GLENCOE
WORLD HISTORY

Unit 3 Resources

The Early Modern World
1400–1800

CHAPTER 12 **Renaissance and Reformation**

CHAPTER 13 **The Age of Exploration**

CHAPTER 14 **Crisis and Absolutism in Europe**

CHAPTER 15 **The Muslim Empires**

CHAPTER 16 **The East Asian World**

CHAPTER 17 **Revolution and Enlightenment**

CHAPTER 18 **The French Revolution and Napoleon**

 **Glencoe**

New York, New York   Columbus, Ohio   Chicago, Illinois   Woodland Hills, California

Book Organization

Glencoe offers resources that accompany *Glencoe World History* to expand, enrich, review, and assess every lesson you teach and for every student you teach.

HOW THIS BOOK IS ORGANIZED

Each Unit Resources book offers blackline masters at unit, chapter, and section levels. Each book is divided into three parts—unit-based resources, chapter-based resources, and section-based resources. Tabs facilitate navigation.

UNIT-BASED RESOURCES

We have organized this book so that all unit resources appear at the beginning. Although you may choose to use the specific activities at any time during the course of unit study, Glencoe has placed these resources up front so that you can review your options. For example, the Economics and History Activities and World Literature Readings appear in the front of this book, but you may plan to use these resources in class at any time during the study of the unit.

CHAPTER-BASED AND SECTION-BASED RESOURCES

Chapter-based resources follow the unit materials. For example, Chapter 12 blackline masters appear in this book immediately following Unit 3 materials. The materials appear in the order you teach—Chapter 12 activities; Chapter 12 section activities; Chapter 13 activities; Chapter 13 section activities; and so on.

A COMPLETE ANSWER KEY

A complete answer key appears at the back of this book. This answer key includes answers for all activities in this book in the order in which the activities appear.

The McGraw-Hill Companies

 Glencoe

Send all inquiries to:
Glencoe/McGraw-Hill
8787 Orion Place
Columbus, Ohio 43240-4027

ISBN: 978-0-07-878224-4
MHID: 0-07-878224-4

Printed in the United States of America.

1 2 3 4 5 6 7 8 9 10   079   10 09 08 07

Table of Contents

To the Teacher vi

Unit 3 Resources 1
Charting and Graphing Activity 3 3
Economics and History Activity 3 5
World Literature Reading 3 9

Chapter 12 Resources 17
Reading Skills Activity 12 19
Historical Analysis Skills Activity 12 20
Differentiated Instruction Activity 12 21
English Learner Activity 12 23
Content Vocabulary Activity 12 25
Academic Vocabulary Activity 12 27
Skills Reinforcement Activity 12 29
Critical Thinking Skills Activity 12 30
History and Geography Activity 12 31
Mapping History Activity 12 33
Historical Significance Activity 12 34
Cooperative Learning Activity 12 35
History Simulation Activity 12 37
Time Line Activity 12 39
Linking Past and Present Activity 12 40
People in World History Activity 12, Profile 1 41
People in World History Activity 12, Profile 2 42
Primary Source Reading 12 43
World Art and Music Activity 12 45
Reteaching Activity 12 47
Enrichment Activity 12 48

Chapter 12 Section Resources 49
Guided Reading Activity 12-1 50
Guided Reading Activity 12-2 51
Guided Reading Activity 12-3 52

Chapter 13 Resources 55
Reading Skills Activity 13 57
Historical Analysis Skills Activity 13 58
Differentiated Instruction Activity 13 59
English Learner Activity 13 61

Content Vocabulary Activity 13 63

Academic Vocabulary Activity 13 65

Skills Reinforcement Activity 13 67

Critical Thinking Skills Activity 13 68

History and Geography Activity 13 69

Mapping History Activity 13 71

Historical Significance Activity 13 72

Cooperative Learning Activity 13 73

History Simulation Activity 13 75

Time Line Activity 13 77

Linking Past and Present Activity 13 78

People in World History Activity 13, Profile 1 79

People in World History Activity 13, Profile 2 80

Primary Source Reading 13 81

World Art and Music Activity 13 83

Reteaching Activity 13 85

Enrichment Activity 13 86

Chapter 13 Section Resources 87

Guided Reading Activity 13-1 88

Guided Reading Activity 13-2 89

Guided Reading Activity 13-3 90

Chapter 14 Resources 91

Reading Skills Activity 14 93

Historical Analysis Skills Activity 14 94

Differentiated Instruction Activity 14 95

English Learner Activity 14 97

Content Vocabulary Activity 14 99

Academic Vocabulary Activity 14 101

Skills Reinforcement Activity 14 103

Critical Thinking Skills Activity 14 104

History and Geography Activity 14 105

Mapping History Activity 14 107

Historical Significance Activity 14 108

Cooperative Learning Activity 14 109

History Simulation Activity 14 111

Time Line Activity 14 113

Linking Past and Present Activity 14 114

People in World History Activity 14, Profile 1 115

People in World History Activity 14, Profile 2 116

Primary Source Reading 14 117

World Art and Music Activity 14 119

Reteaching Activity 14 121

Enrichment Activity 14 122

Chapter 14 Section Resources 123

Guided Reading Activity 14-1 124
Guided Reading Activity 14-2 125
Guided Reading Activity 14-3 126
Guided Reading Activity 14-4 127

Chapter 15 Resources 129

Reading Skills Activity 15 131
Historical Analysis Skills Activity 15 132
Differentiated Instruction Activity 15 133
English Learner Activity 15 135
Content Vocabulary Activity 15 137
Academic Vocabulary Activity 15 139
Skills Reinforcement Activity 15 141
Critical Thinking Skills Activity 15 142
History and Geography Activity 15 143
Mapping History Activity 15 145
Historical Significance Activity 15 146
Cooperative Learning Activity 15 147
History Simulation Activity 15 149
Time Line Activity 15 151
Linking Past and Present Activity 15 152
People in World History Activity 15, Profile 1 153
People in World History Activity 15, Profile 2 154
Primary Source Reading 15 155
World Art and Music Activity 15 157
Reteaching Activity 15 159
Enrichment Activity 15 160

Chapter 15 Section Resources 161

Guided Reading Activity 15-1 162
Guided Reading Activity 15-2 163
Guided Reading Activity 15-3 164

Chapter 16 Resources 165

Reading Skills Activity 16 167
Historical Analysis Skills Activity 16 168
Differentiated Instruction Activity 16 169
English Learner Activity 16 171
Content Vocabulary Activity 16 173
Academic Vocabulary Activity 16 175
Skills Reinforcement Activity 16 177
Critical Thinking Skills Activity 16 178

History and Geography Activity 16.. 179

Mapping History Activity 16... 181

Historical Significance Activity 16... 182

Cooperative Learning Activity 16 183

History Simulation Activity 16 185

Time Line Activity 16... 187

Linking Past and Present Activity 16 188

People in World History Activity 16, Profile 1 189

People in World History Activity 16, Profile 2 190

Primary Source Reading 16 191

World Art and Music Activity 16 193

Reteaching Activity 16... 195

Enrichment Activity 16 196

Chapter 16 Section Resources 197

Guided Reading Activity 16-1 198

Guided Reading Activity 16-2 199

Guided Reading Activity 16-3 200

Chapter 17 Resources 203

Reading Skills Activity 17 205

Historical Analysis Skills Activity 17 206

Differentiated Instruction Activity 17 207

English Learner Activity 17 209

Content Vocabulary Activity 17.. 211

Academic Vocabulary Activity 17 213

Skills Reinforcement Activity 17 215

Critical Thinking Skills Activity 17 216

History and Geography Activity 17.. 217

Mapping History Activity 17... 219

Historical Significance Activity 17... 220

Cooperative Learning Activity 17.. 221

History Simulation Activity 17 223

Time Line Activity 17... 225

Linking Past and Present Activity 17 226

People in World History Activity 17, Profile 1............................. 227

People in World History Activity 17, Profile 2............................. 228

Primary Source Reading 17 229

World Art and Music Activity 17 231

Reteaching Activity 17 233

Enrichment Activity 17 234

Chapter 17 Section Resources 235

Guided Reading Activity 17-1 236
Guided Reading Activity 17-2 237
Guided Reading Activity 17-3 238
Guided Reading Activity 17-4 239

Chapter 18 Resources 241

Reading Skills Activity 18 243
Historical Analysis Skills Activity 18 244
Differentiated Instruction Activity 18 245
English Learner Activity 18 247
Content Vocabulary Activity 18 249
Academic Vocabulary Activity 18 251
Skills Reinforcement Activity 18 253
Critical Thinking Skills Activity 18 254
History and Geography Activity 18 255
Mapping History Activity 18 257
Historical Significance Activity 18 258
Cooperative Learning Activity 18 259
History Simulation Activity 18 261
Time Line Activity 18 263
Linking Past and Present Activity 18 264
People in World History Activity 18, Profile 1 265
People in World History Activity 18, Profile 2 266
Primary Source Reading 18 267
World Art and Music Activity 18 269
Reteaching Activity 18 271
Enrichment Activity 18 272

Chapter 18 Section Resources 273

Guided Reading Activity 18-1 274
Guided Reading Activity 18-2 275
Guided Reading Activity 18-3 276

Answer Key 277

To the Teacher

Charting and Graphing Activities—help students learn and think through the use of charts and graphs.

Economics and History Activities—familiarize students with basic economics and its place in historical developments.

World Literature Readings—guide students through literature excerpts related to the period.

Reading Skills Activities—provide specific strategies and activities linked to chapter content.

Historical Analysis Skills Activities—allow students to practice historical analysis skills.

Differentiated Instruction Activities—suggest ways to adapt chapter activities for students of all learning styles.

English Learner Activities—focus on word usage, grammar and comprehension for vocabulary related to chapter content.

Content Vocabulary Activities—review and reinforce history terms from the student text.

Academic Vocabulary Activities—review and reinforce general academic vocabulary.

Skills Reinforcement Activities—introduce and reinforce social studies, critical thinking, technology, and writing skills.

Critical Thinking Skills Activities—develop independent thinking and assessment skills for history topics.

History and Geography Activities—guide students in using geography to support and expand their understanding of history.

Mapping History Activities—present maps related to chapter content for analysis and interpretation.

Historical Significance Activities—make connections for students between past events or developments and today's world.

Cooperative Learning Activities—enrich learning through group projects on historical topics and issues.

History Simulation Activities—explore historical themes and issues through games or simulations for small groups.

Time Line Activities—promote students' understanding of chronology through time-line centered questions.

Linking Past and Present Activities—emphasize the universal elements in political, social, and cultural developments so students can see connections to the past.

People in World History Profiles—highlight the historical roles of famous figures in world events.

Primary Source Readings—guide students through primary excerpts and offer meaningful questions on them.

World Art and Music Activities—show students how art and music shape and reflect the history of a period.

Reteaching Activities—help students see relationships betweeen historical events through the use of graphic organizers.

Enrichment Activities—introduce content related to the themes and topics in the text.

Guided Reading Activities—present outlines, sentences, and other exercises for students to complete as they read along in the text.

GLENCOE

WORLD HISTORY

Unit 3 Resources
The Early Modern World, 1400–1800

CHARTING AND GRAPHING ACTIVITY 3
European Crises   3

ECONOMICS AND HISTORY ACTIVITY 3
The Rise of National Economies   5

WORLD LITERATURE READING 3
From *Macbeth*   9

Charting and Graphing Activity 3

UNIT 3

European Crises

Directions: For each crisis listed, identify the conflict that resulted and the resolution to that conflict. Follow the example given below to fill in each of the boxes.

Crisis	Conflict	Resolution
Issue: French Wars of Religion French Protestants, called Huguenots, and Catholics were in a power struggle to win the hearts and minds of Europeans.	The debate turned violent; thousands died over a 30-year period.	Battles raged until Henry of Navarre, a Huguenot, became king in 1589 and converted to Catholicism.
Issue: The Spanish Armada Philip II harbored a desire to invade England and restore Catholicism as the dominant religion.		
Issue: Witchcraft Craze A deadly hysteria about witchcraft overtook Europe.		
Issue: The Thirty Years' War Begun as a regional conflict between Calvinists and Catholics, the religious war eventually embroiled half of Europe.		

The Rise of National Economies

Mercantilism and Colonization In the 1500s and 1600s, most European nations subscribed to the theory of mercantilism. This economic theory links a country's wealth to its supply of gold and silver. The mercantilist nations of Europe had two goals: to increase their supply of gold and silver by finding (and controlling) new gold and silver mines and to create a positive trade balance. A trade balance is the balance between a nation's imports and exports. A positive trade balance means that the value of a country's exports exceeds the value of its imports.

The process of colonization helped the nations of Europe achieve both their goals: The Latin American colonies were rich in gold and silver, and the colonies helped with the balance of trade. The colonies were a great source of cheap raw materials—unfinished products that are used to make something else. For example, cotton is a raw material used in producing yarn; coffee beans are a raw material used in producing coffee; and sugar cane is a raw material in producing refined sugar. In the 1500s and 1600s, raw materials were brought back to the "mother country" in Europe, where they were used in the manufacturing process. Then the finished products were shipped back to and sold in the colonies. To ensure a positive trade balance, the mother countries imposed high taxes on any finished products that were exported from the colonies and imported into the mother country.

The Four Resources One reason that European nations sought colonies as a source of gold and raw materials is that such items are limited resources. There are four categories of limited resources or factors of production: land, labor, capital, and entrepreneurial ability. Land can be valuable for many reasons. It might hold many valuable resources within it, such as gold or oil; it might be near a specific location, such as the coast or a capital city; or

it might provide a location necessary for a business to function.

Like land, labor also has different types of value. For example, the work that doctors do has a value in part due to its specialization— only certain people can perform the work. Yet the skills provided by a doctor have another value: the perceived importance to the client. In the thirteen American colonies, labor was far scarcer than it was in the mother country. As a result, free workers prospered in the Northern Colonies, and a system of slave labor developed in the Southern Colonies. Until the turn of the twentieth century in the United States, much of the technology developed was used to offset the need for labor in our country's vast agricultural spaces and in its manufacturing plants.

Capital is the term used to describe all the equipment and tools used to produce goods and services. Some examples of capital are stores, office buildings, computers, trucks, and railroads. The finances that are invested in businesses are also considered capital. In mercantile theory, the mother country controlled capital and often outlawed manufacturing in the colonies. One of the differences between the British and Spanish colonial experiences was that the Spanish strictly controlled colonial manufacturing, whereas the British let the New England colonists develop shipbuilding, iron foundries, and other forms of capital investment.

Entrepreneurial ability is the human know-how or knowledge that is necessary to create new businesses. A person must have more than just know-how to start a business; land, labor, or capital is also necessary. In much the same way, land, labor, and capital would have far less impact on an economy without the entrepreneurial spirit.

Each of the four types of resources is considered to be a limited resource because its supply is limited. There is only so much land in any given country. There are only so many

UNIT 3

Economics and History Activity 3

UNIT 3

people who can provide labor. There is only so much capital. There are also only so many people with entrepreneurial abilities. Although the resources are limited, there are many ways for each resource to be used. For example, an acre of land can be used for a park, a factory, a school, or wildlife reserve.

The Three Questions of Economics Limited resources are used to produce goods and services. But what will be produced, who will produce it, and for whom will it be produced? These are the three basic questions of economics.

The first question "What goods will be produced?" refers to more than just what one company or one economic sector will make. It relates to the national economy. In other words, "What type of products will the nation expend the greatest portion of its resources producing?"

The second question "How will these goods be produced?" relates to the actual producer of goods. There are really only two possible answers: the private sector (small businesses and corporations) or the public sector (government). In most countries, both the private and public sectors contribute to the production of goods. However, one of the groups usually acts as the dominating force in an economy. In the United States, while the public sector is quite large, it is the private sector that is the dominant force in the production of goods. In the People's Republic of China, the public sector is dominant. Yet, while the Chinese government actually decides what will be produced, it allows the private sector to produce many of these goods and services.

The third question "For whom will the goods be produced?" refers to the ability to obtain the goods produced. In other words, will anyone who is able and willing to pay the price for the goods be able to obtain them? In some economic systems, the government decides who will have the goods, not the

consumers. In the United States, it is the middle class, the largest consumer group, that dictates much of what is produced.

Determining who actually answers, or is responsible for, the three economic questions can identify the type of economy of a nation. In command economies, such as mercantilism, socialism, and other forms of government in which government officials make all or most of the decisions, the government—whether it is a king, ruling group, or parliament—determines the answer to the three questions of economics. You will read more about socialism in Unit 5 of your textbook. In the mercantile system discussed previously, the government of the mother country answered the three questions of economics for its colonies. Historically, most economies have been principally command economies, with the monarch or ruling group making the final economic decisions.

Free-Enterprise System In a free-enterprise system, it is the business owners and ultimately the consumers who answer the three questions of economics. Adam Smith, an eighteenth-century economist, wrote *The Wealth of Nations*, which formed the basis for the American economic system. In his book, Smith described a laissez-faire system in which businesses were free from government controls. In Smith's opinion, government had three main responsibilities: to provide an army, to provide police, and to provide public services such as roads and canals. Smith did not want governments to answer any of the three economic questions.

In capitalism, or the free-enterprise system, the market determines what will be produced. A company cannot successfully sell a product or service if people do not want or need it. Therefore, it is the consumer who is actually the decision-maker. In this way, the free-enterprise system is directly opposed to the system of mercantilism that was dominant at the height of colonialism.

Economics and History Activity 3

Applying Economics to History

Directions: Use the information you have read to answer the following questions on a separate sheet of paper.

Recalling Information
1. What is mercantilism?
2. Explain the difference between raw materials and finished products.
3. Who was Adam Smith?

Critical Thinking
4. **Making Comparisons** Compare mercantilism to capitalism in terms of the three economic questions.

5. **Synthesizing Information** Explain how a positive trade balance would help a country increase its supply of gold and silver.
6. **Making Inferences** Identify three types of value that labor might have. Give an example of the type of worker or job that holds the value you have identified.

Making Connections
7. Think about your local community. Give a specific example of each of the four limited resources from your community. For example, you might cite the woman who owns a local bakery as an example of entrepreneurial ability.

World Literature Reading 3

Shakespeare wrote *The Tragedy of Macbeth* in 1605 or 1606; the drama was first performed in 1606. The central character is the tragic hero Macbeth, a Scottish lord and a brave man who suffers from a tragic flaw—a fatal weakness—that results in his eventual downfall.

About the Author Because of the power and beauty of his language and his deep understanding of humanity, **William Shakespeare** (1564–1616) is generally ranked as the greatest English writer of all time. Shakespeare was born in the small town of Stratford-on-Avon, the son of a successful businessman. By the time he was 30 years old, Shakespeare had moved to London and had become the main playwright for a successful theater company. A few years later, the company built the Globe Theatre, where most of Shakespeare's plays were performed. In addition to his 37 plays, Shakespeare wrote more than 150 sonnets and two long narrative poems.

GUIDED READING As you read this excerpt from *Macbeth*, Act I, think about how Macbeth reacts to the witches' prophecies.

From *Macbeth*

ACT I

Scene I. [Scotland. An open place.]

Thunder and lightning. Enter three Witches.

1 Witch. When shall we three meet again
In thunder, lightning, or in rain?
2 Witch. When the hurlyburly's done,
When the battle's lost and won.
3 Witch. That will be ere the set of sun.
1 Witch. Where the place?
2 Witch. Upon the heath.
3 Witch. There to meet with Macbeth.
1 Witch. I come, Graymalkin!
2 Witch. Paddock calls.
3 Witch. Anon!

All. Fair is foul, and foul is fair.
Hover through the fog and filthy air.

Exeunt.

Scene II. [A camp near Forres.[1]]

Alarum within. Enter King[2] [Duncan],
Malcolm[3], Donalbain[4], Lennox[5], *with*
Attendants, *meeting a bleeding* Captain.

---

[1] **Forres:** city on the northern coast of Scotland
[2] **King:** Duncan I, king of Scotland
[3] **Malcolm:** son of Duncan
[4] **Donalbain:** son of Duncan
[5] **Lennox:** Scottish lord

World Literature Reading 3

From *Macbeth* (continued)

King. What bloody man is that? He can
   report,
As seemeth by his plight, of the revolt
The newest state.
Malcolm. This is the sergeant
Who like the good and hardy soldier fought
'Gainst my captivity. Hail, brave friend!
Say to the King the knowledge of the broil
As thou didst leave it.
Captain. Doubtful it stood,
As two spent swimmers that do cling
   together
And choke their art. The merciless
   Macdonwald
(Worthy to be a rebel, for to that
The multiplying villainies of nature
Do swarm upon him) from the Western
   Isles
Of kerns[6] and gallowglasses[7] is supplied;
And Fortune, on his damned quarrel
   smiling,
Showed like a rebel's whore. But all's too
   weak;
For brave Macbeth (well he deserves that
   name),
Disdaining Fortune, with his brandished
   steel,
Which smoked with bloody execution
(Like valor's minion), carved out his
   passage
Till he faced the slave;
Which ne'er shook hands nor bade farewell
   to him
Till he unseamed him from the nave to the
   chops
And fixed his head upon our battlements.
King. O valiant cousin! worthy gentleman!
Captain. As whence the sun 'gins his
   reflection
Shipwracking storms and direful thunders
   break,
So from that spring whence comfort
   seemed to come

Discomfort swells. Mark, King of Scotland,
   mark.
No sooner justice had, with valor armed,
Compelled these skipping kerns to trust
   their heels
But the Norweyan[8] lord, surveying vantage,
With furbished arms and new supplies of
   men,
Began a fresh assault.
King. Dismayed not this
Our captains, Macbeth and Banquo?
Captain. Yes,
As sparrows eagles, or the hare the lion.
If I say sooth, I must report they were
As cannons overcharged with double
   cracks, so they
Doubly redoubled strokes upon the foe.
Except they meant to bathe in reeking
   wounds,
Or memorize another Golgotha.
I cannot tell—
But I am faint; my gashes cry for help.
King. So well thy words become thee as
   thy wounds;
They smack of honor both. Go get him
   surgeons.

       [*Exit* Captain, *attended*.]

    Enter Ross[9] *and* Angus[10].

Who comes here?
Malcolm. The worthy Thane[11] of Ross.
Lennox. What haste looks through his eyes!
   So should he look
That seems to speak things strange.
Ross. God save the King!
King. Whence cam'st thou, worthy thane?
Ross. From Fife, great King,
Where the Norweyan banners flout the sky
And fan our people cold. Norway himself,
With terrible numbers,
Assisted by that most disloyal traitor

---

[6] **kerns:** lightly armed Irish soldiers
[7] **gallowglasses:** heavily armed Irish soldiers

[8] **Norweyan:** of Norway
[9] **Ross:** Scottish lord
[10] **Angus:** Scottish lord
[11] **Thane:** Feudal lord, second only to the king

World Literature Reading 3

From *Macbeth* (continued)

The Thane of Cawdor, began a dismal
  conflict,
Till that Bellona's bridegroom, lapped in
  proof,
Confronted him with self-comparisons,
Point against point, rebellious arm 'gainst
  arm,
Curbing his lavish spirit; and to conclude,
The victory fell on us.
King. Great happiness!
Ross. That now
Sweno, the Norways' king, craves
  composition;
Nor would we deign him burial of his men
Till he disbursed, at Saint Colme's Inch,
Ten thousand dollars to our general use.
King. No more that Thane of Cawdor shall
  deceive
Our bosom interest. Go pronounce his
  present death
And with his former title greet Macbeth.
Ross. I'll see it done.
Duncan. What he hath lost noble Macbeth
  hath won.

                               Exeunt.

    Scene III. [A heath near Forres.]

   Thunder. Enter the three Witches.

1 Witch. Where hast thou been, sister?
2 Witch. Killing swine.
3 Witch. Sister, where thou?
1 Witch. A sailor's wife had chestnuts in
  her lap
And mounched and mounched and
  mounched.
"Give me," quoth I.

"Aroint thee, witch!" the rump-fed ronyon
  cries.
Her husband's to Aleppo gone, master o'
  the "Tiger";
But in a sieve I'll thither sail
And, like a rat without a tail,
I'll do, I'll do, and I'll do.
2 Witch. I'll give thee a wind.
1 Witch. Th' art kind.
3 Witch. And I another.
1 Witch. I myself have all the other,
And the very ports they blow,
All the quarters that they know
I' the shipman's card.
I'll drain him dry as hay.
Sleep shall neither night nor day
Hang upon his penthouse lid.
He shall live a man forbid.
Weary sev'nights, nine times nine,
Shall he dwindle, peak, and pine.
Though his bark cannot be lost,
Yet it shall be tempest-tost.
Look what I have.
2 Witch. Show me! show me!
1 Witch. Here I have a pilot's thumb,
Wracked as homeward he did come.

                             Drum within.

3 Witch. A drum! a drum!
Macbeth doth come.
All. The Weird Sisters, hand in hand,
Posters of the sea and land,
Thus do go about, about,
Thrice to thine, and thrice to mine,
And thrice again, to make up nine.
Peace! The charm's wound up.

    Enter Macbeth *and* Banquo[12].

Macbeth. So foul and fair a day I have not
  seen.
Banquo. How far is't called to Forres? What
  are these,

---

[12] **Banquo:** Scottish nobleman, friend to Macbeth

World Literature Reading 3

From *Macbeth* (continued)

So withered, and so wild in their attire,
That look not like the inhabitants o' the
    earth,
And yet are on't? Live you? or are you
    aught
That man may question? You seem to
    understand me,
By each at once her choppy finger laying
Upon her skinny lips. You should be
    women,
And yet your beards forbid me to interpret
That you are so.
Macbeth. Speak, if you can. What are you?
1 Witch. All hail, Macbeth! Hail to thee,
    Thane of Glamis!
2 Witch. All hail, Macbeth! Hail to thee,
    Thane of Cawdor!
3 Witch. All hail, Macbeth, that shalt be
    King hereafter!
Banquo. Good sir, why do you start and
    seem to fear
Things that do sound so fair? I' the name of
    truth,
Are ye fantastical, or that indeed
Which outwardly ye show? My noble partner
You greet with present grace and great
    prediction
Of noble having and royal hope,
That he seems rapt withal. To me you
    speak not.
If you can look into the seeds of time
And say which grain will grow and which
    will not,
Speak then to me, and neither beg nor fear
Your favors nor your hate.
1 Witch. Hail!
2 Witch. Hail!
3 Witch. Hail!
1 Witch. Lesser than Macbeth, and greater.
2 Witch. Not so happy, yet much happier.
3 Witch. Thou shalt get kings, though thou
    be none.
So all hail, Macbeth and Banquo!
1 Witch. Banquo and Macbeth, all hail!

Macbeth. Stay, you imperfect speakers, tell
    me more!
By Sinel's[13] death I know I am Thane of
    Glamis,
But how of Cawdor? The Thane of Cawdor
    lives,
A prosperous gentleman; and to be King
Stands not within the prospect of belief,
No more than to be Cawdor. Say from
    whence
You owe this strange intelligence, or why
Upon this blasted heath you stop our way
With such prophetic greeting. Speak, I
    charge you.

Witches vanish.

Banquo. The earth hath bubbles, as the
    water has,
And these are of them. Whither are they
    vanished?
Macbeth. Into the air, and what seemed
    corporal melted
As breath into the wind. Would they had
    stayed!
Banquo. Were such things here as we do
    speak about?
Or have we eaten on the insane root
That takes the reason prisoner?
Macbeth. Your children shall be kings.
Banquo. You shall be King.
Macbeth. And Thane of Cawdor too. Went
    it not so?
Banquo. To the selfsame tune and words.
    Who's here?

Enter Ross *and* Angus.

Ross. The King hath happily received,
    Macbeth,
The news of thy success; and when he
    reads
Thy personal venture in the rebels' fight,
His wonders and his praises do contend
Which should be thine or his. Silenced with
    that,
In viewing o'er the rest o' the selfsame day,

---

[13] **Sinel:** Macbeth's father

World Literature Reading 3

From *Macbeth* (continued)

He finds thee in the stout Norweyan ranks,
Nothing afeard of what thyself didst make,
Strange images of death. As thick as hail
Came post with post, and every one did
   bear
Thy praises in his kingdom's great defense
And poured them down before him.
Angus. We are sent
To give thee from our royal master thanks;
Only to herald thee into his sight,
Not pay thee.
Ross. And for an earnest of a greater
   honor,
He bade me, from him, call thee Thane of
   Cawdor;
In which addition, hail, most worthy Thane!
For it is thine.
Banquo. What, can the devil speak true?
Macbeth. The Thane of Cawdor lives. Why
   do you dress me
In borrowed robes?
Angus. Who was the Thane lives yet,
But under heavy judgment bears that life
Which he deserves to lose. Whether he was
   combined
With those of Norway, or did line the rebel
With hidden help and vantage, or that with
   both
He labored in his country's wrack, I know
   not;
But treason's capital, confessed and
   proved,
Have overthrown him.
Macbeth. [*Aside*] Glamis, and Thane of
   Cawdor!
The greatest is behind.—[*To* Ross *and* Angus]
   Thanks for your pains.
[*Aside to* Banquo] Do you not hope your
   children shall be kings,
When those that gave the Thane of Cawdor
   to me
Promised no less to them?
Banquo. [*Aside to Macbeth*] That, trusted
   home,

Might yet enkindle you unto the crown,
Besides the Thane of Cawdor. But 'tis
   strange!
And oftentimes, to win us to our harm,
The instruments of darkness tell us truths,
Win us with honest trifles, to betray's
In deepest consequence.—
Cousins, a word, I pray you.
Macbeth. [*Aside*] Two truths are told,
As happy prologues to the swelling act
Of the imperial theme.—I thank you,
   gentlemen.—
[*Aside*] This supernatural soliciting
Cannot be ill; cannot be good. If ill,
Why hath it given me earnest of success,
Commencing in a truth? I am Thane of
   Cawdor.
If good, why do I yield to that suggestion
Whose horrid image doth unfix my hair
And make my seated heart knock at my
   ribs
Against the use of nature? Present fears
Are less than horrible imaginings.
My thought, whose murder yet is but
   fantastical,
Shakes so my single state of man that
   function
Is smothered in surmise and nothing is
But what is not.
Banquo. Look how our partner's rapt.
Macbeth. [*Aside*] If chance will have me
   King, why, chance may crown me,
Without my stir.
Banquo. New honors come upon him,
Like our strange garments, cleave not to
   their mold
But with the aid of use.
Macbeth. [*Aside*] Come what come may,
Time and the hour runs through the rough-
   est day.
Banquo. Worthy Macbeth, we stay upon
   your leisure.
Macbeth. Give me your favor. My dull brain
   was wrought

World Literature Reading 3

From *Macbeth* (continued)

With things forgotten. Kind gentlemen, your pains
Are registered where every day I turn
The leaf to read them. Let us toward the King.
[*Aside to Banquo*] Think upon what hath chanced, and, at more time,
The interim having weighed it, let us speak
Our free hearts each to other.
Banquo. [*Aside to Macbeth*] Very gladly.
Macbeth. [*Aside to Banquo*] Till then, enough—Come, friends.

                                    Exeunt.

Scene IV. [Forres. The Palace.]

Flourish. Enter King [Duncan], Lennox, Malcolm, Donalbain, *and* Attendants.

King. Is execution done on Cawdor? Are not
Those in commission yet returned?
Malcolm. My liege,
They are not yet come back. But I have spoke
With one that saw him die; who did report
That very frankly he confessed his treasons,
Implored your Highness' pardon, and set forth
A deep repentance. Nothing in his life
Became him like the leaving it. He died
As one that had been studied in his death
To throw away the dearest thing he owed
As 'twere a careless trifle.
King. There's no art
To find the mind's construction in the face.
He was a gentleman on whom I built
An absolute trust.

    Enter Macbeth, Banquo, Ross, *and* Angus.

O worthiest cousin,

The sin of my ingratitude even now
Was heavy on me! Thou art so far before
That swiftest wing of recompense is slow
To overtake thee. Would thou hadst less deserved,
That the proportion both of thanks and payment
Might have been mine! Only I have left to say,
More is thy due than more than all can pay.
Macbeth. The service and the loyalty I owe,
In doing it pays itself. Your Highness' part
Is to receive our duties; and our duties
Are to your throne and state children and servants,
Which do but what they should by doing everything
Safe toward your love and honor.
King. Welcome hither.
I have begun to plant thee and will labor
To make thee full of growing. Noble Banquo,
That hast no less deserved, nor must be known
No less to have done so, let me infold thee
And hold thee to my heart.
Banquo. There if I grow,
The harvest is your own.
King. My plenteous joys,
Wanton in fullness, seek to hide themselves
In drops of sorrow. Sons, kinsmen, thanes,
And you whose places are the nearest, know
We will establish our estate upon
Our eldest, Malcolm, whom we name hereafter
The Prince of Cumberland; which honor must
Not unaccompanied invest him only,
But signs of nobleness, like stars, shall shine
On all deservers. From hence to Inverness,

World Literature Reading 3

From *Macbeth* (continued)

And bind us further to you.
Macbeth. The rest is labor, which is not used for you.
I'll be myself the harbinger, and make joyful
The hearing of my wife with your approach;
So, humbly take my leave.
King. My worthy Cawdor!
Macbeth. [*Aside*] The Prince of Cumberland! That is a step
On which I must fall down, or else o'erleap,
For in my way it lies. Stars, hide your fires!
Let not light see my black and deep desires.
The eye wink at the hand; yet let that be,
Which the eye fears, when it is done, to see. *Exit.*
King. True, worthy Banquo: he is full so valiant,
And in his commendations I am fed;
It is a banquet to me. Let's after him,
Whose care is gone before to bid us welcome.
It is a peerless kinsman.

Flourish. Exeunt.

Scene V. [Inverness[14]. Macbeth's Castle.]

Enter Macbeth's Wife[15], *alone, with a letter.*

Lady. [*Reads*] "They met me in the day of success; and I have learned by the perfect'st report they have more in them than mortal knowledge. When I burned in desire to question them further, they made them-selves air, into which they vanished. Whiles I stood rapt in the wonder of it, came missives from the King, who all-hailed me Thane of Cawdor, by which title, before, these Weird Sisters saluted me, and referred me to the coming on of time with 'Hail, King that shalt be!' This have I thought good to deliver thee, my dearest partner of greatness, that thou mightst not lose the dues of rejoicing by being ignorant of what greatness is promised thee. Lay it to thy heart, and farewell."
Glamis thou art, and Cawdor, and shalt be
What thou art promised. Yet I do fear thy nature.
It is too full o' the milk of human kindness
To catch the nearest way. Thou wouldst be great;
Art not without ambition, but without
The illness should attend it. What thou wouldst highly,
That wouldst thou holily; wouldst not play false,
And yet wouldst wrongly win. Thou'ldst have, great Glamis,
That which cries "Thus thou must do," if thou have it;
And that which rather thou dost fear to do
Than wishest should be undone. Hie thee hither,
That I may pour my spirits in thine ear
And chastise with the valor of my tongue
All that impedes thee from the golden round
Which fate and metaphysical aid doth seem
To have thee crowned withal.

---

[14] **Inverness:** city on the north coast of Scotland, approximately 20 miles (37 kilometers) west of Forres
[15] **Macbeth's Wife:** called Lady Macbeth in the script

World Literature Reading 3

From *Macbeth* (continued)

DIRECTIONS: Answer the following questions in the space provided.

Interpreting the Reading

1. What do the three witches predict for Macbeth?

_____

_____

_____

_____

2. How does Macbeth perform in battle?

_____

_____

_____

_____

3. What honor does the king give Macbeth?

_____

_____

_____

_____

_____

Critical Thinking

4. Making Comparisons How do Banquo and Macbeth react to the witches' predictions? What do the reactions of the two men reveal about their characters?

_____

_____

_____

_____

_____

_____

_____

_____

UNIT 3

GLENCOE
WORLD HISTORY

Chapter 12 Resources
Renaissance and Reformation, 1350–1600

READING SKILLS ACTIVITY 12
Summarizing 19

HISTORICAL ANALYSIS SKILLS ACTIVITY 12
Identifying Bias and Prejudice 20

DIFFERENTIATED INSTRUCTION ACTIVITY 12
The Effect of the Renaissance 21

ENGLISH LEARNER ACTIVITY 12
Renaissance and Reformation 23

CONTENT VOCABULARY ACTIVITY 12
Renaissance and Reformation, 1350–1600 25

ACADEMIC VOCABULARY ACTIVITY 12
Renaissance and Reformation 27

SKILLS REINFORCEMENT ACTIVITY 12
Summarizing Information 29

CRITICAL THINKING SKILLS ACTIVITY 12
Identifying Assumptions 30

HISTORY AND GEOGRAPHY ACTIVITY 12
Venice, Queen of the Adriatic 31

MAPPING HISTORY ACTIVITY 12
The Success of Reform 33

HISTORICAL SIGNIFICANCE ACTIVITY 12
Renaissances 34

COOPERATIVE LEARNING ACTIVITY 12
The Renaissance in Italy 35

HISTORY SIMULATION ACTIVITY 12
A Renaissance Fair 37

TIME LINE ACTIVITY 12
Renaissance and Reformation 39

LINKING PAST AND PRESENT ACTIVITY 12
Supporting the Arts: Past and Present 40

PEOPLE IN WORLD HISTORY ACTIVITY 12
Profile 1: Johannes Gutenberg (c. 1397–1468) 41
Profile 2: Martin Luther (1483–1546) 42

PRIMARY SOURCE READING 12
The Autobiography of Benvenuto Cellini 43

WORLD ART AND MUSIC ACTIVITY 12
Michelangelo 45

RETEACHING ACTIVITY 12
Renaissance and Reformation 47

ENRICHMENT ACTIVITY 12
The State of the World, 1516 48

Reading Skills Activity 12

Summarizing

LEARNING THE SKILL

Summarizing is an important skill for developing the ability to read critically. It requires you to use your own words to capture the main ideas of a reading. It is also essential for taking the notes that help you remember what you read to discuss topics in class or to prepare for an exam. When you summarize, you put ideas into your own words. By doing so, you are actively synthesizing the material. One way to get a start on summarizing a complex reading is to use a graphic organizer.

PRACTICING THE SKILL

DIRECTIONS: Read the following excerpt from The Renaissance Philosophy of Man edited by Ernst Cassirer, Paul Kristeller, and John Randall, Jr. (1948). On a separate sheet of paper, summarize this statement about the importance of individualism in a few sentences.

Pico della Mirandola, a Renaissance philosopher, said in his Oration on the Dignity of Man:

You, constrained by no limits in accordance with your own free will, shall ordain for yourself the limits of your nature. We have set you at the world's center that you may from there more easily observe whatever is in the world. We have made you neither of heaven nor of earth, neither mortal nor immortal, so that with freedom of choice and with honor, as though the maker and molder of yourself, you may fashion yourself in whatever shape you shall prefer.

APPLYING THE SKILL

DIRECTIONS: Read the excerpt about women's position in society on page 000 of your textbook. Summarize Christine de Pizan's argument in one or two sentences.

_____

_____

_____

_____

_____

_____

_____

_____

_____

_____

CHAPTER 12

Identifying Bias and Prejudice

CHAPTER 12

LEARNING THE SKILL

Historians themselves take a point of view when they interpret the past, but they try to take a balanced point of view. In order to do this, they must be able to recognize bias and prejudice in the primary sources they consult. A source that seems extreme in its position may still be valid, but the historian would want to check to see what facts support an extreme point of view.

PRACTICING THE SKILL

DIRECTIONS: Read the following excerpt from Chapter 12 about statements made by a wealthy merchant in Florence during the Renaissance.

> *Those that are lazy in a way that does harm to the city, and who can offer no just reason for their condition, should either be forced to work or expelled from the city. The city would thus rid itself of that most harmful part of the poorest class.*

1. What bias does the merchant hold towards citizens of Florence?

   _____

   _____

   _____

   _____

2. What do you think he was trying to accomplish by writing this?

   _____

   _____

   _____

   _____

APPLYING THE SKILL

DIRECTIONS: Bias can play a very strong role in religion and politics. It is important for a reader to read statements and speeches of religious leaders carefully to detect the point of view. Search the Internet or in library source material to locate a primary source from the Protestant Reformation. Read the source carefully and think critically. Then on a separate sheet of paper, describe the speaker's point of view. What is the religious leader saying between the lines about people of different religions? Provide a copy of the primary source with your description.

Differentiated Instruction Activity 12

The Effect of the Renaissance

As you learned in the chapter, the word renaissance means rebirth. Between 1350 and 1550, the Renaissance period, emphasized secularism, awareness of ties to ancient Greek and Roman worlds, and the ability of the individual. Society, politics, art, education, literature, architecture, and religion were all affected by this rebirth.

DIRECTIONS: Using your textbook, choose one area affected by the Renaissance and list examples of the influence and impact this period had.

The Renaissance and _____

1. _____

_____

_____

2. _____

_____

_____

3. _____

_____

_____

4. _____

_____

_____

5. _____

_____

_____

CHAPTER 12

(continued)

Differentiated Instruction Activity **12**

For the Teacher

TEACHING STRATEGIES FOR DIFFERENT LEARNING STYLES

The following activities are ways the basic lesson can be modified to accommodate students' different learning styles:

English Learners (EL) Review the assignment with students, explaining any terminology they may not understand, including renaissance.

Advanced Learners (AL) Have students research an individual whose work in the area they chose to focus on was prominent during the Renaissance. Students should write an essay based on their research to illustrate the individual's influence. Have students present the individual's contributions to the class.

Below Grade Level (BL) Review the chapter vocabulary with students. Assist them in reading through the text and compiling a short list of examples of one area affected by the Renaissance.

On Grade Level (OL) Have students complete the activity as written. Give students the opportunity to share their research with other students who chose an area different than their own.

English Learner Activity 12

Renaissance and Reformation

✪ A. PRE-READING ACTIVITY: IMPROVING READING COMPREHENSION

Directions: *Before reading "The Italian Renaissance" on pages 398–400, answer the following questions.*

1. The title of this chapter is *Renaissance and Reformation*. What do these terms mean? What changes do you think will occur during this period? What type of reformation have you been part of?

   _____

   _____

   _____

   _____

2. As you read, list the three most important characteristics of the Italian Renaissance.

   _____

   _____

   _____

   _____

✪ B. WORD BUILDING ACTIVITY: MATCHING SYNONYMS

Directions: *Match the meaning of the words in the numbered column with their synonyms in the lettered column. Remember that synonyms are words that have similar meanings.*

1.	goal	**a.**	attack
2.	criticize	**b.**	convince
3.	characteristic	**c.**	custom
4.	culture	**d.**	purpose
5.	independent	**e.**	match
6.	imitate	**f.**	stress
7.	persuade	**g.**	self-governing
8.	emphasize	**h.**	trait

CHAPTER 12

(continued)

English Learner Activity 12

✖ C. READING COMPREHENSION ACTIVITY: SENTENCE COMPLETION

Directions: *After you have read "Need for Reform" on pages 413–414, complete the sentences below by circling the best answer.*

1. Corruption in the Catholic church led to

   a. persuade.   **b.** reform.   **c.** culture.

2. Popes were often more concerned with Italian politics and world interests than with spiritual

   a. matters.   **b.** rebirth.   **c.** leaders.

3. Church officials often used their church offices to advance their own careers and

   a. wealth.   **b.** duties.   **c.** responsibilities.

4. Because leaders of the Church were unable to offer advice and instruction on the matter, people began collecting relics as a popular means to

   a. careers.   **b.** instruction.   **c.** salvation.

5. People began to seek the certainty of salvation through the movement known as Modern

   a. Church.   **b.** Devotion.   **c.** Luther.

✖ D. LANGUAGE STUDY ACTIVITY: COMBINING SENTENCES

Directions: *Combine the following words into sentences by rereading "Anabaptistis" on page 421 in your textbook. The first one has been done for you.*

1. True Christian church / undergone spiritual rebirth

   Anabaptists believed the true Christian church was a voluntary community of adult

   believers who had undergone spiritual rebirth and had been baptized.

2. Anabaptist church / chose

   _____

   _____

3. Christians / considered

   _____

   _____

4. Anabaptists / regarded

   _____

   _____

Content Vocabulary Activity 12

Renaissance and Reformation, 1350–1600

DIRECTIONS: Fill in the term for each definition listed below, writing one letter in each square. Then use the letters in the shaded squares to answer the question that follows.

1. money brought by a bride to her husband at marriage

2. worldly rather than spiritual

3. having the characteristics of the city or city life (two words)

4. acceptance into Heaven

5. doctrine that held that a person can be deemed good because of faith alone (three words)

6. doctrine that held that God determines everything that happens in the past, present, and future

7. interest in and study of classical writing, art, and society

8. movement that resulted in the creation of Protestant churches

9. soldier serving for pay

10. certificates issued by the Catholic Church that could reduce or even eliminate someone's punishment for sins

11. painting on fresh, moist plaster with pigments dissolved in water

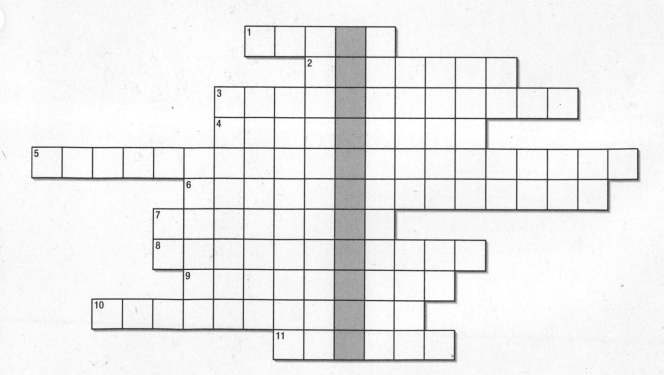

12. What was the period of the awakening of learning and great change?

_____

Academic Vocabulary Activity 12

Renaissance and Reformation

Key Words

Academic Words	Words with Multiple Meanings	Content Vocabulary
attain	Renaissance	urban society
decline		dowry
ignorant		
instability		
justification		
precise		
published		
rebirth		

A. Word Meaning Activity

Word Classification

DIRECTIONS: Three of the words or phrases in each line below are similar in meaning to the underlined word, but one word is not. Circle the word that is NOT similar in meaning.

1. <u>achieve</u>   accomplish   attain   attempt   gain

2. <u>decline</u>   turn down   deteriorate   refuse   incline

3. <u>unaware</u>   ignorant   studious   illiterate   unlearned

4. <u>instability</u>   sound   unpredictable   unstable   shakiness

5. <u>rationalize</u>   defend   justification   support   damage

6. <u>kind</u>   design   tool   style   genre

7. <u>accurate</u>   definite   exact   incorrect   precise

8. <u>publish</u>   prepare   broadcast   reveal   image

(continued)

Academic Vocabulary Activity 12

B. Word Meaning Activity
Matching Definitions
DIRECTIONS: Match the definition to the given words.

1. rebirth
2. ignorant
3. published
4. precise
5. attain
6. instability
7. justification
8. style

a. untutored
b. design
c. reach
d. definite
e. renewal
f. rationalize
g. release
h. unstable

C. Word Meaning Activity
Vocabulary in Writing
DIRECTIONS: Choose five of the following words to use in sentences that describe The Renaissance period: *style, rebirth, ignorant, attain, decline, published, justification.*

_____

_____

_____

_____

_____

_____

_____

_____

_____

_____

_____

_____

Skills Reinforcement Activity 12

Summarizing Information

The ability to summarize information is a part of note taking. Summarizing allows you to record and remember the most important ideas and facts from your reading. When you summarize, you record main ideas in your own words.

DIRECTIONS: Read the following excerpt from your textbook, page 398. Then answer the questions that follow in the space provided.

The word *renaissance* means rebirth. A number of people who lived in Italy between 1350 and 1550 believed that they had witnessed a rebirth of the ancient Greek and Roman worlds. To them, this rebirth marked a new age. Historians later called this period the Renaissance, or Italian Renaissance—a period of European history that began in Italy and spread to the rest of Europe. What are the most important characteristics of the Italian Renaissance?

First, Renaissance Italy was largely an urban society. As the Middle Ages progressed, powerful city-states became the centers of Italian political, economic, and social life. Within this growing urban society, a secular, or worldly, viewpoint emerged as increasing wealth created new enjoyment of material things.

Second, the Renaissance was an age of recovery from the disasters of the fourteenth century—the plague, political instability, and a decline of Church power. Recovery went hand in hand with a rebirth of interest in ancient culture. Italian thinkers became aware of their own Roman past—the remains of which were to be seen all around them. They also became intensely interested in the culture that had dominated the ancient Mediterranean world. This revival affected both politics and art.

Third, a new view of human beings emerged as people in the Italian Renaissance emphasized individual ability. As Leon Battista Alberti, a fifteenth-century Italian, said, "Men can do all things if they will." A high regard for human worth and a realization of what individuals could achieve created a new social ideal. The well-rounded, universal person could achieve much in many areas. Leonardo da Vinci, for example, was a painter, sculptor, architect, inventor, and mathematician.

1. What are the main ideas of these paragraphs?

_____

_____

_____

2. Write a brief summary of two or three sentences to help you remember the important details of these paragraphs.

_____

_____

_____

_____

CHAPTER 12

Critical Thinking Skills Activity 12 | Identifying Assumptions

Identifying assumptions means recognizing that authors usually assume their readers share certain beliefs. It is important to identify these assumptions so you can understand what the author is arguing. The following is an excerpt from a letter written in 1417 by Franciscus Barbarus, a Venetian military leader, statesman, and humanist. It is addressed to Poggius Bracciolini, a scholar who traveled throughout Europe searching for and discovering many works of literature that had been lost for a thousand years. The recovery of these works led to much of the renewed interest in learning and ancient works that is associated with the Renaissance. Franciscus Barbarus is praising Poggius for the work he has already done and the books he has already found.

DIRECTIONS: Read the excerpt. Then answer the questions that follow.

> You have revived so many illustrious men and such wise men, who were dead for eternity, through whose minds and teachings not only we but our descendants will be able to live well and honorably. If our ancestors decided that a triumph should be awarded to those who had captured forts and cities and provinces and if I had as much dignity, power, and gratitude as they who were the most important in the literary Senate and in the house of the Muses, I should decree a triumph for you, since surely their learning and their reasoning power could bring the human race more benefit by far than the deeds of a few illustrious generals ever brought. For as these deeds have sometimes freed a few soldiers or a single city or occasionally one province from impending dangers with great slaughter of men and have turned men from frugality to every and all kinds of lust, so there must be no doubt that culture and mental training, which are adapted to a good and blessed life and fair speech, can bring no trifling advantages not only to private concerns but to cities, nations, and finally to all mankind.
>
> —From *Two Renaissance Book Hunters: The Letters of Poggius Bracciolini to Nicolaus de Niccolis*

1. What does Franciscus Barbarus think people assume about military leaders as opposed to people who pursue learning and literature?

_____

_____

_____

2. Compare Franciscus Barbarus's assumption about people with Niccolò Machiavelli's assumption about the characteristics of a prince found in Section 1.

_____

_____

_____

★ HISTORY AND GEOGRAPHY ACTIVITY 12

Venice, Queen of the Adriatic

"Desponsamus te, mare" (We wed thee, O sea) exclaimed the Doge of Venice, standing at the bow of the state gallery and hurling a consecrated gold ring into the Adriatic Sea. In Renaissance Venice, this symbolic marriage of the city to the sea was performed each year in a splendid water festival that included choirs, trumpets, banners, and a flotilla of gondolas. How did Venice become Queen of the Adriatic—the commercial center of the world at that time?

The city of Venice reached its commercial and political power and glory as a trading center during the 1300s and 1400s. The French ambassador Philippe de Comines in 1495 called Venice's Grand Canal the "handsomest avenue . . . in the whole world." Venetian merchants crowded the canals with their gondolas filled with all manner of goods. "There were so many boats it seemed as if all the gardens of the world must be there," remarked a merchant from Milan when he saw the maze of market boats loaded with produce from the mainland. Far more valuable goods than vegetables, however, were traded on the Venetian canals.

Venice was the hub of commercial activity for the whole Mediterranean. Fleets of merchant ships set out from the northern Adriatic, in the heart of Europe, to move large quantities of diverse products throughout the Mediterranean and Black Seas. Sailors loaded tons of precious East Indian spices onto their ships in Alexandria to be sold in places as far away as England. Some fleets loaded furs, silks, and dyes from Black Sea ports; others carried wool and leather from Spain; and still others transported enslaved people, gold, and ivory from Africa.

Christian pilgrims boarded Venetian ships to sail to the Holy Land. Venetian trade routes began and ended in Venice—the center of the wealthiest trading network in Europe. A medieval monk complained that St. Mark's Square "seems perpetually filled with Turks, Libyans, and Parthians," evidence of Venice's cosmopolitan character

> *Sun-grit city, thou hast been*
> *Ocean's child, and then his queen;*
> *Now is come a darker day,*
> *And thou soon must be his prey.*
>
> —Percy Bysshe Shelley, "Lines written amongst the Euganean Hills," 1818

Venice is located on 120 islands in the Adriatic Sea, separated from Italy's mainland by a lagoon. A system of canals branch off the Grand Canal, clearly visible in this 1500 engraving by Jacopo Dei Barberi. A large complex of shipyards once dominated the eastern tip of the city. There, shipwrights constructed the merchant ships that sailed from Venice to all major ports in the Mediterranean.

HISTORY AND GEOGRAPHY ACTIVITY 12 (continued)

even in its early days. As Venetians moved goods and people across the Mediterranean Sea, cultural and political ideologies traveled with them and spread throughout the region.

Human movement, initiated by human needs and wants, can create patterns and centers of activity. Situated on the Mediterranean Sea and midway between the markets of Asia and western Europe, Venice used its advantageous location to establish Mediterranean trade routes linking these markets. Trade movement brought goods as well as money to Venice, making the city a great commercial center where banking, shipbuilding, and maritime-supply industries thrived. Later, the Portuguese established an Asian trade route around Africa, bypassing the Venetian trade network. Then the center of commercial activity moved from Venice to several cities located along the Atlantic coast.

APPLYING GEOGRAPHY TO HISTORY

DIRECTIONS: Answer the questions below in the space provided.

1. How does human movement create patterns and centers of activity?

_____

2. Study the engraving on the previous page and explain the advantage of having the Grand Canal run through the city.

_____

3. How did Venice's geographic location lead to its becoming an important trading center?

_____

Critical Thinking

4. **Determining Relevance** The expectation of financial profits motivated the Venetians to send fleets throughout the Mediterranean and Black Seas. List other factors that motivate people to move themselves, goods, or ideas from one place to another.

_____

_____

Activity

5. Use an atlas to locate the places where Venetian fleets traveled. Start with a list of the places mentioned on the previous page. Then research to find the largest trading centers in the world today and locate them on maps.

Mapping History Activity 12

The Success of Reform

The Protestant and Catholic Reformations during the Renaissance changed the face of religion in Europe. Instead of being almost exclusively Catholic, now Europe was divided among several different religions: Catholic, Calvinist, Lutheran, Anglican (Church of England), and others. Meanwhile, the Ottoman Empire in the east remained Orthodox, whereas the majority of the eastern Mediterranean and North Africa remained Muslim.

DIRECTIONS: The map below shows the distribution of religions in Europe in 1560. Use the map to answer the questions and complete the activity that follow. Use a separate sheet of paper.

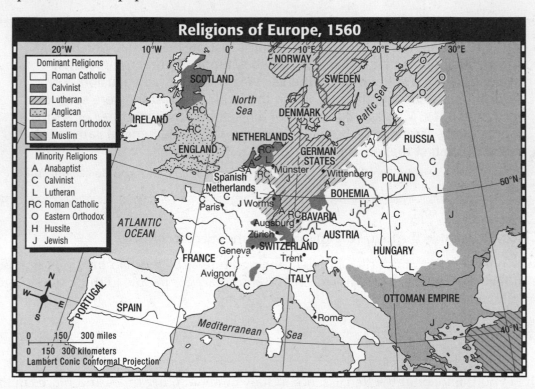

Religions of Europe, 1560

1. Approximately what percent of Europe north and west of the Ottoman Empire was Catholic? What percent was Protestant?

2. Look at the list of towns and cities in the chart. Locate each town or city on the map. Circle Protestant towns in blue and Catholic towns in red.

3. What does this tell you about how successful the Protestant and Catholic Reformations were?

Date	Event	Location
1517	Luther presents a list of Ninety-five Theses to his church superiors.	Wittenberg
1521	Luther rejects council's attempt to reclaim him.	Worms
1525	Ulrich Zwingli establishes theocracy.	Zürich
1534	Anabaptists seize control of city.	Münster
1541	John Calvin establishes Consistory.	Geneva
1542	Inquisition begins.	Rome
1545	Pope Paul III calls for Council to reform doctrine.	Trent

Historical Significance Activity 12

CHAPTER 12

Renaissances

"There is something about the present which we would not exchange, though we were offered a choice of all past ages to live in."

In this 1925 statement, Virginia Woolf points to a human tendency of each generation to privilege its present age. Writers and historians in the Renaissance were the first to describe their age as a "renaissance," literally a rebirth of culture and a new age for Europe. Since then, a long line of scholars have praised the years 1400 to 1600 as a high point for art and humankind. Read the following famous description of the end of the Middle Ages and the beginning of the Renaissance. Note that the new age is contrasted with medieval times by belittling and trivializing the years before the Renaissance.

> In the Middle Ages both sides of human consciousness—that which was turned within as that which was turned without—lay dreaming or half awake beneath a common veil. The veil was woven of faith, illusion and childish prepossession, through which the world and history were seen clad in strange hues. Man was conscious of himself only as a member of a race, people, party, family or corporation—only through some general category. In Italy this veil first melted into air. . . .
>
> —From *The Civilization of the Renaissance in Italy*, by Jacob Burckhardt, 1860

DIRECTIONS: Answer the following questions in the space provided.

1. Many philosophers and writers think of their culture as better than previous ages and claim their own age as a "renaissance." Is it important for people to think of one age as better than a previous age?

   _____

   _____

2. When you think about the Renaissance in Italy or about other times and places in the past, do you think the world today is better than those ages? Would you describe the people of those times as "half awake" or "childish"?

   _____

   _____

3. On a separate sheet of paper, write a short essay on the status of the world today. How will you present society? What do you think are its great achievements? How will you convince your readers that this age is not beneath a "veil" of ignorance? Imagine that your essay will be put in a time capsule that will be opened in 500 years.

★ Cooperative Learning Activity 12 ★

The Renaissance in Italy

BACKGROUND

The Renaissance began in Italy and spread from there throughout the southern part of Europe and then northward. Between A.D. 1350 and 1550, a number of urban intellectuals who lived in the independent northern and central Italian city-states rediscovered Greek and Roman cultures. This rediscovery awakened a new spirit of humanism, trade, and culture in Europe. By working as a group to examine the states and regions of Renaissance Italy, you will note the conditions that paved the way for the Renaissance.

GROUP DIRECTIONS

1. As a group, draw a map of Italy during the Renaissance on a poster-sized sheet of paper. Have individual group members use Chapter 12 in their textbook and other sources to identify the major Italian states that existed during this time. Be sure to include the following:

   the republic of Venice   the duchy of Milan
   the kingdom of Naples   the republic of Florence

2. Each member of the group researches one or more of the states. Group members should identify specific people and events from the state and make notes on note cards about the characteristics of that state.

3. On the map, list or illustrate and label key events and important figures for each state and draw a line from each event to the place where it happened. For example, Leonardo da Vinci painted *The Last Supper* in Milan.

4. Post and share the maps with the class.

ORGANIZING THE GROUP

1. **Group Work/Decision Making** As a group, create a large map of Italy. Identify the locations of the major states and note their similar or dissimilar geographic situations: Are they situated in the north, south, east, or west of Italy? Which have ready access to trade routes? Which have harbors? Decide what standard information to gather and what headings to use for every state. Assign one or more of the states to individual group members for research according to the agreed-upon headings.

2. **Individual Work** Use available sources to gather information about the state(s) assigned to you. Record your information on note cards, using the headings your group decided to use.

3. **Group Work/Decision Making** Share your research with your group. Invite comments on and extensions of individuals' ideas. Determine if additional research is needed for any of the states. Together, decide what information will be included as call outs (boxes that highlight information) on the map.

Cooperative Learning Activity 12 (continued)

4. **Additional Group Work** Create the call outs and illustrations for the map. Assemble the elements of the map and include a map key as needed to explain shading or other geographic elements included on the map. Attach the summary note cards to the back of the map.

5. **Group Sharing** Present the maps to the other groups.

6. **Extended Group Work/Sharing** Invite the members of the class to identify common and distinct elements that took place in the states. Discuss how such events might have given birth to Renaissance thinking.

GROUP PROCESS QUESTIONS

- What is the most important thing you learned about Renaissance Italy from this activity?

- What part of the project did you enjoy most?

- What problems did you have?

- How did you solve the problems?

Quick **CHECK** ✔

1. Was the goal of the assignment clear at all times?

_____

_____

_____

_____

2. How was using a map to present the information different from other types of projects? Was it helpful or would some other presentation method have been more effective?

_____

_____

_____

_____

_____

A Renaissance Fair

As the Italian Renaissance spread to northern Europe and Europeans accepted ideas of humanism and secularism, many cities and towns supported the works of artists, writers, and philosophers.

TEACHER MATERIAL

Learning Objective To broaden students' knowledge and deepen their appreciation of the contributions of Renaissance culture.

Activity Groups of students work together to prepare fair booths (tables) representing selected aspects of Renaissance culture. Each group chooses a cultural focus, researches information about that Renaissance topic, and prepares an exhibit or a demonstration such as posters, poetry, play readings, or models. On a designated day, all the groups present their displays or demonstrations. Group members take turns hosting their booths and answering questions about their chosen Renaissance topics. Students create and distribute surveys to visitors.

Teacher Preparation Provide for each group: poster board, colored markers, paper, tape, ruler. Make a copy of the worksheet on the next page for each student. On the day of the fair, make available a folding table or a few desks for each group and clear a large area of the classroom, or schedule the use of another room for the fair.

Activity Guidelines

1. Introduce the activity to students by explaining its objective and general steps.

2. Organize students into groups of three or four and give a copy of the worksheet to each student.

3. Direct each group to choose one cultural aspect of the Renaissance, using the list of subjects provided. Tell students that they may narrow their subject by focusing on one city or country. For example, architecture in

Rome, literature in England, or painting in northern Europe.

4. Have each group write its subject on the board. Point out that two groups may choose the same subject if they change the focus, such as Italian painting and Dutch painting.

5. Set a date for the fair. Advertise it throughout the school.

6. Direct students to research their topics, consulting with art, literature, or music teachers and librarians as needed. Have groups plan and prepare posters for their booths. Depending on the subject, a booth might also include pictures of paintings, sculptures, or buildings. Encourage groups to cooperate in sharing resources, making copies from books if necessary. If groups are staging demonstrations or readings from literature, advise them to schedule rehearsals.

7. Before the day of the fair, direct groups to make schedules for hosting their booths so that all students will have time to view the various displays and demonstrations. As a class, design and create a survey form that can be handed out to visitors during the fair. The survey should include questions asking visitors what they have learned about the Renaissance and elicit further comments about the booths.

8. After the fair, have students review and discuss visitors' responses.

CHAPTER 12

HANDOUT MATERIAL

A Renaissance Fair—Worksheet

Steps for Staging a Renaissance Fair

1. Choose a subject from the list.

2. Choose a city or country on which to focus.

3. Plan and conduct research.

4. Share research findings with your group members.

5. Plan a poster and pictures, readings, or demonstrations for the fair booth.

6. Prepare the poster. Plan the layout of the booth pictures or rehearse readings or demonstrations.

7. Make a schedule showing the time for each group member to host the booth. The host should be prepared to answer questions.

Subjects for Renaissance Fair Booths

☐ Painting
☐ Architecture
☐ Sculpture
☐ Literature
☐ Music
☐ Sports and Games

Focus City or Country

☐ Germany and Low Countries
☐ Florence
☐ Rome
☐ Venice
☐ Italy
☐ France
☐ England

Items for Fair Booths

- Poster identifying subject and providing key information
- Pictures of paintings, sculptures, or buildings
- Readings from literature
- Musical recordings
- Demonstrations of sports or games

Time Line Activity 12

Renaissance and Reformation

DIRECTIONS: The years A.D. 1350–1600 were a time of development and diffusion of cultural and political activity and a time of dissension and reform within religious institutions. New styles of art, learning, and commerce helped to generate important criticisms of the Catholic Church and, ultimately, the formation of Protestant religions. Read the time line below. Then answer the questions that follow.

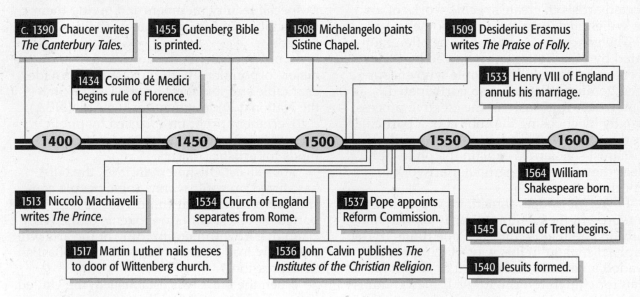

1. Which event on the time line was most important for spreading the ideas of the Renaissance and Reformation?

   _____

2. What was the earliest critique of the practices of the Catholic Church?

   _____

3. Which critique of the practices of the Catholic Church led to the establishment of the first main Protestant religion?

   _____

4. What happened in 1533 that led to the Church of England's separating from Rome?

   _____

5. Which events on the time line helped curtail the spread of Protestantism?

   _____

6. Which book was written before Gutenberg's movable type was developed for printing?

   _____

7. Who wrote a book in 1536 that influenced religious reformers for years to come?

   _____

Supporting the Arts: Past and Present

THEN During the Renaissance, many artists were supported by wealthy patrons. These patrons—who included popes, monarchs, and the rulers of city-states—frequently invited artists to join their households as court artists. Artists were also funded by guilds and local religious organizations. These groups contracted artists to create specific works of art, for which they were paid handsomely.

The generosity of patrons was often motivated by their desire to be viewed by their peers as being cultured people who encouraged geniuses. Patrons also participated, somewhat vicariously, in the creative process, usually by choosing the subject of a particular work of art. More modest patrons hired humanist scholars to explain the philosophical ideas they wanted a particular artwork to reflect.

Powerful leaders sometimes induced artists to represent them, either directly or symbolically, in a religious context. Pope Julius II used Raphael's talent in this way. Having persuaded an ecumenical council to accept his plan for church reform, Julius II then commissioned Raphael to paint a biblical scene, *The Expulsion of Heliodorus*. The picture shows God intervening on behalf of a Jewish high priest. The audience of the day would have recognized that the high priest symbolized Julius and that the pope, like the high priest, was also supported by God.

Although self-interest played a part in their generosity, Renaissance patrons did not usually stifle artists' essential visions. Perhaps this was because patrons and protégés shared an open, exploratory attitude toward life.

NOW Art is still supported by wealthy individuals. Today, artists display their works in galleries with the hope that the works of art will be bought. In today's art market, successful artists are those who most please the tastes of the buyer. Universities and colleges also support well-known artists by hiring them as special faculty members and giving them the facilities and time to pursue their own projects.

In most countries, the government and major corporations both buy art and provide charitable support for it. In the United States, the National Endowment for the Arts (NEA), a government program financed by public money or taxes, is an important source of funds for artistic projects.

Since its establishment in 1965, the NEA has stirred up controversy. Some people consider art a luxury that should not be supported by taxes. Other opponents of the NEA claim that government funding of the arts will inevitably lead to the political control of artistic expression.

When the NEA was established, the United States Congress stressed that, in accordance with the Constitution, the program was required to allow freedom of expression. However, in 1989 Congress cut the NEA's budget by $45,000 to punish it for supporting art that many citizens found objectionable. Congress also passed a bill that prohibited the NEA from financing similar works.

CRITICAL THINKING

Directions: Answer the following questions on a separate sheet of paper.

1. **Drawing conclusions:** How did Renaissance patrons influence artistic expression?

2. **Making inferences:** How is the United States Congress able to influence artistic expression?

3. **Synthesizing information:** Why do some people want to ban hip hop music? Do research in the library and on the Internet to examine some of the differing opinions on the relevance and importance of hip hop music in contemporary American culture. Write a brief report on your findings, state with which viewpoint you agree, and explain your reasoning.

CHAPTER 12

People in World History Activity 12 — Profile 1

CHAPTER 12

Johannes Gutenberg (c. 1397–1468)

He who first shortened the labour of copyists by device of Movable Types was disbanding hired armies, and cashiering most Kings and Senates, and creating a whole new democratic world: he had invented the art of printing.

From *Sartor Resartus* (1834) by Thomas Carlyle

The Gutenberg Bible, set and printed in 1455, is perhaps the most famous book in history. It is the product of the first successful attempt to use movable type and the printing press in an efficient way. These developments made it possible to print books and other materials quickly. During the centuries since then, the spread of books around the world—and the ideas they carry—has altered human life in profound ways. In developing this method of printing, Johannes Gutenberg secured his place in history.

Johannes Gutenberg was born to an aristocratic family in Mainz, Germany, in about 1397. Mainz was a center for goldsmiths, and Gutenberg may have been trained in goldsmithing as a young man. When he was about 40, Gutenberg began his experiments with printing. He combined movable type, type molds, oil-based inks, and a special printing press to create a workable printing system. Many of these ideas existed, but Gutenberg improved, refined, and, most important, combined them. The basic method of printing he developed remained in use well into the 1900s.

In 1446 Gutenberg entered a partnership with a man named Johannes Fust. Fust, a goldsmith, lent money to Gutenberg to help him pursue his printing work. When the partnership failed after five years—Gutenberg was apparently unable to repay the loan when Fust demanded it—Gutenberg was forced to surrender his printing equipment and supplies to Fust. Fust and his son-in-law continued printing.

Gutenberg found patronage under a wealthy man in Mainz, thus enabling him to continue to print. Apparently, he gave up printing in 1465, perhaps due to failing eyesight. When he died in 1468, at nearly 70 years old, he was not a wealthy man. He probably never knew, though he may have dreamed, how his work would affect the world in the centuries to come. Today, Mainz honors its most famous son through the Gutenberg Museum and Johannes Gutenberg University. His original workshop has been restored and preserved. Fittingly, printing is an important industry in the hometown of Johannes Gutenberg.

REVIEWING THE PROFILE

Directions: Answer the following questions on a separate sheet of paper.

1. In what trade was Gutenberg trained?

2. **Critical Thinking** Making Inferences. How might Gutenberg's early training have helped him develop his method of printing?

3. **Critical Thinking** Drawing Conclusions. Write a paragraph in which you assess the impact and influence of Gutenberg's work.

People in World History Activity 12   Profile 2

CHAPTER 12

Martin Luther (1483–1546)

A mighty fortress is our God,
A bulwark never failing.
Our helper He amid the flood
Of mortal ills prevailing.

Hymn based on "Ein' Feste Burg" (1529) by Martin Luther

Martin Luther was raised in the mining town of Mansfield, Germany. In keeping with his father's wishes, Luther enrolled at the University of Erfurt in 1501 to study law, but he abandoned his legal studies in 1505 and entered a monastery instead. It was a hard, disciplined life. He lived in an unheated cell, leaving only to receive instruction, take meals in silence, and join others in the chapel for services. Luther was ordained a Roman Catholic priest and celebrated his first Mass in 1507. Luther continued his studies and, by 1512 was a professor of biblical theology at the University of Wittenberg.

The Roman Catholic Church had developed indulgences as a way to release sinners from part of the penance for their sins. For example, instead of going on a pilgrimage as a penalty for one's sins, an indulgence permitted the person to make a contribution to a worthy cause. In 1515 the pope authorized the sale of indulgences to raise money to build St. Peter's Basilica in Rome.

In response to what he saw as the abuse of indulgences, Luther wrote a letter explaining that by seeking escape from divine punishment through indulgences, people were led away from true sorrow for their sins and into a sense of false security. This letter became known as the Ninety-five Theses.

The Theses marked the beginning of Luther's disillusionment with the Church and the start of the Reformation. Luther went on to publish other highly influential works questioning the Church's teachings.

In April 1521, Luther was given a hearing before a meeting at Worms, Germany. Although urged to retract his teachings, Luther refused. The emperor then declared Luther an outlaw. Luther's supporters hid him at Wartburg Castle, where he spent time studying and writing. During his year there, he translated the Bible into German. He took care to write simply and in common everyday language. Together with hymns he had written, this German Bible was to become a mighty force of the Reformation.

Luther remained a professor at the university where some 16,000 students studied the teaching of Luther and his successors in the theological faculty, spreading the new Lutheran religion across Germany.

REVIEWING THE PROFILE

Directions: Answer the following questions on a separate sheet of paper.

1. Before Luther criticized the Catholic Church, how did he make his living?

2. What did Luther write that had a great influence on the Reformation?

3. **Critical Thinking** **Determining Cause and Effect.** Do you think Luther's study of the law had any influence on his later criticisms of the Catholic Church? Why or why not?

PRIMARY SOURCE READING 12

The Autobiography of Benvenuto Cellini

Benvenuto Cellini (1500–1571), Florentine goldsmith and writer, embodies two of the defining characteristics of the Renaissance. First, like his contemporaries Michelangelo and Leonardo da Vinci, Cellini created great works of art in more than one category. He excelled as a goldsmith and sculptor, and his autobiography continues to entertain readers long after its publication. Second, his decision to write down his life story and accomplishments exemplifies the Renaissance humanist belief in the importance of creative achievement on the earth.

Guided Reading *In this selection, read to learn what life was like for a struggling young artist in Renaissance Florence.*

XV

I had come to know some worthy men among the goldsmiths . . . but I also met with others reputed honest, who did all they could to ruin me, and robbed me grossly. When I perceived this, I left their company, and held them for thieves and blackguards. One of the goldsmiths . . . kindly accommodated me with part of his shop. . . . There I finished several pretty pieces, and made good gains, and was able to give my family much help. This aroused the jealousy of the bad men among my former masters. . . . On becoming aware of their evil will against me, I complained to certain worthy fellows, and remarked that they ought to have been satisfied with the thieveries they practised on me under the cloak of hypocritical kindness. This coming to their ears, they threatened to make me sorely repent of such words; but I, who knew not what the colour of fear was, paid them little or no heed.

XVI

It chanced one day that I was leaning against a shop of one of these men, who called out to me, and began partly reproaching, partly bullying. I answered that had they done their duty by me, I should have spoken of them what one speaks of good and worthy men; but as they had done the contrary, they ought to complain of themselves and not of me. While I was standing there and talking, one of them, named Gherardo Guasconti, their cousin, having perhaps been put up to it by them, lay in wait till a beast of burden went by. It was a load of bricks. When the load reached me, Gherardo pushed it so violently on my body that I was very much hurt. Turning suddenly round and seeing him laughing, I struck him such a blow on the temple that he fell down, stunned, like one dead. Then I faced round to his cousins, and said: "That's the way to treat cowardly thieves of your sort"; and when they wanted to make a move upon me, trusting to their numbers, I, whose blood was now well up, laid hands to a little knife I had, and cried: "If one of you comes out of the shop, let the other run for the confessor, because the doctor will have nothing to do here." These words so frightened them that not one stirred to help their cousin. . . . The magistrates had me summoned. . . . I, inexperienced in such matters, had not spoken to any of them, trusting in the goodness of my cause. I said that, having received such outrage and insult from Gherardo, and in my fury having only given him a box on the ear, I did not think I deserved such a vehement reprimand. . . . Prinzivalle spoke thus in my defence to his brother judges: "Mark, sirs, the simplicity of this poor young man. . . . He is a young man of admirable talents, and supports his poor family by his labour in great abundance; I would to God that our city had plenty of this sort, instead of the present dearth of them."

XVII

. . . The chancellor bound us over upon bail on both sides; but only I was punished by having to pay the four measures of meal [flour]. Albeit just then I felt as though I had been massacred, I sent for one of my cousins . . . desiring that he should go to bail for me. He refused to

PRIMARY SOURCE READING 12

come, which made me so angry, that, fuming with fury and swelling like an asp, I took a desperate resolve. . . . I left the palace, ran to my shop, seized a dagger, and rushed to the house of my enemies, who were at home and shop together. I found them at table; and Gherardo, who had been the cause of the quarrel, flung himself upon me. I stabbed him in the breast, piercing the doublet and jerkin through and through to the shirt, without however grazing his flesh or doing him the least harm in the world. When I felt my hand go in, and heard the clothes tear, I thought that I had killed him; and seeing him fall terror-struck to earth, I cried: "Traitors, this day is the day on which I mean to murder you all." . . . I ran storming down the staircase; and when I reached the street, I found

all the rest of the household, more than twelve persons; one of them had seized an iron shovel, another a thick iron pipe, one had an anvil, some of them hammers, and some cudgels. When I got among them, raging like a mad bull, I flung four or five to the earth, and fell down with them myself, continually aiming my dagger now at one and now at another. . . . but inasmuch as God does sometimes mercifully intervene, He so ordered that neither they nor I did any harm to one another. I only lost my cap, on which my adversaries seized, though they had run away from it before, and struck at it with all their weapons. Afterwards, they searched among their dead and wounded, and saw that not a single man was injured.

INTERPRETING THE READING

Directions *Use the information from the reading to answer the following questions. If necessary, use a separate sheet of paper.*

1. Who were Cellini's enemies in Florence?

_____

2. What was the outcome of the quarrel?

_____

_____

Critical Thinking

3. **Recognizing Bias** How reliable do you find Cellini as a narrator? Why?

_____

_____

_____

_____

4. **Making Inferences** What kind of person was Cellini? Use details from the excerpt to support your answer.

_____

_____

_____

_____

World Art and Music Activity 12

Michelangelo

Michelangelo is considered one of the greatest and most important artists of the Renaissance. He lived for 89 years, and for 70 of those years, he created sculptures, paintings, and architecture that continue to influence and inspire people all over the world.

DIRECTIONS: Read the passage below about this Italian artist. Then answer the questions in the space provided.

Michelangelo Buonarroti was born in 1475 in Caprese, near Florence, Italy. He studied under the master fresco painter Domenico Ghirlandaio, then became a student of a sculptor working for the Medicis. When he was only 24, he completed his *Pietà,* which was immediately hailed as a masterpiece. Michelangelo loved the three-dimensional quality of sculpture. In a sense, he thought the figure was already within the marble and that the sculptor "released" it.

Michelangelo's best-known sculpture is his 13-foot-high marble statue of David, which he created while still in his twenties. The perfectly proportioned David, who has just slain Goliath, stands strong yet relaxed, muscular yet graceful. The statue was given a place of honor outside Florence's Palazzo Vecchio, the seat of the Medici government.

In both the *Pietà* and *David,* Michelangelo placed emphasis on the figures' faces. Sadness and humility can be seen in Mary's face as she gazes at her dead son. David looks calm but tense, as if ready for whatever may occur.

Other Florentine sculptors of the time were envious of Michelangelo's talent and success. The large Sistine Chapel in the Vatican needed artwork for its ceiling. Michelangelo's fellow sculptors persuaded Pope Julius II to commission him to paint the ceiling, thus eliminating their competition in the world of sculpture. Everyone—even Michelangelo himself—expected him to fail.

For more than four years (1508–1512), Michelangelo toiled on the 40-foot by 133-foot ceiling from scaffolding 68 feet above the floor. When he was finished, he had painted 145 pictures with more than

Michelangelo, *Pietà,* 1499, St. Peter's Basilica, Rome

300 figures. This great fresco tells a great story: the creation of the world, Adam and Eve's expulsion from Eden, and humanity's ultimate reconciliation with God. God appears in the sky and with a gesture creates Adam. Later we see an anguished Adam and Eve being forced to leave Eden. The story continues with Noah

> *Until you have seen the Sistine Chapel, you can have no adequate conception of what man is capable of accomplishing.*
>
> —Johann Wolfgang von Goethe

(continued)

World Art and Music Activity 12

and the flood. Heroic figures act out their epic roles in broad brushstrokes and an astonishing range of colors.

Michelangelo returned to the Sistine Chapel more than 20 years later, in 1534. This time he painted *The Last Judgment,* a vast fresco that covers the entire altar wall. Hundreds of figures (including a self-portrait of Michelangelo), the blessed and damned alike, all beg for God's mercy. Each figure is different, with a unique facial expression. It is an intense work, less optimistic than the ceiling.

During the last 30 years of his life, Michelangelo shifted his focus to architecture. In his paintings and sculpture, he learned from his predecessors and improved on their techniques. His architecture was similarly innovative. This is apparent in his Laurentian Library in Florence, which Michelangelo designed to house all of the Medici family's books and

manuscripts. Michelangelo's design for the building uses basic classical elements—columns, pilasters, and entablatures—yet they are arranged in a way that defies the ideals of classical perspective.

Michelangelo went on to redesign the Campidoglio, the top of the Capitoline Hill in Rome, into a monumental square. After walking up a flight of steps, the visitor is suddenly in an "outdoor room," surrounded on the other three sides by long two-story buildings. It remains the most imposing civic center ever built and a model for countless others.

Michelangelo's last achievement was St. Peter's Basilica in Rome. The building's elegant dome draws the eye upward from the body of the church. Everything reinforces this journey to the heavens. Unfortunately, Michelangelo died in 1564, without seeing the dome completed.

Reviewing the Selection

1. What are Michelangelo's major works?

_____

2. What are the characteristics of his art?

_____

3. What effect does the *Pietà* sculpture have on you? Explain.

_____

_____

Critical Thinking

4. Identifying Central Issues What is the main idea in this reading? What are the supporting details?

_____

_____

5. Drawing Conclusions Michelangelo loved sculpting, yet his fame rests more on his Sistine Chapel frescoes. Which do you think gave him more pleasure? Explain your answer.

_____

_____

Reteaching Activity 12

Renaissance and Reformation

The years 1350 to 1600 were a time of new ideas in government, art, scholarship, and religion. The Renaissance began as Italian intellectuals revisited the Greek and Roman cultures. The Reformation spread new ideas in religion.

DIRECTIONS: The outline below lists five cultural areas in which innovations, as well as rediscoveries of techniques that had fallen into disuse, occurred. Under each heading, write the innovations and rediscoveries, selecting from the following list.

- Petrarch is called the father of Italian Renaissance humanism.
- Architects used columns and arches to create a human-centered environment.
- Artists created lifelike, freestanding statues.
- Humanists wrote in the vernacular.
- Using new techniques, artists made paintings more lifelike.
- Reformers removed decorations from Protestant churches.
- Protestantism was born as a result of Luther's conflicts with the Catholic Church.
- With a new method of printing, books became more widely available.
- Northern European painters developed the technique of painting in oils.
- The Catholic Reformation began in reaction to the spread of Protestantism.

Innovations and Rediscoveries

A. Painting

  1. _____

  2. _____

B. Architecture

  1. _____

  2. _____

C. Sculpture

  1. _____

D. Literature

  1. _____

  2. _____

  3. _____

E. Religion

  1. _____

  2. _____

★ Enrichment Activity 12

The State of the World, 1516

Section 2 describes the way northern Europe was affected by the Renaissance and humanist ideas. The following excerpt from Sir Thomas More's *Utopia* (1516) shows the author's critical vision of the state of Europe at this time.

When I run over in my mind the various commonwealths flourishing today, so help me God, I can see in them nothing but a conspiracy of the rich, who are fattening up their own interests under the name and title of the commonwealth. They invent ways and means to hang onto whatever they have acquired by sharp practice, and then they scheme to oppress the poor by buying up their toil and labor as cheaply as possible. These devices become law as soon as the rich, speaking through the commonwealth—which, of course, includes the poor as well—say they must be observed.

And yet when these insatiably greedy and evil men have divided among themselves goods which would have sufficed for the entire people, how far they remain from the happiness of the Utopian Republic, which has abolished not only money but with it greed! What a mass of trouble was cut away by that one step! What a thicket of crimes was uprooted! Everyone knows that if money were abolished, fraud, theft, robbery, quarrels, brawls, seditions, murders, treasons, poisonings, and a whole set of crimes which are avenged but not prevented by the hangman would at once die out. If money disappeared, so would fear, anxiety, worry, toil, and sleepless nights. Even poverty, which seems to need money more than anything else, would vanish if money were entirely done away with.

Consider if you will this example. Take a barren year of failed harvests, when many thousands of men have been carried off by hunger. If at the end of the famine the barns of the rich were searched, I dare say positively enough grain would be found in them to have kept all those who died of starvation and disease from even realizing that a shortage ever existed—if only it had been divided equally among them. So easily might men get the necessities of life if that cursed money, which is supposed to provide access to them, were not in fact the chief barrier to our getting what we need to live. Even the rich, I'm sure, understand this. They must know that it's better to have enough of what we really need than an abundance of superfluities, much better to escape from our many present troubles than to be burdened with great masses of wealth.

—From *Utopia* by Sir Thomas More, text and translation by Robert M. Adams.

DIRECTIONS: Use a separate sheet of paper to answer the following questions.

1. Compare the belief of Erasmus and others that the popes had corrupted the Catholic Church with the excerpt above. How are they similar? How are they different?

2. Compare the description of commonwealths in More's time with society today. How are they similar? How is society different today?

3. Put yourself in the place of a rich person and argue in favor of a commonwealth. Then put yourself in the place of a poor peasant and argue in favor of a utopia.

GLENCOE

WORLD HISTORY

Chapter 12
Section Resources

GUIDED READING ACTIVITY 12-1   50

GUIDED READING ACTIVITY 12-2   51

GUIDED READING ACTIVITY 12-3   52

GUIDED READING ACTIVITY 12-4   53

SECTIONS

Guided Reading Activity 12-1

The Renaissance

DIRECTIONS: Answer the following questions as you read Section 1.

1. Why was the term *renaissance* used to refer to the time between 1350 and 1550?

_____

_____

2. What are the three most important characteristics of the Italian Renaissance?

_____

_____

3. Which three city-states played crucial roles in Italian politics?

_____

4. How did the location of Milan help to make it rich and powerful?

_____

_____

5. What activities in Florence did the Dominican preacher Savonarola seek to regulate?

_____

6. Which two European countries made Italy their battleground for 30 years?

_____

7. Why did the army of Charles I of Spain sack the city of Rome in 1527?

_____

_____

8. What has been the impact of Niccolo Machiavelli's book *The Prince*?

_____

9. From Machiavelli's point of view, what attitude should a prince have toward power?

_____

_____

10. What did Castiglione say were the three characteristics of a perfect Renaissance noble?

_____

_____

11. How did Italian families have their children declared adults?

_____

SECTION 12-1

Guided Reading Activity 12-2

Ideas and Art of the Renaissance

DIRECTIONS: As you are reading the section, decide if a statement is true or false. Write **T** if the statement is true or **F** if the statement is false. For all false statements, write a corrected statement.

_____ **1.** A key intellectual movement of the Renaissance was secularism.

_____

_____ **2.** Humanists used the works of Cicero as a model for prose and those of Virgil for poetry.

_____

_____ **3.** Dante's masterpiece, the *Divine Comedy*, is the story of two clowns in a medieval circus.

_____

_____ **4.** *The Canterbury Tales* is a collection of stories told by a group of 29 pilgrims headed for the tomb of Saint Thomas à Becket.

_____

_____ **5.** During the Renaissance, studies were called "liberal" because of their non-conservative approach.

_____

_____ **6.** In Renaissance art, God was the focus of attention.

_____

_____ **7.** By the end of the fifteenth century, Italian painters, sculptors, and architects had mastered the new techniques for symbolically portraying the world around them.

_____

_____ **8.** The High Renaissance in Italy is associated with three artistic giants—Leonardo da Vinci, Raphael, and Michelangelo.

_____

_____ **9.** The Flemish painter Jan van Eyck was among the first to use oil paint.

_____

_____ **10.** By 1500 artists from northern Europe had rejected Italian techniques.

_____

SECTION 12-2

Guided Reading Activity 12-3

The Protestant Reformation

DIRECTIONS: Fill in the blanks below as you read Section 3.

SECTION 12-3

I. The Protestant Reformation divided the western Church into _____ and _____ groups.

    A. Christian _____ believed that through _____, humans could improve themselves.

    B. _____ sought _____ within the Catholic Church without breaking away.

        1. Popes were too often concerned with _____ rather than with _____ matters.

        2. Church officials often used their office to advance their careers and grow _____.

II. Martin Luther gained an answer to the problem of the _____ of salvation.

    A. Catholic teaching stressed both faith and _____ to obtain _____.

    B. Luther came to believe that the Bible taught _____ by faith alone.

        1. Luther sent a list of _____ Theses to his church superiors, attacking the sale of _____.

        2. By 1520 Luther called on German princes to overthrow the papacy and establish a _____ church in Germany.

        3. The Church _____ Luther in January 1521.

III. Luther's religious movement became a _____.

    A. German rulers took control of Catholic churches and formed _____ churches.

    B. Luther _____ with the German rulers during a _____ revolt.

    C. Political turmoil and problems in the _____ helped Lutheranism survive.

        1. Lutheran princes were well-_____ by the time Charles V brought military forces to Germany.

        2. An end to religious warfare in Germany came with the _____.

Guided Reading Activity 12-4

The Spread of Protestantism

DIRECTIONS: Fill in the blanks below as you read Section 4.

1. With the Peace of Augsburg, many feared the ideal of Christian _____ was forever lost.

2. _____, a reformer priest in Switzerland, sought an alliance with _____ and the German reformers.

3. When John Calvin converted to _____, he was forced to flee his native _____.

4. Calvin placed much emphasis on the _____ nature of God.

5. In 1534 Henry VIII asked _____ to finalize the break of the Catholic Church in England with the pope in Rome.

6. During the reign of _____, church officials moved the Church of England, or Anglican Church, in a Protestant direction.

7. The _____ were a radical group that strongly disliked giving power to the state to control the affairs of the church.

8. Anabaptists considered all believers to be _____, chose their own ministers, and any member of the community was _____ to be a minister.

9. Protestants developed a new view of the family. They abolished the requirement of _____ for the clergy.

10. Calvin and Luther believed women were to obey their _____ and bear _____.

11. Three chief pillars supported the Catholic Reformation of the sixteenth century: _____, _____, and the _____.

12. After the Council of Trent, the Roman Catholic Church possessed a clear body of _____ and was unified under the supreme _____ of the pope.

SECTION 12-4

Chapter 13 Resources
The Age of Exploration, 1500–1800

READING SKILLS ACTIVITY 13
Time and Sequence   57

HISTORICAL ANALYSIS SKILLS ACTIVITY 13
Interpreting Economics   58

DIFFERENTIATED INSTRUCITON ACTIVITY 13
European Expeditions   59

ENGLISH LEARNER ACTIVITY 13
The Age of Exploration   61

CONTENT VOCABULARY ACTIVITY 13
The Age of Exploration, 1500–1800   63

ACADEMIC VOCABULARY ACTIVITY 13
The Age of Exploration   65

SKILLS REINFORCEMENT ACTIVITY 13
Making Inferences and Drawing
Conclusions   67

CRITICAL THINKING SKILLS ACTIVITY 13
Analyzing Information   68

HISTORY AND GEOGRAPHY ACTIVITY 13
Looking at the Land   69

MAPPING HISTORY ACTIVITY 13
Who Took What?   71

HISTORICAL SIGNIFICANCE ACTIVITY 13
Joint-Stock Companies   72

COOPERATIVE LEARNING ACTIVITY 13
The *New Horizons.info* Web Site   73

HISTORY SIMULATION ACTIVITY 13
The Search for Andronia   75

TIME LINE ACTIVITY 13
The Age of Exploration   77

LINKING PAST AND PRESENT ACTIVITY 13
Exploring Space: Past and Present   78

PEOPLE IN WORLD HISTORY ACTIVITY 13
Profile 1: Francisco Pizarro
(c. 1478–1541)   79
Profile 2: Jacques Cartier
(1491–1557)   80

PRIMARY SOURCE READING 13
A Letter by Christopher Columbus   81

WORLD ART AND MUSIC ACTIVITY 13
African Tribal Masks   83

RETEACHING ACTIVITY 13
The Age of Exploration   85

ENRICHMENT ACTIVITY 13
The European View of the Americas 86

Reading Skills Activity 13

Time and Sequence

LEARNING THE SKILL

When you read about history, the order in which events happened is very important. Placing events in a sequence will help you understand their causes and effects. Authors use various words to show you the order of events in time, called chronological order. These words include *first, second, finally, next, then, since, soon, previously, before, after, meanwhile, at the same time,* and *last.* Dates and times also show you when an event occurred in relation to other events. Timelines also help to place events in sequence. All of these tools are clues you can use in your reading to help you understand how events in history unfold.

PRACTICING THE SKILL

DIRECTIONS: Read the following paragraphs and underline the signal words that show you the chronological order of events.

In November Cortes arrived at Tenochtitlan and was welcomed by the Aztec monarch Montezuma . . .

Eventually tensions arose between the Spaniards and the Aztec. The Spanish took Montezuma hostage and began to pillage the city. In the fall of 1520, one year after Cortes had first arrived, the local population revolted and drove the invaders from the city. Many of the Spanish were killed.

The Aztec soon experienced new disasters, however. As one Aztec related, "But at about the time that the Spaniards had fled from Mexico, there came a great sickness, a pestilence, the smallpox." With no natural immunity to European diseases, many Aztec fell sick and died. Meanwhile, Cortes received fresh soldiers from his new allies; the state of Tlaxcala alone provided 50,000 warriors. After four months, the city surrendered. . . . During the next 30 years, the Spanish expanded their control to all of Mexico.

APPLYING THE SKILL

DIRECTIONS: Think about time and sequence to explore what you have learned in this chapter. Pick a section of the chapter. Go through it, writing down on a separate sheet of paper the words that give you clues to the time sequence of events in the section. Even if you don't have the exact dates of the events, you can still estimate when things happened, using the clue words the author has provided for you in the text.

Historical Analysis Skills Activity 13

Interpreting Economics

LEARNING THE SKILL

One way to understand economics is to look at the relationship between the costs and benefits of an economic policy. For example, European nations became very successful colonizers and traders in the seventeenth century. However, there were destructive, costly aspects to this economic success. Millions of Africans lost their freedom as they were captured and sold as slaves. Almost all people today view the slave trade as morally wrong. But in addition to that, the costs and benefits of the slave trade were wildly unbalanced, making the slave trade an unsuccessful economic policy.

PRACTICING THE SKILL

DIRECTIONS: Reread the information under the headings "Trade, Colonies, and Mercantilism" on pages 440–442. Then answer the following questions about European colonies and trade.

1. What were some of the costs and benefits of the theory of mercantilism?

   _____

   _____

   _____

   _____

   _____

2. European governments granted subsidies to new industries. What is a subsidy? What was the motive for granting them?

   _____

   _____

   _____

   _____

APPLYING THE SKILL

DIRECTIONS: Research the economic costs and benefits experienced by colonial America in the 1700s. How did the trading relationship between England and America help and harm the American economy? Summarize your findings in a couple of paragraphs to present to the class.

Differentiated Instruction Activity 13

European Expeditions

At the end of the fifteenth century, Europeans began to set out on a series of overseas expeditions. Economic gain, religious zeal, and glory and recognition were all motives that led explorers to journey to the new lands.

DIRECTIONS: Using your textbook and other library resources, work in a small group to learn more about one of the early European explorers. Research the explorer's motive for traveling, the travel route they took, discoveries made while on their voyage, and the effects of their expedition had on Europe and other countries.

Present your research in the form of an oral presentation. Include visuals and maps with your presentation. Use the outline below to help organize your research and ideas.

European Explorer: _____

Motive for travel: _____

_____

_____

Travel route: _____

_____

Discoveries made: _____

_____

_____

_____

Effects of the expedition: _____

_____

_____

Other interesting facts: _____

_____

_____

_____

_____

CHAPTER 13

(continued)

Differentiated Instruction Activity 13

For the Teacher

TEACHING STRATEGIES FOR DIFFERENT LEARNING STYLES

The following activities are ways the basic lesson can be modified to accommodate students' different learning styles:

English Learners (EL) Ask students to focus their research on an explorer's discoveries. Have students make a list of the items discovered because of the expedition.

Advanced Learners (AL) Have students write a collection of journal entries imagining they were the explorer they researched. Students' entries should focus on the journey, their discoveries, what the saw, and thoughts on the areas they visited. Have students share one or two entries with their group's presentation.

Below Grade Level (BL) Make sure struggling students are grouped with more advanced learners for this activity. Ensure that all group members play an active role in this project.

On Grade Level (OL) Have students complete the activity as presented.

English Learner Activity 13

The Age of Exploration

✪ A. PRE-READING ACTIVITY: IMPROVING READING COMPREHENSION

Directions: *Before reading "Motives and Means" on pages 430–431, answer the following questions.*

1. What motivated Europeans to explore unknown distant lands? What things motivate you when you are at school or participating in extracurricular activities?

_____

_____

_____

_____

2. What are the benefits of expanding to new territory?

_____

_____

_____

_____

✪ B. WORD BUILDING ACTIVITY: LEARNING WORD FORMS

Directions: *Fill in the blanks with the correct form of the words below.*

1. **exploration**

   Noun: Portugal led the way in European _____ beginning in 1520 under the sponsorship of Prince Henry.

   Verb: Vasco da Gama _____ the coast of India and brought back spices to Portugal making a profit of several hundred percent.

2. **persuade**

   Verb: Christopher Columbus _____ Queen Isabella to finance his exploratory expedition.

   Adjective: Ferdinand Magellan was _____ in obtaining financing for his voyage to Asia through the Western Hemisphere.

3. **arrive**

   Verb: When the British _____ in Benin, they found a society that had been corrupt by slave trade.

   Adjective: Upon their _____ through the Middle Passage, slaves often died from diseases.

(continued)

CHAPTER 13

English Learner Activity 13

✪ C. WORD BUILDING ACTIVITY: WORDS WITH MULTIPLE MEANINGS

> Word Usage Note: <u>Lead</u>
>
> The word *lead* has several meanings:
>
> A. (v.) cause to go with one, especially by guiding or going in front
> B. (n.) amount by which a competitor is ahead of the others
> C. (n.) clue in a case
> D. (n.) leash

Directions: *Match the definition of the underlined word in each sentence with its definition above.*

_____ **1.** Runner number 468 is in the <u>lead</u>.

_____ **2.** The detectives were waiting for a <u>lead</u> that would prove useful.

_____ **3.** Portugal took the <u>lead</u> in European exploration.

_____ **4.** I could not find the dog's <u>lead</u> where I had left it.

✪ D. WORD BUILDING ACTIVITY: SYNONYMS AND ANTONYMS

Directions: *Match each word in the numbered column with its antonym in the lettered column. Remember that antonyms are words with opposite meanings.*

1.	wealthy	**a.**	decrease
2.	expand	**b.**	import
3.	accept	**c.**	urban
4.	rural	**d.**	contract
5.	export	**e.**	needy
6.	increase	**f.**	reject

Content Vocabulary Activity 13

The Age of Exploration, 1500–1800

DIRECTIONS: Match each term with its definition by writing the correct letter on the blank.

A.	balance of trade	**E.**	line of demarcation
B.	conquistador	**F.**	mercantilism
C.	overseas	**G**	Middle Passage
D.	plantation	**H.**	triangular trade

_____ **1.** imaginary division of Spain's and Portugal's spheres of influence

_____ **2.** theory that a state's power depends on its wealth

_____ **3.** formed by ships that sailed from Europe to Africa, from Africa to the Americas, and from the Americas back to Europe

_____ **4.** torturous journey of enslaved people from Africa to the Americas

_____ **5.** across the ocean

_____ **6.** considered favorable when a country exports more goods than it imports

_____ **7.** large agricultural estate

_____ **8.** Spanish conqueror

DIRECTIONS: Identify the sponsoring country for each explorer and write the correct letter on the blank. Letters can be used more than once.

A. England   **B.** Spain   **C.** Portugal

_____ **9.** Hernán Cortés

_____ **10.** Vasco da Gama

_____ **11.** Christopher Columbus

_____ **12.** John Cabot

_____ **13.** Francisco Pizarro

CHAPTER 13

AB Academic Vocabulary Activity 13

The Age of Exploration

A. Word Meaning Activity
Vocabulary in Context

DIRECTIONS: Complete these sentences with one of the following words: *labor, draft, expansion, primary, transportation, lucrative, global age, missions, overseas, percent.*

1. Many European explorers set out on _____ journeys in search of God, glory, and gold.

2. Upon returning to Portugal, de Gama made a profit of several thousand _____ for the spice cargo he picked up in Calicut.

3. Governments improved _____ systems to stimulate and encourage exports.

4. As European _____ increased, there was a dramatic increase in slave trade.

5. Southwest Asia was the _____ market for African slaves in the fifteenth century.

6. Latin American soon became a multiracial society when the Spanish and Portuguese moved in with Native Americans and Africans who brought to be used as _____ .

7. In Peru authorities were allowed to _____ native labor to work in the silver mines.

B. Word Usage Activity
Use Vocabulary in Writing

DIRECTIONS: Choose five of the following words to create five book titles that would have been written during the Age of Exploration: *overseas, global age, transportation, expansion, primary, missions.*

_____

_____

_____

_____

_____

_____

_____

(continued)

Academic Vocabulary Activity 13

C. Word Family Activity
Learning Word Forms

DIRECTIONS: Complete the chart below with the appropriate noun or verb form.

Noun	Verb
1. transportation	
2.	expand
3. enabler	
4.	discover
5. exploration	
6.	regulate

D. Word Meaning Activity
Synonyms or Antonyms

DIRECTIONS: Label the following pairs of words as synonyms (S) or antonyms (A). Remember, synonyms are words that have similar meanings, and antonyms are words that have opposite meanings.

1. _____ worldwide / global

2. _____ expand / decrease

3. _____ primary / original

4. _____ abor / work

5. _____ lucrative / loss

6. _____ keep / transport

CHAPTER 13

Skills Reinforcement Activity 13

Making Inferences and Drawing Conclusions

Many Italians ventured north to trade and share their learning among the Europeans. As they did so, many sent back letters and kept journals of their impressions.

DIRECTIONS: Read the following observations of life among the English by an Italian from about 1500. Then answer the questions that follow in the space provided.

> . . . the English are great lovers of themselves, and of everything belonging to them; they think that there are no other men than themselves, and no other world but England; and whenever they see a handsome foreigner, they say that "he looks like an Englishman," and that "it is a great pity that he should not be an Englishman"; and when they partake of any delicacy with a foreigner, they ask him "whether such a thing is made in *their* country?" . . .
>
> They have an antipathy to foreigners, and imagine that they never come into their island but to make themselves masters of it, and to usurp their goods; neither have they any sincere and solid friendships amongst themselves, insomuch that they do not trust each other to discuss either public or private affairs together, in the confidential manner we do in Italy.
>
> —From *A Relation of the Island of England*, trans. Charlotte A. Sneyd

1. What facts does the author present?

_____

_____

2. What does the author infer from these facts?

_____

_____

3. What conclusions can you draw about the English from this reading?

_____

_____

_____

_____

4. How might you prove or disprove your conclusions?

_____

_____

_____

CHAPTER 13

Critical Thinking Skills Activity 13 | Analyzing Information

Analyzing the information an author presents involves reading carefully to try to understand the author's argument. The following firsthand account is by Mary Prince, a woman who managed to escape slavery in 1828. Prince made her way from the West Indies to England, where she was helped by members of the Society of Friends (Quakers). Her story was first published in 1831.

DIRECTIONS: Read the passage. Then answer the questions that follow.

I am often much vexed, and I feel great sorrow when I hear some people in this country say, that the slaves do not need better usage, and do not want to be free. They believe the foreign people [West Indians], who deceive them, and say slaves are happy. I say, Not so. How can slaves be happy when they have the halter round their neck and the whip upon their back? and are disgraced and thought no more of than beasts?—and are separated from their mothers, and husbands, and children, and sisters, just as cattle are sold and separated? Is it happiness for a driver in the field to take down his wife or sister or child, and strip them, and whip them in a disgraceful manner?—women that have had children exposed in the open field to shame! There is no modesty or decency shown by the owner to his slaves; men, women, and children are exposed alike. Since I have been here I have often wondered how English people can go out into the West Indies and act in such a beastly manner. But when they go to the West Indies, they forget God and all feeling of shame, I think, since they can see and do such things. They tie up slaves like hogs—moor them up like cattle, and they lick them, so as hogs, or cattle, or horses never were flogged;—and yet they come home and say, and make some good people believe, that slaves don't want to get out of slavery. But they put a cloak about the truth. It is not so. All slaves want to be free—to be free is very sweet.

1. What does Mary Prince say about how enslaved people really feel?

   _____

2. What are three reasons Prince gives to support her position on how enslaved people really feel?

   _____

3. In what way do the English change when they arrive in the West Indies, according to Prince? Why might these people change in this way?

   _____

4. Does the fact that the speaker has escaped slavery make her argument more effective or less effective? Explain your answer.

   _____

   _____

CHAPTER 13

★ HISTORY AND GEOGRAPHY ACTIVITY 13

CHAPTER 13

Looking at the Land

European explorers set sail with dreams of glory and discovery in the late 1400s. The vast wilderness of the Americas held the promise of great riches. What form these riches took—gold, furs, or land for settlement—depended on the perception of the adventurer. How did the adventurers' views reflect the goals of the countries they sailed for?

Spanish explorers searched for landscapes in the Americas similar to those of their European homeland. Spaniards had learned to mine the mineral ores from Spain's low mountainous terrain. Knowing the importance of metallurgy to the Spanish economy, the earliest Spanish explorers were drawn to the mountainous areas of Mexico and what is today the southwest United States, where mining operations could be established quickly. They were more eager to make quick profits from mining than to develop self-sufficient colonies based on an agricultural economy.

The French, too, were eager for the profits they could make from North America's natural resources, but they were forced to search in northern North America, because the Spanish had already claimed much of Central America and South America. French explorers Jacques Cartier and Samuel de Champlain explored the St. Lawrence River system and the northern Appalachian area, claiming those places for France. Finding a region teeming with beaver, muskrat, and deer, the French turned to trading metal knives, tools, and guns for furs from animals hunted by Native Americans. The French built a fur-trading monopoly that brought them great wealth without the problems of clearing, farming, and settling the rocky lands of northern New England and Canada.

The English Perception

"There are valleys and plains streaming with the sweet springs. . . . The land is full of minerals and plenty of woods, of which we have a lack in England. There are growing goodly oaks and elms, beech and birch . . . and fir trees in great abundance. The soil is strong and lusty of its own nature."

—Anonymous English writer, early 1600s

European claims to land in North America led to a variety of settlement patterns—from rough wilderness camps to sprawling coastal plantations.

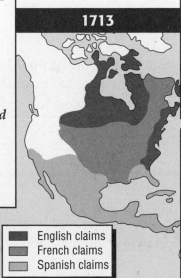

1713

English claims
French claims
Spanish claims

The French Perception

"There is a great number of stags, deer, bears, rabbits, foxes, otters, beavers, weasels, badgers and . . . many other sorts of wild beasts."

—Jacques Cartier, 1530s

The Spanish Perception

"The discovery of the South Sea would lead to the discovery of many islands rich in gold, pearls, precious stones . . . and other unknown and wonderful things."

—Hernán Cortés, 1533

HISTORY AND GEOGRAPHY ACTIVITY 13 (continued)

The English, however, found a land and climate in Virginia that was better suited than their homeland for growing food and producing simple products from the abundance of raw materials available in North America. English colonies of the 1600s grew into farm communities that traded farm products for manufactured English goods.

The different ways in which the Spanish, French, and English explored and colonized the Americas reflect their differing perceptions of the regions. Spanish explorers were enticed to search for legendary cities such as El Dorado, where the streets were said to be paved with gold, and the Seven Cities of Cíbola, which allegedly held enormous treasures. Their dreams of finding these places gave explorers the determination to face hardships and disappointments. French explorers, however, looked at North America as a place where fortunes could be made from the fur trade. Settlements were temporary hunting communities, quite different from English farming colonies, where families had migrated to start a new life in a new land.

APPLYING GEOGRAPHY TO HISTORY

DIRECTIONS: Answer the questions below in the space provided.

1. What makes people perceive regions differently?

   _____

2. What North American resources were important to the Spanish, the French, and the English?

   _____

3. What circumstances in Europe made the English so delighted to find good farmland in North America?

   _____

Critical Thinking

4. **Making Inferences** The Spanish claimed more of the Americas than the French and English combined. What historical event gave the Spanish an advantage in their claims?

   _____

   _____

Activity

5. With a partner, select a region of the world and then write separate one-page descriptions of what you think are the important aspects of that region. When you finish writing, compare your perceptions. How are they similar, and how are they different?

Mapping History Activity 13

Who Took What?

As European explorers arrived in the Americas, they took land from Native Americans and claimed it for their home countries. The map below shows the locations of Native American peoples before the arrival of Europeans.

DIRECTIONS: Use the map to answer the questions and complete the activities that follow.

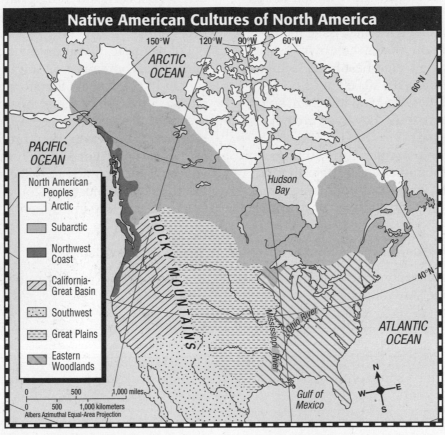

Native American Cultures of North America

North American Peoples
- Arctic
- Subarctic
- Northwest Coast
- California–Great Basin
- Southwest
- Great Plains
- Eastern Woodlands

0   500   1,000 miles
0   500   1,000 kilometers
Albers Azimuthal Equal-Area Projection

1. Choose three colors to represent the Spanish, English, and French holdings in North America. Show this information in a key.

2. Use the following information to indicate on the map the lands held by Spain, England, and France:

   By the mid-1600s, England controlled most of New England and all but the westernmost tip of Long Island, as well as the eastern shore of Chesapeake Bay. Spain had northern South America, Central America, Mexico, and the entire coast of Florida. France controlled the St.

   Lawrence River, Nova Scotia, Prince Edward Island, and the eastern portion of New Brunswick.

3. From which Native American peoples did the Spanish take land?

   _____

4. From which Native American peoples did the English take land?

   _____

5. From which Native American peoples did the French take land?

   _____

Historical Significance Activity 13

Joint-Stock Companies

During the period of colonial expansion, the major joint-stock companies that sought to do business in Asia were known as the East India Companies. These companies were given unprecedented political authority by their home countries. Within their territories, they had power to pass legislation, wage war, negotiate treaties, issue their own currency, and administer their own justice. At its height, the Dutch East India Company maintained more than 10,000 of its own soldiers, 40 warships, and 150 merchant ships. Joint-stock companies, however, are not just a thing of the past.

Today joint-stock companies still function but without the same degree of authority. Contemporary joint-stock companies are still organized by individuals who invest a specific sum of money. Each investor is given a share of stock in the company in proportion to the amount of money he or she has invested. Although the purpose of the company is to make money for all of the stockholders, an individual stockholder can never lose more than he or she initially invested.

For example, if you invested $5,000 in a joint-stock company, you might own 5 percent of its total stock; therefore, you would receive 5 percent of the company's total profit for the year. If the company made a profit of $50,000, you would receive 5 percent of this profit or $2,500. If the company you invested in failed to make a profit or lost money, the most you could lose was your initial $5,000 investment.

DIRECTIONS: Answer the following questions in the space provided.

1. What might be some advantages of investing in a joint-stock company rather than starting one's own business?

   _____

   _____

2. What might be some of the disadvantages to owning stock in a joint-stock company?

   _____

   _____

3. How do you think joint-stock companies have changed since they were first started in the Age of Exploration?

   _____

   _____

4. Imagine that a friend wants your advice: should he start his own business or invest his money in a joint-stock company? On a separate sheet of paper, write a letter to your friend, giving and justifying your advice. How would your answer be different if you were writing your letter in the late 1600s?

★ Cooperative Learning Activity 13 ★

The *New Horizons* Web Site

BACKGROUND

Many European nations became involved in overseas expansion and exploration starting in the fifteenth century. Trade opportunities, Christianization, and an emerging spirit of nationalist adventure drove many of the nations to seek new empires and new trade windows in Asia, Africa, and the Americas. Mercantilism and increasing international trade became the basis of economic thinking. By working as a group to create a *New Horizons* news Web site (or newspaper) to cover events in the Age of Exploration, you will develop a heightened sense of the energy and motivation that surrounded the era.

GROUP DIRECTIONS

1. Your group will create a news Web site (live or ready-to-post) called *New Horizons* covering events in the Age of Exploration.

2. The group needs to select an editor and two assistant editors who will assign articles and schedule due dates, proofreading, page layouts, and other tasks. All questions should be directed to this senior editorial team.

3. Each member of the group will write a news article about one or more events in the Age of Exploration and create an advertisement for the Web site, plus complete other assignments such as maps, illustrations, and adding Web links as directed by the editorial group. The group should also select members to type the articles, design the Web pages, create the graphics, and post the text and graphics files.

4. Include the following in the site:
   - name for the site
   - illustrations
   - historical advertisements
   - maps
   - articles on any of the following:

     causes for exploration and expansion   Papal Demarcation Line
     Bartholomeu Dias   Prince Henry the Navigator
     Christopher Columbus   Vasco da Gama
     Amerigo Vespucci   Ferdinand Magellan
     Hernán Cortés   Francisco Pizarro

ORGANIZING THE GROUP

1. **Decision Making** As a group, select the editorial team. Then brainstorm ideas for advertisements and other features for the site. The editorial team should assign stories to the team members and determine responsibilities for other editing, design, illustration, and posting tasks.

Cooperative Learning Activity 13 (continued)

2. **Individual Work** Conduct research as needed and write your story in proper newspaper style, adding any visuals that would enhance your story's value to your readership. Consider the historical context and create an advertisement to accompany your article. Edit and proofread your article and advertisement.

3. **Group Work/Decision Making** The editorial team should read and edit the articles and advertisements submitted by the team members and make any changes required, discussing the changes with the reporters as needed.

4. **Group Work/Decision Making** Decide on the basic design and navigation of the Web site. Consider the types of links that you would like to include, both within the site and to external sources. Gather the files, including graphics, that will be required to complete the Web site.

5. **Additional Group Work** Prepare the files for posting and build the Web site. Your school's technology team should be able to provide any technical expertise that the team will need to create its Web site. You may even want to post the information on (or link to) your school's Web site. If possible, include a method for visitors to the Web site to contact the team members via e-mail.

6. **Group Sharing** Invite the members of your class to visit your Web site and, if possible, to e-mail comments to your team.

GROUP PROCESS QUESTIONS

- What is the most important thing you learned about building Web sites and about news Web sites in particular from this activity?

- What part of the project did you enjoy most?

- What problems did you have?

- How did you solve the problems?

- How was it helpful to work with others?

Quick **CHECK** ✔

Answer the following questions on a separate sheet of paper.

1. Was the goal of the assignment clear at all times?

2. How was designing a Web site and preparing articles for the Web site different from other types of projects?

3. Did you have technical problems or problems working together? If so, how did you solve them?

4. Were you satisfied with your work on this project? Why or why not?

HISTORY SIMULATION ACTIVITY 13

The Search for Andronia

During the Age of Exploration, European explorers used unsophisticated instruments to navigate their small sailing ships, searching for a water route to Asia. They faced the dangers of long voyages at sea—storms, lack of fresh food, disease, accidents, and the emotional stress of being away from home and family.

TEACHER MATERIAL

Learning Objective To understand the difficulties and risks explorers faced in charting unknown territories.

Activity Groups role-play a voyage of exploration searching for the fabled wealthy planet of Andronia. Voyagers draw one card at a time from a stack of game cards, each of which describes a part of the journey. The group then decides how to respond to that event; points are awarded according to their response. When all groups have completed their journeys, they compare their point totals.

Teacher Preparation Cut the game cards apart, keeping them in sets. Each group needs one copy of the handout, paper and pencil for keeping score, and a coin to flip.

Activity Guidelines

1. Explain the objective and general directions.

2. To help students prepare for the game, set the following scene:
   Andronia is a planet of fabulous wealth. It contains enormous deposits of gold and silver, huge veins of which can clearly be seen in the bare sides of cliffs. However, no ship has ever returned from a journey to Andronia. What is known of the planet comes secondhand from traders from other planets in the galaxy. It is uncertain whether the planet's location is shown accurately on existing star maps. Furthermore, there are many dangers: black holes that swallow ships whole; electromagnetic fields that burn a ship's electronic system, leaving it adrift in space; and reaching the edge of the known universe and slipping into the Great Void, from which there is no return.

3. Organize the class into small groups and have each group choose a captain. Give each

group 1,000 points. Tell them that the captain has absolute authority. In the case of mutiny, the group will elect a new captain.

4. Distribute one set of game cards, turned facedown, to each group.

5. Groups begin the game by choosing a card and reading it aloud. They then discuss the situation and decide on the response—go on, turn back, or take some other course of action. The captain makes the final decision, either by consulting the group or by making the decision unilaterally. The group has the option of mutiny at any time. The game continues until the crew turns back, stays in one location, or uses all game cards.

6. When all groups have completed the game, have the groups that did not turn back or settle on another planet choose outcome letter *a*, *b*, or *c*. Then read the outcome each group selected from the list below. Groups count their points. The group with the most points wins.
   a. Andronia is even richer than legend has told. All crew members become fabulously wealthy and return home to live happily ever after. Add 50,000 points.
   b. Andronia contains no riches. It does, however, have enough food and water to sustain life and reprovision the ship for the journey home. Deduct 20,000 points.
   c. The crew realizes too late that the ship has been pulled off course by electromagnetic forces. It sails into oblivion. Deduct all points.

7. Have groups compare the difficulties each group faced to the hardships of European explorers in the 1500s.

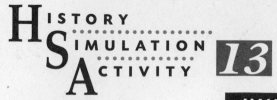

HANDOUT MATERIAL

The Search for Andronia—Game Cards

The Search for Andronia

Game Card 1

You have been traveling for more than two months and should have reached Andronia long ago. You may be nearing the edge of the Great Void.

Turn Back

Your voyage is over. 500 points

Or—flip a coin:

HEADS, you recheck your map and figure out where you are. 15,000 points

TAILS, you wander for five years before returning to familiar territory. 2,000 points

The Search for Andronia

Game Card 2

You have drifted into fierce solar winds from a nearby star. If you continue, your ship may break apart.

Turn Back

Your voyage is over. 500 points

Or—flip a coin:

HEADS, you survive. 2,000 points

TAILS, your ship is damaged. −2,000 points

The Search for Andronia

Game Card 3

The fuel regenerator has broken and might not be repairable. You have fuel for two weeks, after which your ship will drift aimlessly in space. If you turn back now, you will reach home before fuel runs out.

Turn Back

Your voyage is over. 500 points

Or—flip a coin:

HEADS, you fix the regenerator. 3,000 points

TAILS, it cannot be fixed. Sail on and cross your fingers. −3,000 points

The Search for Andronia

Game Card 4

You are approaching an asteroid belt. If you attempt to navigate through it, your ship will almost surely be crushed.

Turn Back

Your voyage is over. 500 points

Or—flip a coin:

HEADS, you survive. 3,000 points

TAILS, your ship is damaged. −3,000 points

The Search for Andronia

Game Card 5

You have encountered an uncharted planet much like Earth, with many resources. The inhabitants are friendly and invite you to stay. You may be able to set up a trading station on the planet.

Stay

Your voyage is over. 5,000 points

Continue

15,000 points

The Search for Andronia

Game Card 6

Food is running very low. Each crew member is rationed to two slices of bread each day. Some crew members are becoming ill from a lack of vitamins in their diet.

Turn Back

Your voyage is over. 500 points

Or—flip a coin:

HEADS, no one becomes seriously ill. 3,000 points

TAILS, some crew members are incapacitated. −3,000 points

Time Line Activity 13

The Age of Exploration

DIRECTIONS: The explorations of the fifteenth and sixteenth centuries brought great changes to many civilizations. Read the time line below. Then answer the questions that follow.

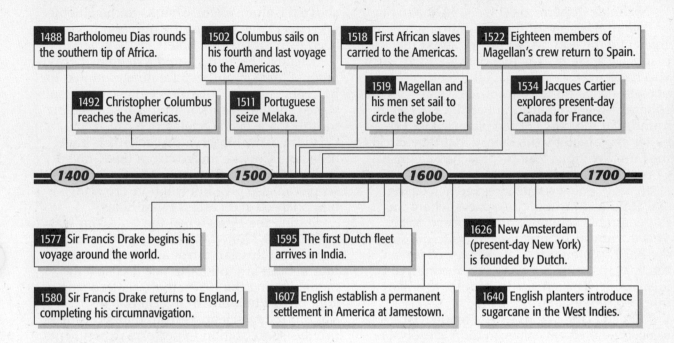

1488 Bartholomeu Dias rounds the southern tip of Africa.

1502 Columbus sails on his fourth and last voyage to the Americas.

1518 First African slaves carried to the Americas.

1522 Eighteen members of Magellan's crew return to Spain.

1492 Christopher Columbus reaches the Americas.

1511 Portuguese seize Melaka.

1519 Magellan and his men set sail to circle the globe.

1534 Jacques Cartier explores present-day Canada for France.

1400   **1500**   **1600**   **1700**

1577 Sir Francis Drake begins his voyage around the world.

1595 The first Dutch fleet arrives in India.

1626 New Amsterdam (present-day New York) is founded by Dutch.

1580 Sir Francis Drake returns to England, completing his circumnavigation.

1607 English establish a permanent settlement in America at Jamestown.

1640 English planters introduce sugarcane in the West Indies.

CHAPTER 13

1. How long did it take Magellan's crew to circumnavigate the world?

   _____

2. How long did it take Sir Francis Drake to complete a similar trip?

   _____

3. How many years passed between Europeans first reaching the Americas and sugarcane being introduced in the West Indies?

   _____

4. When did Cartier explore present-day Canada for France?

   _____

5. Who first founded a settlement in the present-day United States: the English or the Dutch? What was it called?

   _____

Exploring Space: Past and Present

THEN During the Age of Exploration, Europeans grew more curious about the world around them and began to travel to distant places. As their view of Earth changed, they began to revise their concepts of the heavens.

Nicholas Copernicus (1473–1543), a native of Poland, was one of the first astronomers to challenge the authorized theory about the planetary system. This theory stated that Earth was fixed in place and that all the other planets—encased in concentric crystal spheres—revolved around Earth. Copernicus found that the paths of the planets could be better explained by the theory that they circle the Sun. Religious leaders preached against Copernicus's ideas.

In 1577 a new comet streaked across the sky. It passed through the spaces where the impenetrable spheres were supposed to be. This event caused more scientists to question the Earth-centered model. As they observed the heavens, they began to set preconceived ideas aside. This enabled scientists to collect more objective data.

Galileo Galilei (1564–1642) made it possible to observe the heavens even more closely. He improved the recently invented telescope so that he could see the moons that orbit Jupiter. Partly inspired by this evidence that all heavenly bodies do not circle Earth, he wrote a book supporting the Sun-centered model. Outraged leaders of the Catholic Church forced Galileo to take back his assertions. His ideas endured, however, eventually paving the way for modern space exploration.

NOW Today advanced instruments and spacecraft help us explore and learn more about outer space. Galileo would envy the telescopes of today's astronomers. One such telescope—the Hubble space telescope—orbits Earth high above the atmosphere. Thanks to the Hubble telescope, large parts of the universe have been seen for the first time.

Scientists have measured a degree of gravitational force in outer space not accounted for by visible masses. Scientists believe that a substance known as dark matter is responsible for this force. Using a telescope called the Chandra X-ray Observatory, scientists have been able to make images from the X-rays emitted by the dark matter. The Chandra telescope can also give information about invisible collapsed stars called black holes.

During the 1960s when the Cold War was at its height, United States astronauts competed with Russian astronauts to place satellites in orbit around Earth and to reach the moon. During the 1990s, these rivals began a joint project to build an international space station. Today, scientists from many countries use this space station to perform experiments about the effects of living in space.

Unmanned spacecraft now explore our solar system and land on planets. These craft contain robots that control flight, take photographs, and collect samples from the surfaces of planets. One such craft may some day tell us if some form of life exists or has ever existed on Mars.

CRITICAL THINKING

Directions: Answer the following questions on a separate sheet of paper.

1. **Drawing conclusions:** Why did the appearance of a new comet challenge the Earth-centered model of our planetary system?

2. **Making inferences:** How do you think Earth's atmosphere interferes with observing distant parts of the universe?

3. **Synthesizing information:** Why do some scientists believe life forms either exist or once existed on Mars? Do research in the library and on the Internet to learn about the exploration of Mars by *Pathfinder* in 1997. Write a brief report describing that mission.

People in World History Activity **13**   **Profile 1**

Copyright © Glencoe/McGraw-Hill, a division of The McGraw-Hill Companies, Inc.

CHAPTER 13

Francisco Pizarro (c. 1478–1541)

There lies Peru with its riches here, Panama and its poverty. Choose, each man, what best becomes a brave Castilian. For my part, I go to the South.

Francisco Pizarro, tracing a line on the sand and looking south

Raised in Spain by poor relatives of his mother, Francisco Pizarro never learned to read and write. Service in the Spanish infantry, however, taught him about fighting—and conquering. The Spanish infantry was noted for three things: courage, cruelty, and greed.

Pizarro set out for the West Indies in 1502, when he was in his early twenties. He served as Vasco Núñez de Balboa's chief lieutenant and was at Balboa's side when he marched across the Isthmus of Panama to the Pacific Ocean in 1513. Years later Pizarro heard stories of an incredibly rich empire to the south. He wanted to find it and take its wealth for himself.

Pizarro and his business manager, Diego de Almagro, organized an expedition in 1524. After battling bad weather and attacks by native populations, the voyagers reached their goal in what is now Peru. Pizarro and his followers were the first Europeans to set foot in Peru. The first peoples they encountered wore shiny yellow ornaments—gold! Peru had more silver and gold than any other part of the Americas.

Pizarro returned to Spain and reported his findings to King Charles I, who appointed him governor of Peru. Returning from Spain, Pizarro founded the city of San Miguel de Tangarara (now Piura) in northern Peru. Although the Inca civil war was over, the land was still in turmoil. Had Pizarro tried to invade Peru earlier, he would have been met by a united empire; but now the Inca were split, giving him the opportunity to play one side against the other. In a surprise attack, Pizarro's men captured the Inca ruler, Atahuallpa, slaughtering between 3,000 and 4,000 Inca in the process. Pizarro held Atahuallpa captive, promising to spare his life if a ransom was paid. After receiving the ransom, Pizarro and his men executed Atahuallpa anyway.

Eight years after reaching Peru, Pizarro founded the city of Lima as Peru's capital, setting himself up as the governor. While he was governor, many Spaniards settled in Peru. They mined great amounts of silver and gold and built many cities. With Peru as its base, Spain conquered most of South America. In the late 1530s, war broke out over who was to rule the area around Cuzco—Pizarro or his old ally Almagro. Pizarro's forces won the conflict and executed Almagro. In 1541 followers of Almagro's son killed Pizarro.

REVIEWING THE PROFILE

Directions: Answer the following questions on a separate sheet of paper.

1. How was Pizarro associated with Balboa?

2. How did Pizarro conquer the Inca?

3. **Critical Thinking** **Making Inferences.** What do you think was the Inca people's opinion of Pizarro?

People in World History Activity **13** Profile 2

Jacques Cartier (1491–1557)

Jacques Cartier was born in the seaport of St. Malo, France, and trained in navigation at Dieppe, a French center for navigators. Other details of Cartier's early life, however, remain a mystery. Some historians believe he sailed to Newfoundland with a fishing fleet in his early teens and was with the Italian navigator Verrazano on French expeditions to North America during the 1520s. Historians do know that when King Francis I of France sent Cartier to North America in 1534 to search for gold, Cartier appeared to be familiar with Newfoundland waters. An experienced sailor, Cartier sailed his two ships into what is now the Gulf of St. Lawrence and claimed the Gaspé Peninsula for France.

Cartier established friendly relations with a group of Iroquois—so friendly, in fact, that Chief Donnacona let two of his sons sail to France with Cartier. On this voyage, Cartier brought a supply of corn that was probably the first corn ever seen in northern Europe. Nine months later, the king sent Cartier on a second expedition to Canada, and the two Iroquois boys returned home. On this trip, Cartier continued up the northern coast of the Gaspé Peninsula and entered a large bay on the feast day of St. Lawrence. In honor of the saint, Cartier named the bay St. Lawrence Bay. He also found the mouth of a great river he named after the saint. Cartier continued his exploration up the river to the foot of a mountain, which he named Mont Réal (Mount Royal). It became the site of the city of Montreal.

In 1541 King Francis I sent an expedition led by Sieur de Roberval to establish a permanent settlement in Canada. Cartier sailed ahead on his own voyage, not waiting for Roberval's official voyage. Some of Cartier's men built a settlement on the St. Lawrence River on what is now Cap Rouge, near Quebec City. Cartier continued to search for gold in the name of the king but found no precious metals.

During this time, the Iroquois had become distrustful of the French and killed several Frenchmen. Fearful of Iroquois hostilities, Cartier started back for France but met Roberval in Newfoundland. Roberval ordered Cartier to remain in Canada, but Cartier refused, warning Roberval about the Iroquois, and returned to France. Roberval's colonizing efforts were a failure due to hostilities with the Iroquois and winter hardships, and he and other survivors returned to France in 1543. Eventually, Jacques Cartier, who had seen so much of the world, returned to St. Malo, where he wrote about his travels.

REVIEWING THE PROFILE

Directions: Answer the following questions on a separate sheet of paper.

1. How did the city of Montreal get its name?

2. **Critical Thinking** **Making Inferences.** Why do you think Cartier took Chief Donnacona's two sons with him to France?

PRIMARY SOURCE READING 13

A Letter by Christopher Columbus

As you know, Christopher Columbus was trying to reach China when he "discovered" America and the islands of the Caribbean. On February 13, 1493, he wrote a letter to Santangel, the Spanish government official who had persuaded Queen Isabella to finance his expedition. Below is part of Columbus's letter, followed by an interpretation by modern historian Daniel J. Boorstin.

Guided Reading *In this selection, read to learn Columbus's account of the voyage and compare it to Boorstin's interpretation.*

When I reached Juana [Cuba], I followed its coast to the westward, and found it so large that I thought it must be the mainland,—the province of Cathay [China]; and, as I found neither towns nor villages on the seacoast, but only a few hamlets, with the inhabitants of which I could not hold conversation because they all immediately fled, I kept on the same route. . . .

. . . The lands are high and there are many very lofty mountains. . . . [The islands] are all most beautiful, of a thousand different shapes, accessible, and covered with trees of a thousand kinds of such great height that they seemed to reach the skies. . . . The nightingale was singing as well as other birds of a thousand different kinds; and that, in November, the month in which I myself was roaming amongst them. There are palm-trees of six or eight kinds, wonderful in their beautiful variety; but this is the case with all the other trees and fruits and grasses; trees, plants, or fruits filled us with admiration. It contains extraordinary pine groves, and very extensive plains. There is also honey, a great variety of birds, and many different kinds of fruits. In the interior there are many mines of metals and a population innumerable. . . . The inhabitants of this and of all the other islands I have found or gained intelligence of, both men and women, go as naked as they were born. . . . They have neither iron, nor steel, nor arms, nor are they competent to use them, not that they are not well-formed and of handsome stature, but because they are timid to a surprising degree.

On my reaching the Indies, I took by force, in the first island that I discovered, some of these natives that they might learn our language and give me information in regard to what existed in these parts; and it so happened that they soon understood us and we them, either by words or signs, and they have been very serviceable to us. . . . I find that they . . . believe that I come from heaven. . . .

They assure me that there is another island . . . in which the inhabitants have no hair. It is extremely rich in gold. . . . Finally, and speaking only of what has taken place in this voyage . . . their Highnesses may see that I shall give them all the gold they require, if they will give me but a little assistance; spices also, and cotton, as much as their Highnesses shall command to be shipped; and mastic [resin used in varnishes], hitherto found only in Greece . . . slaves, as many of these idolators as their Highnesses shall command to be shipped. I think also I have found rhubarb and cinnamon, and shall find a thousand other valuable things.

Boorstin's Interpretation

On shipboard off the Azores in mid-February 1493, returning from his first voyage, Columbus wrote his own report of what he thought, and wanted others to think, that he had accomplished. . . .

Columbus, having convinced himself that a trip across the Western Ocean would take him to the Indies, now set about convincing a wider audience. He had a heavy vested interest in his destination actually being the Indies. . . . Columbus was careful not to mention disasters or near disasters—the loss of the flagship, *Santa Maria*, the insubordination of Martín Alonso Pinzón, the commander of the *Pinta*, or the

81

PRIMARY SOURCE READING 13

mutinous spirit of the crew. Following the national-security regulations of his day, he omitted information on the courses taken or the precise distance covered in order to prevent competitors from following where he had led. While Columbus conceded that he had not actually seen the Great Khan or the court of gold-rich Cipangu, he detailed numerous clues reinforcing his belief that he was just off the coast of China. The resplendent Great Khan, he was confident, would be found just a little farther on, doubtless on the next voyage.

Although Columbus was a hardheaded observer of the winds and the waves, on the crucial question of where he had arrived he remained the slave of his hopes. He was determined to find signs everywhere that he had reached the fringes of Asia. Botany, still a vague wilderness whose images where not yet standardized by printing, was his happy hunting ground. From the moment when he first touched the north coast of Cuba on his first voyage, he had no trouble finding the Asiatic flora. A shrub that smelled like cinnamon he eagerly called cinnamon and so made it a hint of untold spice treasures. The aromatic West Indies gumbo-limbo, he insisted, must be an Asiatic form of the mastic tree of the Mediterranean that yielded resin. . . . The ship's surgeon examined some roots that the men had dug up and obligingly pronounced them valuable medicinal Chinese rhubarb, a strong cathartic [laxative] drug. Actually it was only the common garden rhubarb, that we now use for pies and tarts. . . . But so many false scents somehow seemed to add up the authentic odor of the Orient.

INTERPRETING THE READING

Directions *Use information from the readings to answer the following questions. If necessary, use a separate sheet of paper.*

1. What impressed Columbus about the land he discovered?

_____

_____

2. Where did Columbus think he had landed?

_____

3. What did Columbus offer to the king and queen of Spain?

_____

_____

4. According to Boorstin, what information did Columbus omit from his letter to Santangel? Why?

_____

_____

Critical Thinking

5. Evaluating Information Based on Columbus's letter and Boorstin's comments on it, do you think Columbus really believed he had reached Asia? Explain your answer.

_____

Name _____ Date _____ Class _____

World Art and Music Activity **13**

African Tribal Masks

Masks are not unique to Africa. Paleolithic cave paintings show hunting scenes with masked dancers. Masks were used in Chinese theater, in Japanese No drama, and in devil-dancing ceremonies and theatrical performances in India, Ceylon, and Java. Native Americans in North America all used face masks. Masks were used in Mexico and South America, as well as by some aboriginal people in Australia. Masks are used for theater and dance, religious ceremonies, and tribal rituals of fertility, hunting, and agriculture.

DIRECTIONS: Read the passage below about the use of African tribal masks. Then answer the questions in the space provided.

African tribal rituals celebrate religious and cultural events. The dancer who wears the mask may be introducing a spirit or transmitting the genealogy of the ancestors of the group, showing the history of the migration, the institution of ceremonies, or the techniques of agriculture or hunting. The image on the mask therefore might be a mythic or grotesque human representation, an animal, or a spirit.

The dancer who wore the mask had to have exceptional strength and special skill. The dances were technically complicated, and the dancer had to undergo special training to learn the dance. The masks were also heavy and had an uncomfortable structure. The dancer was usually wrapped in a costume that covered his body, and the warm climate would sap the dancer's strength.

Ritual masks were used in four different kinds of ceremonies. (1) Rituals of myth transmitted history of the group or celebrated legendary heroes and animals. (2) Fertility rituals celebrated or encouraged spirits to provide fertility in crops and human births; masks were also used in the opposite end of fertility rituals—funerals or burials. (3) Initiations or rites of passage included celebrations of different stages of life, such as the passage of a boy into manhood or the initiation of members into a secret society. (4) Other related ceremonies were celebrated or solemnized with

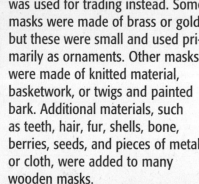

Two masks of the Congo Bakwele tribe, known for highly abstract face masks

masks, such as healing, divination, exorcism, protection, presenting petitions, averting disaster, welcoming chiefs and visitors, and law enforcement and judging disputes.

Most masks were made of wood because it was abundantly available in the forests in Africa. A small percentage were carved in ivory from elephant tusks; however, most of the ivory harvested was used for trading instead. Some masks were made of brass or gold, but these were small and used primarily as ornaments. Other masks were made of knitted material, basketwork, or twigs and painted bark. Additional materials, such as teeth, hair, fur, shells, bone, berries, seeds, and pieces of metal or cloth, were added to many wooden masks.

Mask carvers served a period of apprenticeship to a master carver. Often the knowledge of carving was transmitted from father to son through many generations, but sometimes a young man was selected because he showed talent in carving. Mask carvers were usually given high status; however, with some people, such as the Bambara or Senufo, the mask carver was either feared or from a low caste, and lived isolated from the village. The most common tool for carving the masks was the adze, although smaller knives might be used for finer work.

(continued)

World Art and Music Activity 13

The masks were usually considered sacred and were consecrated by the priest, medicine man, or magician to give the mask the proper power. There were rituals of cleansing before donning the mask and desecration after using the mask. The tools of the mask carver were believed to have their own power, and the tools were also prepared with special rituals before use. When a master carver died, often the best student inherited his tools as it was believed that the tools also contained the skill of the master.

The faces on masks sometimes had natural features and sometimes had idealized features. Some of the masks had frightening features. The type of face depended on the special function of the mask; some were even considered comic and were used in plays.

Masks with animal features or a combination of animal and human features were common. Tribes believed that man could acquire qualities attributed to different animals, such as the strength of a lion, the agility of an antelope, or the power of a bull. If an animal was killed, its spirit was liberated and might take revenge upon the hunter; a mask would be made to capture such a spirit to give the hunter control over the spirit.

Reviewing the Selection

1. What are four general uses of African tribal masks?

   _____

   _____

   _____

2. What actions are evidence that the people of Africa believed that masks had spiritual power?

   _____

   _____

   _____

   _____

Critical Thinking

3. **Making Inferences** What would be the attitude of Africans toward tribal masks in a nationalist movement?

   _____

   _____

   _____

   _____

   _____

Reteaching Activity 13

The Age of Exploration

During the age of European exploration, one nation after another sought to gain territory, goods, or trading partners. Keeping track of the explorers that the major powers of Europe sent out can be challenging because explorers were not always born in the country that sponsored their voyages.

DIRECTIONS: Use the chart below to record the names of the early explorers under the country each represented.

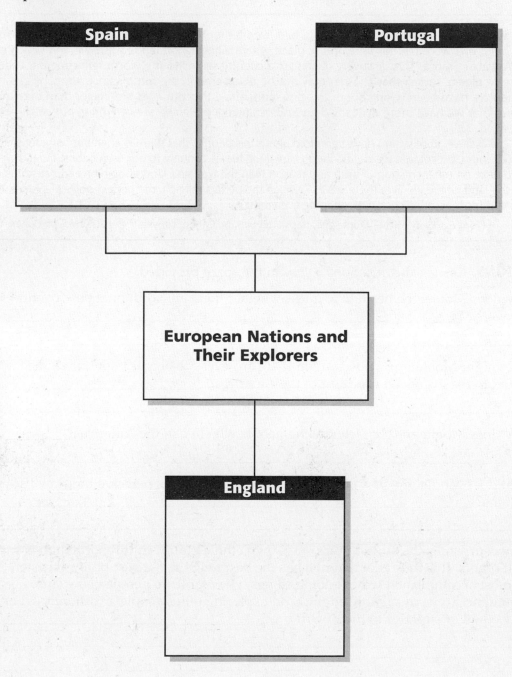

★ Enrichment Activity 13

The European View of the Americas

As European explorers made discoveries on their ocean voyages, many writers began to consider the proper way to relate to new people and different ways of life. A lawyer by profession, Michel Montaigne (1533–1592) retired to his estate in the Bordeaux region of France in 1571 to write a collection of essays that was first published in 1580. In his *Essais*, Montaigne gives his personal opinion on a range of issues of the day. Read the following excepts from his essay "On Cannibals."

I had with me for a long time a man who had lived ten or twelve years in that other world which has been discovered in our time, in the place where Villegaignon landed [Brazil], and which he called Antarctic France. This discovery of so vast a country seems to me worth reflecting on. I should not care to pledge myself that another may not be discovered in the future, since so many greater men than we have been wrong about this one. I am afraid that our eyes are bigger than our stomachs, and that we have more curiosity than understanding. We grasp at everything, but catch nothing except wind. . . .

I do not believe, from what I have been told about this people, that there is anything barbarous or savage about them, except that we call barbarous anything that is contrary to our own habits. Indeed we seem to have no other criterion of truth and reason than the type and kind of opinions and customs current in the land where we live. There we always see the perfect religion, the perfect political system, the perfect and most accomplished way of doing everything.

—From *Essais* by Michel Montaigne, translated by J. M. Cohen, copyright © 1958 by J. M. Cohen.

DIRECTIONS: Answer the questions below in the space provided.

1. Why does Montaigne hesitate to guess whether there are additional new countries to be discovered? _____

_____

2. How might Montaigne's observation that "our eyes are bigger than our stomachs" be related to the European conquest of the Americas? _____

_____

3. How does Montaigne characterize the people who live in the Americas? _____

_____

4. What does Montaigne find faulty with the way Europeans perceive their own social customs? _____

_____

5. Ethnocentrism is the attitude that one's own ethnic group, culture, or nation is superior to all others. It is the belief that one has the best religion, the best political system, and the most accomplished way of doing things. How far have people come since Montaigne's time in acknowledging and exploring other people's "differences" as potentially equal or superior to their own? _____

_____

WORLD HISTORY

Chapter 13
Section Resources

GUIDED READING ACTIVITY 13-1   88

GUIDED READING ACTIVITY 13-2   89

GUIDED READING ACTIVITY 13-3   90

SECTIONS

Guided Reading Activity 13-1

Exploration and Expansion

DIRECTIONS: Fill in the blanks below as you read Section 1.

1. Why were westerners unable to travel by land from Europe to Asia in the fourteenth century?

   _____

2. What three motives prompted adventurers to begin seeking a better sea route to Asia?

   _____

3. Which country took the lead in European exploration?

   _____

4. Why were traders ready to duplicate the voyage of da Gama to the coast of India?

   _____

5. How did the Spanish differ from the Portuguese in searching for a route to Asia?

   _____

6. What lands did Christopher Columbus reach in his four voyages?

   _____

7. What rights were agreed upon by Spain and Portugal in the Treaty of Tordesillas?

   _____

8. How effective were the Spanish in gaining control of Latin America?

   _____

9. How did one Aztec describe another consequence of the Spanish invasion?

   _____

10. What other European countries joined Spain and Portugal in their explorations?

    _____

Guided Reading Activity 13-2

The Atlantic Slave Trade

DIRECTIONS: As you are reading the section, decide if a statement is true or false. Write **T** if the statement is true or **F** if the statement is false. For all false statements, write a corrected statement.

_____ **1.** The primary market for African slaves was Southwest Asia, where most slaves were used as field hands.

_____

_____ **2.** The demand for slaves changed dramatically with the discovery of the Americas and the planting of sugarcane there.

_____

_____ **3.** In 1518 a Spanish ship carried the first boatload of African slaves directly from Africa to Spain.

_____

_____ **4.** As many as 10 million African slaves were brought to the Americas between the early sixteenth and the late nineteenth centuries.

_____

_____ **5.** Local slave traders first obtained their supplies of slaves from the interior of Africa. As the demand increased, however, they had to move to coastal areas to find more slaves.

_____

_____ **6.** The population in West Africa was so great that the slave trade had little effect on their numbers.

_____

_____ **7.** Slave traders rarely took the youngest and strongest men and women from a village.

_____

_____ **8.** A brilliant and creative society in the sixteenth century, the country of Benin deteriorated because of slave trade.

_____

_____ **9.** European feeling against slavery began to build after the Society of Friends, known as the Quakers, began to condemn slavery in the 1770s.

_____

SECTION 13-2

Guided Reading Activity 13-3

SECTION 13-3

Colonial Latin America

DIRECTIONS: Fill in the blanks below as you read Section 3.

I. In the sixteenth century, Spain established a colonial empire that included North

America, Central America, and most of _____.

    A. Colonial Latin America was divided into social classes that included the

    _____ at the top.

    B. The second social class, called the _____, was made up of descendents

    of Europeans born in Latin America.

    C. Two groups, the _____ and _____, helped produced a

    unique multiracial society in Latin America.

II. The Portuguese and the Spanish found ways to _____ from their

colonies.

    A. One source of wealth was _____ and _____.

    B. _____ also became a long-lasting source of prosperity.

    C. The Spanish created large _____.

    D. To maintain a supply of labor, the Spanish made use of the _____

    system.

        1. In Peru, the Spanish made use of the _____.

        2. This allowed authorities to _____ Native Americans to work in the

        silver mines.

III. Spanish and Portuguese rulers were determined to _____ the native

people.

    A. _____ established more than 30 missions in the region.

    B. The Catholic Church also built cathedrals, _____,

    _____, and _____ in the colonies.

GLENCOE
WORLD HISTORY

Chapter 14 Resources
Crisis and Absolutism in Europe, 1550–1715

READING SKILLS ACTIVITY 14
Synthesizing 93

HISTORICAL ANALYSIS SKILLS ACTIVITY 14
Validating Arguments 94

DIFFERENTIATED INSTRUCTION ACTIVITY 14
The Reign of Absolutism and the Divine Right of Kings 95

ENGLISH LEARNER ACTIVITY 14
Europe in Crisis: The Wars of Religion 97

CONTENT VOCABULARY ACTIVITY 14
Crisis and Absolutism in Europe, 1550–1715 99

ACADEMIC VOCABULARY ACTIVITY 14
Crisis: The Wars of Religion 101

SKILLS REINFORCEMENT ACTIVITY 14
Making Generalizations 103

CRITICAL THINKING SKILLS ACTIVITY 14
Drawing Conclusions 104

HISTORY AND GEOGRAPHY ACTIVITY 14
Britain's Toehold in Europe 105

MAPPING HISTORY ACTIVITY 14
The Hapsburg Empire 107

HISTORICAL SIGNIFICANCE ACTIVITY 14
Saving the "Wooden O" 108

COOPERATIVE LEARNING ACTIVITY 14
Influential Europeans in Absolute Profile 109

HISTORY SIMULATION ACTIVITY 14
King or Queen for a Day 111

TIME LINE ACTIVITY 14
Crisis and Absolutism in Europe 113

LINKING PAST AND PRESENT ACTIVITY 14
Attempts to Maintain Centralized Power: Past and Present 114

PEOPLE IN WORLD HISTORY ACTIVITY 14
Profile 1: Guy Fawkes (1570–1606) 115
Profile 2: Blaise Pascal (c. 1623–1662) 116

PRIMARY SOURCE READING 14
A Day at the Court of the Sun King 117

WORLD ART AND MUSIC ACTIVITY 14
Rembrandt 119

RETEACHING ACTIVITY 14
Crisis and Absolutism in Europe 121

ENRICHMENT ACTIVITY 14
Addressing the Troops 122

Reading Skills Activity 14

Synthesizing

LEARNING THE SKILL

Synthesizing is a critical skill to practice. Synthesizing is a process of making connections between bits of knowledge to draw conclusions about their relationships or to discover over-arching themes. Piecing together information from different places in a textbook—or from other books—and relating them to each other helps a person build knowledge.

PRACTICING THE SKILL

DIRECTIONS: Read the following quotations from two French men in the 1700s on the subject of ruling a country. Using what you know from your reading of the chapter, describe on a separate sheet of paper whether or not these two men agreed on how a country should be ruled.

> *But kings, although their power comes from on high . . . should not regard themselves as masters of that power to use it at their pleasure . . . they must employ it with fear and self-restraint, as a thing coming from God and of which God will demand an account.*
>
> —Jacques-Benigne Bossuet, *Political Treatise*

> *Soon you will be King of a great kingdom . . . Try to remain at peace with your neighbors. I loved war too much. Do not follow me in that or in overspending . . . Lighten your people's burden as soon as possible, and do what I have had the misfortune not to do myself.*
>
> —King Louis XIV to his successor on his deathbed

APPLYING THE SKILL

DIRECTIONS: Russian Czar Peter the Great was determined to "Europeanize" Russia. Research and write a paragraph about which western ideas Peter the Great synthesized into Russian culture.

📖 Historical Analysis Skills Activity 14

Validating Arguments

LEARNING THE SKILL

Determining the validity of an argument requires close, objective examination of how the information is presented. Extreme words, such as *never* and *always*, clue in the reader to rare, and therefore suspect, occurrences. Arguments that set down a "no exceptions" fact are also suspect because most of these statements can't be proven. Arguments that use more cautious descriptions and that reveal both sides of an issue are more likely to prove valid. However, a valid argument may also take risks by relying on several people's perspectives of an event or situation to support claims. In addition, information presented as factual should be readily available and fairly easy to prove.

PRACTICING THE SKILL

DIRECTIONS: Read the following excerpts from the *Malleus Maleficarum* (*The Hammer of the Witches*), published in 1486. This was a guidebook to help inquisitors identify and prosecute witches. On a separate sheet of paper, answer the questions that follow.

> *Whether the belief that there are such beings as witches is so essential a part of the Catholic faith that obstinately to maintain the opposite opinion manifestly savours of heresy.*

> *The evils which are perpetrated by modern witches exceed all other sin which God has ever permitted to be done.*

1. Summarize the arguments being made in the two excerpts.

2. Are the arguments convincing? What does or does not seem valid about these arguments?

APPLYING THE SKILL

DIRECTIONS: How difficult is it to spot an argument that is not supported with evidence? Search various news magazines for an article that presents obvious bias toward an issue or event. Research the topic, looking for evidence regarding the argument. Use reliable, well-known sources. On a separate sheet of paper, present your evidence and answer the questions: did your research validate or invalidate the argument? How? Be sure to use proper documentation in your paper to support your conclusion and provide copies of the article and your sources.

Differentiated Instruction Activity 14

The Reign of Absolutism and the Divine Right of Kings

Absolutism began in the seventeenth century as a way to seek stability after years of conflict and war. In this system, a ruler holds total power and the divine right of kings. The ruler has the ability to make laws, levy taxes, administer justice, control officials, and determine foreign policy.

Jacques-Benigne Bossuet explained his perception of the divine right of kings:

> *Rulers . . . act as the ministers of God and as his lieutenants on earth. It is through them that God exercises his empire. But kings, although their power comes from on high . . . should not regard themselves as masters of that power to use it at their pleasure . . . they must employ it with fear and self-restraint, as a thing coming from God and of which God will demand an account.*

DIRECTIONS: Use your text to review the reign of Louis XIV beginning in 1661. Fill in the chart below to organize your ideas about how his leadership affected the government, religion, economy, and war.

Decide whether Jacques-Benigne Bossuet would have approved of the way Louis XIV ruled. Write a one-page essay defending your position.

Under the Leadership of Louis XIV

Government	Religion	Economy	War

(continued)

Differentiated Instruction Activity 14

For the Teacher

TEACHING STRATEGIES FOR DIFFERENT LEARNING STYLES

The following activities are ways the basic lesson can be modified to accommodate students' different learning styles:

English Learners (EL) Provide students with a partially completed chart. Students should then work in pairs to complete the organizer and determine if Jacques-Benigne Bossuet would have approved of the way Louis XIV ruled. Have students discuss their stance instead of writing a one-page essay.

Advanced Learners (AL) Have students present their essays to the class in a debate-style forum. Ask students with opposing positions to share their essays as if they were in a debate.

Below Grade Level (BL) Work with the students to scan the chapter locating the section where information about Louis XIV can be found. Direct students' attention to the bold headings, highlighted vocabulary, and illustrations that will help them find the information they are looking for. Help students write their notes in the correct columns. Have students discuss their stance instead of writing a one-page essay.

On Grade Level (OL) Have students fill in the chart as instructed. Have students trade essays with a partner for peer review.

English Learner Activity 14

Europe in Crisis: The Wars of Religion

✪ A. PRE-READING ACTIVITY: IMPROVING READING COMPREHENSION

Directions: *Before reading "Spain's Conflicts" on pages 454–456, answer the following questions.*

1. How are Calvinism and Catholicism different?

   _____

   _____

   _____

   _____

2. What religious wars are we still fighting today? Which countries are involved in them. What effects have these wars had on the countries and people involved?

   _____

   _____

   _____

   _____

✪ B. READING COMPREHENSION ACTIVITY: MULTIPLE CHOICE

Directions: *After you have read "The Thirty Years' War" on page 460, complete the sentences below by circling the best answer.*

1. Religious disputes continued in Germany after the Peace of Augsburg because Calvinism
   a. was not a religion.   **b.** ended   **c.** had not been recognized.

2. Religion started the Thirty Years' War, but political and territorial issues
   a. were also a cause.   **b.** weren't evident.   **c.** ended.

3. All major European countries became involved in the Thirty Years' War
   a. except England.   **b.** German.   **c.** Rome.

4. The Peace of Westphalia divided the states of the Holy Roman Empire and gave them the power to conduct their own foreign policy and determine
   a. their leadership   **b.** their own religion.   **c.** their motives.

(continued)

⬧ English Learner Activity 14

✖ C. READING COMPREHENSION ACTIVITY: TRUE / FALSE

Directions: *After you have read "Art after the Renaissance" on pages 472–474, complete the exercise below. Write* **T** *if the sentence is true and* **F** *if the sentence if false.*

1. _____ Enthusiasm sparked by the Renaissance declined as people grew uncertain and wished for spiritual experience.

2. _____ Mannerism emerged in Germany in the 1520s and 1530s.

3. _____ The Baroque Period replaced Mannerism.

4. _____ Artists from the Baroque Period brought classical ideals from Renaissance art with the spiritual feelings of the sixteenth century.

5. _____ The interior of Saint Peter's Basilica is filled with many masterpieces of Mannerism art.

6. _____ Some of Caravaggio's work depicted religious figures as common people.

7. _____ Artemisia Gentileschi, the first woman to be elected to the Florentine Academy of Design, is famed for her pictures of New Testament heroines.

✖ D. WORD MEANING ACTIVITY: DEFINE WORDS

Directions: *Write the definition of each word.*

1. authority

_____

2. resistance

_____

3. successor

_____

4. motives

_____

5. absolute

_____

Content Vocabulary Activity 14

Crisis and Absolutism in Europe, 1550–1715

DIRECTIONS: Write one of the following terms on each numbered line below to complete the paragraphs.

- absolutism
- armada
- baroque
- boyars
- commonwealth
- czar
- divine right
- heretics
- inflation
- Mannerism
- natural rights
- witchcraft

The rule of Philip II in Spain was an example of **(1)** _____, as he held virtually unlimited power over his subjects. Philip sent an **(2)** _____ to invade England, but many of the ships sank. Spain, as well as other European countries, also faced **(3)** _____, which sent prices soaring.

During the sixteenth and seventeenth centuries, the religious zeal that led to the Inquisition and the hunt for **(4)** _____ was extended to concern about **(5)** _____, or magic.

Following the death of England's Queen Elizabeth I, James I ascended to the throne with his belief in **(6)** _____, the conviction that a ruler derives complete authority to govern directly from God and is responsible to God alone.

In 1642 England slipped into a civil war between the supporters of the king and the parliamentary forces. Victorious, Parliament abolished the monarchy and the House of Lords and declared England a republic, or **(7)** _____.

In the sixteenth century, Russia's Ivan IV became the first ruler to take the title of **(8)** _____, the Russian word for caesar. Ivan IV took steps against the **(9)** _____ to reduce their potential threat to his throne.

The artistic Renaissance came to an end when a new movement, called **(10)** _____, emerged in Italy. It distorted elements such as scale and perspective. This movement eventually was replaced by **(11)** _____, known for its use of dramatic effects to arouse the emotions.

John Locke, an English political thinker, argued against absolutism. Locke believed that humans had certain **(12)** _____, including life, liberty, and property.

Academic Vocabulary Activity 14

Europe in Crisis: The Wars of Religion

Key Words

Academic Words	Words with Multiple Meanings	Content Vocabulary
authority	rule	militant
conflict		armada
convert		
creative		
drama		
policy		
restoration		
stability		

A. Word Usage Activity

Scenario Response

DIRECTIONS: In the following activity, answer the questions in complete sentences using the underlined word.

Would you be surprised if…
one individual in our country was given supreme <u>authority</u>?

_____

_____

an old building in your community was <u>restored</u> after being ignored for many years?

_____

_____

students were assigned their classes based on how <u>creative</u> they were?

_____

_____

<u>conformity</u> was expected in our world?

_____

_____

everyone had to <u>convert</u> to the same religion?

_____

_____

CHAPTER 14

(continued)

Academic Vocabulary Activity 14

B. Word Use Activity

Word Web

DIRECTIONS: Use the following words in a word web to show how they are connected:
Louis XIV, absolutism, Catholicism, military, France, debt, mercantilism.

Louis XIV links all these words together. Write *Louis XIV* in the center oval, and write the other related words in the surrounding ovals. For each of the related words, write a sentence that clearly shows the word's relationship to Louis XIV. You can write sentences inside the ovals or, if you need more space, use a separate sheet of paper.

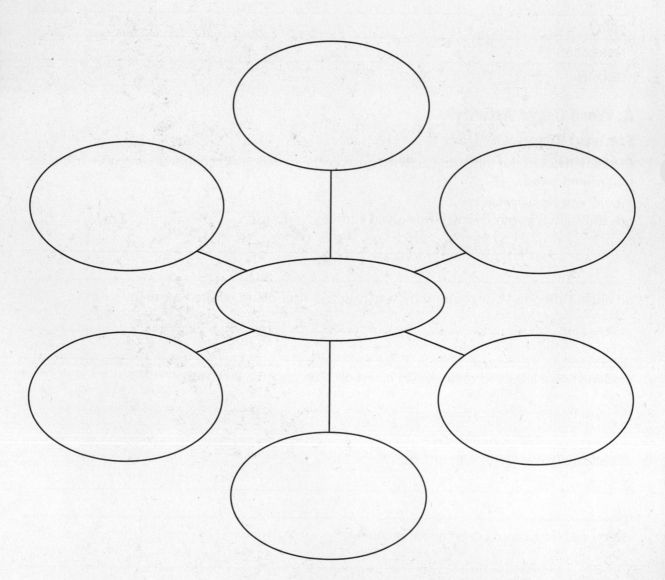

Skills Reinforcement Activity 14

Making Generalizations

Historians must be careful when they make generalizations based on observed data. They must back up each generalization they make with specific references to the sources they have used so that others can trace the reasoning that went into making the generalization. A generalization made without reference to specific historical sources is usually viewed as an opinion and therefore not necessarily accurate.

DIRECTIONS: Read "Protestantism in England," page 455 of your text. Then read the following excerpt from a reply made by Elizabeth I to some English bishops who wanted to continue Mary's pro-Catholic policies. Answer the questions below in the space provided.

On Religion, 1559

Sirs,

As to your entreaty for us to listen to you we waive it; yet do return you this our answer. Our realm and subjects have been long wanderers, walking astray, whilst they were under the tuition of Romish pastors, who advised them to own a wolf for their head (in lieu of a careful shepherd) whose inventions, heresies and schisms be so numerous, that the flock of Christ have fed on poisonous shrubs for want of wholesome pastures. And whereas you hit us and our subjects in the teeth that the Romish Church first planted the Catholic within our realm, the records and chronicles of our realm testify the contrary; and your own Romish idolatry maketh you liars; witness the ancient monument of Gildas unto which both foreign and domestic have gone in pilgrimage there to offer. This author testifieth Joseph of Arimathea to be the first preacher of the word of God within our realms. Long after that, when Austin came from Rome, this our realm had bishops and priests therein, as is well known to the learned of our realm by woeful experience, how your church entered therein by blood; they being martyrs for Christ and put to death because they denied Rome's usurped authority.

---

1. What generalizations does the author of your textbook make about Elizabeth I in regard to religion?

_____

2. What statements does Elizabeth make about religion in her reply to the English bishops?

_____

3. What generalizations can you make based on Elizabeth's statements?

_____

4. Does Elizabeth's reply support the generalizations made in your text? Why or why not?

_____

_____

Critical Thinking Skills Activity 14   Drawing Conclusions

When you draw conclusions, you make decisions about information presented. A conclusion is a logical generalization you make by putting together the details you read about with what you already know about the topic. For example, you might read about a king who, without consulting his advisers, invades a neighboring country. From this information, you might conclude that the king is impulsive or aggressive.

DIRECTIONS: Read the passage below. Then answer the questions that follow to draw conclusions.

From 1577 to 1580, the great English explorer Sir Francis Drake sailed around the world in a ship called the *Golden Hind*. However, the ship started its voyage with a different name—the *Pelican*. Sir Francis Drake suddenly renamed the ship after one of his sailors, Thomas Doughty, sparked a mutiny. Drake ruthlessly suppressed the mutiny by beheading Doughty, but this action created a political crisis. Doughty had been the secretary to Sir Christopher Hatton, a major investor in the voyage and one of Queen Elizabeth's favorites. The Hatton family coat of arms (a family crest or shield) was decorated with a golden female deer, called a hind. A few days after Doughty's execution, Drake renamed the *Pelican* the *Golden Hind*. Under that name, the ship achieved great fame.

1. From the information above, what can you conclude about Sir Francis Drake's leadership approach? State and support at least two conclusions. _____
    _____
    _____
    _____

2. What conclusion can you draw about why Sir Francis Drake changed the name of the flagship from the *Pelican* to the *Golden Hind*? Explain your answer. _____
    _____
    _____
    _____

3. At sea, captains took the law into their own hands. Explain why this conclusion is or is not supported by the information above. _____
    _____
    _____
    _____

★ HISTORY AND GEOGRAPHY ACTIVITY 14

Britain's Toehold in Europe

Since 1704 England and Spain have been quarreling over Gibraltar, a 2.25 square mile (5.83 sq m) rocky outcropping in the Straits of Gibraltar linked to Spain by a narrow isthmus. Today Gibraltar remains an overseas territory of the United Kingdom. Why do the two powers contest control of "the Rock"?

England plucked Gibraltar from Spain during the War of the Spanish Succession, which began when Louis XIV accepted the Spanish crown on behalf of his grandson, Philip of Anjou. In the spring of 1704, Britain and the Netherlands dispatched fleets to the Mediterranean to assist Charles of Austria in his claim to the crown. Unable to attain their original objective and not wishing to return empty-handed, the fleet's commanders attacked Gibraltar on July 23

and took possession of its gates the next day. To the naval commanders of Britain, control of the point at the southern tip of Spain where the Atlantic joins the Mediterranean proved irresistible.

Some 200 years later during World War II, Britain's judgment of Gibraltar's strategic importance proved correct. In November 1942, General Eisenhower set up a command center in Gibraltar from which he launched the invasion of North Africa known as Operation Torch. Troop convoys assembled in Gibraltar's harbor. A cave within the rocks served as the point from which Eisenhower communicated with Washington, London, and the field commanders landing in Africa. From this strategic point, the Allies launched the campaign that eventually allowed them to regain Europe.

Launched from Gibraltar, landings near Casablanca, Oran, and Algiers started the campaign that eventually allowed Allied forces to occupy Europe during World War II.

HISTORY AND GEOGRAPHY ACTIVITY 14 (continued)

People choose to settle in certain locations for many reasons. Soil, climate, and energy sources provide the basic elements for human survival. Geographic features such as deep harbors or navigable rivers allow people to transport goods and passengers to other markets or population centers. At the time that the British acquired Gibraltar, the seas were a primary means of commerce and transportation, allowing Britain to support a community in a location where rocky soil and salty water prevent crops from being grown.

> ## Gibraltar Made It Possible
>
> *In November, 1942, the Allied nations possessed, except for the Gibraltar Fortress, not a single spit of ground in all the region of Western Europe . . . Gibraltar made possible the invasion of northern Africa.*
>
> —Dwight D. Eisenhower

APPLYING GEOGRAPHY TO HISTORY

DIRECTIONS: Answer the questions in the space provided or on a separate sheet of paper.

1. What factors typically affect the location of a settlement?

_____

2. Why might the advantages of a location not be apparent to a visitor?

_____

3. What aspects of Gibraltar's geography made it valuable during World War II?

_____

Critical Thinking

4. **Making Inferences** Many British civil servants and dockworkers married women from neighboring Spain and settled in Gibraltar. Which elements do you think Gibraltar might have adopted from each culture?

_____

_____

Activity

5. Look for articles in newspapers, news magazines, or geographic magazines that describe the economic activities of Gibraltar today. Explain in a brief report how Gibraltar's location is related to its economy.

Mapping History Activity 14

The Hapsburg Empire

The Hapsburgs reached their greatest power before the end of the 1500s. Charles V annexed Milan in 1535, Philip II conquered Portugal in 1580, and Spain expanded its holdings in the Americas. However, the Hapsburg power structure would collapse over the next decades.

DIRECTIONS: The map below shows the Hapsburg holdings in the mid-1500s. Use the map to answer the questions and complete the activities that follow. Use a separate sheet of paper.

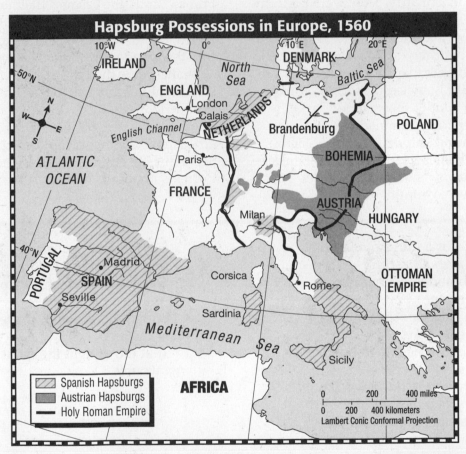

Hapsburg Possessions in Europe, 1560

1. Locate the lands held by the Spanish Hapsburgs. Based on the arrangement of holdings, what location might have made a better capital than Madrid? Why?

2. The Spanish Armada suffered a disastrous defeat at the hands of the English. What other countries do you think Philip II could have had better success at conquering? Support your opinion with information from the map.

3. Use an atlas from your classroom, library, or the Internet to help you draw in the borders of the countries of present-day Europe. How have the configurations of the borders changed in more than 400 years? How have they stayed the same?

Historical Significance Activity 14

Saving the "Wooden O"

The English-speaking theater achieved its greatest height in Elizabethan England. No playwright of this time was more important than William Shakespeare, and no theater was more important than the "wooden O"— the Globe—referred to in the passage below. Yet, in 1598, the future of Shakespeare and his acting company, the Lord Chamberlain's Men, were in jeopardy. They were performing at The Theatre, but their lease was up. The landlord told the company he planned to tear the building down and "convert the wood and timber thereof to some better use."

Faced with homelessness, the company took action. Under the cover of darkness, the members disassembled the theater themselves and shipped the pieces across the River Thames to an area called Bankside. The company's new home would be built there. All were counting on Bankside becoming London's next theatrical center, and they were correct.

In 1599 the Globe—made of wood and probably round, like the letter O—opened its doors to the public and much success. Its sign showed Hercules bearing the world on his shoulders. Apparently Shakespeare believed that not only the "vastly fields of France" and "the casques [helmets] that did affright the air at Agincourt," but the whole world, could be crammed imaginatively into the wooden O of the theater.

Shakespeare died in 1616, but the English stage continued to enjoy its greatest period until 1642. In that year, the Puritans closed London's theaters because they thought theatrical entertainment would corrupt citizens. Secondly, the English royalty, whom the Puritans opposed, supported the theater.

O, for a Muse of fire, that
would ascend
The brightest heaven of invention!
   A kingdom for a stage, princes to act,
   And monarchs to behold the swelling scene!
   Then would the warlike Harry, like himself,
   Assume the port of Mars . . .

But pardon, gentles all . . .
Can this cockpit hold
The vastly fields of France?
Or may we cram
   Within this wooden O the very casques
   That did affright the air at Agincourt?

—William Shakespeare,
Prologue to Act I,
The Life of King Henry the Fifth

DIRECTIONS: Answer the following questions on a separate sheet of paper.

1. Who is Mars and why does he fit in the prologue about King Henry the Fifth (Harry)?

2. What event happened at Agincourt?

3. Why did the Puritans object to plays being performed?

4. Were the members of the Lord Chamberlain's Men right or wrong in dismantling the theater in the middle of the night to build the Globe across the Thames? When you answer, keep in mind that their lease actually gave them the right to move the theater, but the lease had expired.

★ Cooperative Learning Activity 14 ★

Influential Europeans in Absolute Profile

BACKGROUND

The late sixteenth century through to the beginning of the eighteenth century was a time of great change in the nations of Europe. European monarchs sought to consolidate and expand their authority, often in the context of religious wars and disputes driven by a desire for greater political power. A number of absolute monarchs and rulers played key roles in Europe. In this activity, your group will choose one historical figure from the era of state building in Europe, research the subject's role in the great changes that took place in Europe, and present their findings as a multimedia presentation to the class.

GROUP DIRECTIONS

1. Your group should discuss, then select, one of the following figures to research.

Elizabeth I	Peter the Great
William and Mary	Oliver Cromwell
Louis XIV	Frederick William the Great
Charles II	James II
Philip II	Henry of Navarre

2. As a group, decide on the aspects of the subject to be researched and presented, including details from his or her personal life, and the impact that the person had on changes in Europe as a whole. Assign specific areas of research to individual group members.

3. Complete your research assignment and include ideas for visuals and props that can be included in the multimedia presentation about your subject.

4. Present your multimedia presentation to the class and have the class complete the "listener's guide."

ORGANIZING THE GROUP

1. **Decision Making/Group Work** Decide on a subject from the list provided or suggest another subject to your teacher for approval. Brainstorm as a group the general areas that will be used to organize the research on the subject's life and historical significance. Record the results. Assign specific topics to individual team members to research. Team members should be aware of all research areas determined by the team, not just their own, so they can point teammates to sources of information that they may find for different research assignments.

2. **Individual Work** Start with your textbook, but draw upon at least three sources of information to research the subject area you were assigned. Be sure to include personal information you can find about the subject and identify sources of maps, paintings, documents, information about personal effects, and other information that can be used in visuals. Share any information you find that other team members might need or want to include in their own assignments and encourage them to share with you any information they encounter related to your own specific area of focus. Keep track of all reference sources used.

Cooperative Learning Activity 14 (continued)

3. **Group Work/Decision Making** Share your research with your group. Invite comments on, and build extensions of, individuals' ideas. Together, decide what information to prioritize, using information that the group considers most significant and interesting. Collect ideas and references to visuals that can be used in the presentation. Collectively agree on the significance of the subject to the larger European scene. Assign writing, editing, further research, and assembling visuals tasks to the members of the group. Decide what role the group members will play in making the multimedia presentation. Also assign one or more members of the team to design, create, and duplicate a one-page "listener's guide" with questions to be answered by the audience during the presentation. Have this same group work with your teacher to create a rubric, or criteria, students can use to evaluate your presentation.

4. **Individual Work** Complete additional assignments made by the team to prepare the multimedia presentation.

5. **Group Sharing** Distribute the one-page listener's guide handouts and present your multimedia presentation to the class. Tell the audience in advance that they will be asked to complete an evaluation of the presentation. Have the team members observe the audience's attentiveness, reactions, and apparent interest levels during the presentation.

6. **Extended Group Work/Sharing** Discuss what the members observed and felt about the attentiveness of the audience during the presentation. How could the presentation have better maintained audience interest? Review the answers on the listener guides and compare student responses on the presentation rubric. As a group, create a list of the positive aspects of the presentation and offer suggestions on how it could have been improved.

GROUP PROCESS QUESTIONS

- What is the most important thing you learned about the subject your group researched in this activity?

- Did you omit any important information from your presentation? What was it?

- How effective was the listener's guide in creating audience interest?

Quick CHECK ✔

1. Was the goal of the assignment clear at all times?

2. How was creating and presenting a multimedia presentation different from other types of projects?

3. Did you have problems working together? If so, how did you solve them?

4. Were you satisfied with your work on this project? Why or why not?

HISTORY SIMULATION ACTIVITY 14

King or Queen for a Day

From 1500 to 1700, the age of absolute monarchs brought many social and political changes to the people and the map of Europe. Kings and queens of Europe and Russia wielded absolute power over their subjects. Sometimes their rule brought benefits to the societies they ruled, often at the expense of hardships to some groups.

TEACHER MATERIAL

Learning Objective To review and evaluate the political policies, military strategies, moral convictions, and personal objectives of the absolute monarchs who ruled from 1500 to 1700.

Activity Students will work in five groups to investigate and select the monarch they feel was the most influential to his or her time period and country. Groups should take into consideration how the monarch treated the common people and affected religious beliefs.

Teacher Preparation Bring in supplemental reference books for the students to use in addition to their textbooks. Each group member will need a copy of the worksheet on the next page and a pencil or pen.

Activity Guidelines

1. Introduce this as a chapter-concluding activity that will challenge students to use the knowledge they have gained from their textbooks and independent research to describe and evaluate the absolute monarchs they have studied. Explain the learning objective and briefly review the major figures in the chapter.

2. Organize the class into five groups and assign each group one of the countries involved: France, Spain, England, Prussia, or Russia. Explain that each group's task is to work together to reach a consensus about which monarch from their assigned country they will select to receive the King- or Queen-for-a-day award. Each group should designate one student to present the group's choice to the rest of the class and briefly defend that choice based on the worksheet information. Note: The group assigned to Spain has only one major figure—Philip II.

3. Encourage students to use their textbooks and the supplemental reference books to find facts to support their reasons for selecting a particular monarch.

4. After each group completes the worksheet, ask students to take an informal group vote to determine their choice for the award.

5. Allow at least half of the class period for group research, discussion, and completion of the worksheets and the other half for presentations.

6. After each group's presentation, have members of the class comment on each group's choice, voicing agreement or disagreement, with an explanation of their opinions.

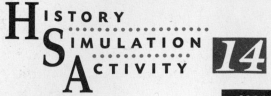

14

HANDOUT MATERIAL

King or Queen for a Day—Worksheet

Complete the following worksheet as you discuss the actions, policies, and personal objectives of the absolute monarchs. Use the information to come to an agreement on who should receive the King- or Queen-for-a-Day award.

Monarchs to Be Considered		
	_____	_____
Political achievements		
Religious policy		
Military successes or failures		
Domestic policy		
Foreign policy		
Innovations during the monarch's rule		
State of the empire after the monarch's reign		

Choice for King- or Queen-for-a-Day award: _____

Time Line Activity 14

Crisis and Absolutism in Europe

DIRECTIONS: The monarchs who ruled Spain, England, France, the German states, and Russia from 1500 to 1750 were intent on expanding their territory and power. Their efforts at national expansion set the stage for Europe's future territorial conflicts. The time line below shows some of the key events in their power struggles. Read the time line. Then answer the questions that follow.

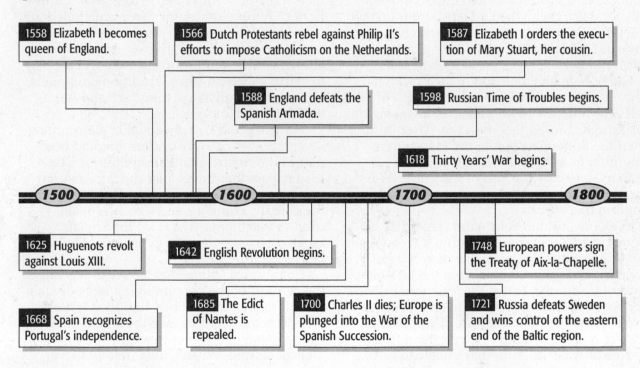

1558 Elizabeth I becomes queen of England.

1566 Dutch Protestants rebel against Philip II's efforts to impose Catholicism on the Netherlands.

1587 Elizabeth I orders the execution of Mary Stuart, her cousin.

1588 England defeats the Spanish Armada.

1598 Russian Time of Troubles begins.

1618 Thirty Years' War begins.

1500   1600   1700   1800

1625 Huguenots revolt against Louis XIII.

1642 English Revolution begins.

1748 European powers sign the Treaty of Aix-la-Chapelle.

1668 Spain recognizes Portugal's independence.

1685 The Edict of Nantes is repealed.

1700 Charles II dies; Europe is plunged into the War of the Spanish Succession.

1721 Russia defeats Sweden and wins control of the eastern end of the Baltic region.

1. Whom did Queen Elizabeth I put to death in 1587? _____

2. When did the Thirty Years' War begin? _____

3. What common factor links the event that occurred in 1566 with the event in 1625?

_____

_____

4. Which country became independent in the mid-seventeenth century? _____

5. Based on the entire time line, how would you characterize Europe in the sixteenth, seventeenth, and early eighteenth centuries?

_____

_____

_____

Attempts to Maintain Centralized Power: Past and Present

CHAPTER 14

THEN As the leaders of the Holy Roman Empire, the Hapsburgs of Austria tried to unify the countries under their rule by converting their populations to Catholicism. In Bohemia (present-day Czechoslovakia), Catholics and Protestants had once coexisted in peace. However, when a Hapsburg monarch closed the Protestant churches there, civil war broke out. This conflict ignited the Thirty Years' War, which raged from 1618 to 1648.

The Bohemians' reaction to an attack on their religion demonstrated the strength of their attachment to their culture. However, the Hapsburgs ignored this message. After putting down the Bohemian revolt, the Hapsburgs attempted to force Catholicism on other German states. By the end of the Thirty Years' War, the Hapsburg king, Ferdinand III, would abandon this effort.

In the meantime, Ferdinand created a strong central government within the countries still under his control. He then wrested Hungary and Transylvania from the Ottoman Empire. Under the Turks, the Hungarians had been free to practice Protestantism and otherwise express their own culture. Their strong sense of national identity helped them resist the rule of Austria. Although unable to break away from the Austro-Hungarian Empire completely, the Hungarians did thwart the Hapsburgs' attempts to establish a totally centralized empire. Over time, strong feelings of nationalism developed within other countries of the empire, which also challenged Austria's authority.

NOW Some governments still ignore peoples' right to choose their own way of life. The "empire" of the former Soviet Union included countries in Eastern Europe, in which the Soviets had set up puppet governments. Like the countries in the Austro-Hungarian Empire, Eastern Europe under the Soviets included a variety of ethnic groups. Hoping to maintain strong centralized rule, the Soviets did not allow the different groups in Eastern Europe to express their cultures. Traditional religions, economies, family structures, art, and literature were all banned.

Hungary and Czechoslovakia were among several Soviet-ruled countries that had been part of the Austro-Hungarian Empire. The nationalism that developed during Austrian rule intensified under Soviet control. Repeatedly, Hungary and Czechoslovakia tried to free themselves from the Soviets. Finally they succeeded as the Soviet Union began to crumble.

Communist China also has tried to change the cultures of the peoples living in its domain. Tibet is a notable example. Buddhist leaders, called lamas, once ran the Tibetan government. Consequently, religion formed the core of Tibetan culture. When China first took over, Chinese leaders promised the Tibetans that their religious freedom would be respected. However, in 1956, many Buddhist monasteries were closed and the Dalai Lama was forced to seek refuge in India. Buddhism forbids the use of violence. Therefore, the Dalai Lama has tried to free his country of Chinese tyranny through peaceful means—so far without much success.

CRITICAL THINKING

Directions: Answer the following questions on a separate sheet of paper.

1. **Making comparisons:** How were the Hapsburgs and the Soviets similar in the way they ruled conquered countries? How were they different?
2. **Making inferences:** Why might leaders feel that controlling a group's culture will help them govern that group?
3. **Synthesizing information:** Do you think that peaceful resistance, such as strikes and boycotts, are worthwhile methods of protesting injustice or occupation? Do research in the library and on the Internet to learn about people who have used peaceful means of resisting oppression. Write a brief report of your findings.

People in World History Activity **14**   Profile 1

Guy Fawkes (1570–1606)

Remember, remember the fifth of November,
Gunpowder treason and plot;
I see no reason why Gunpowder Treason
Should ever be forgot.

Chant sung by children on Guy Fawkes Day

Guy Fawkes, kneeling, being interrogated by James I

Each November 5 in the British Commonwealth, children repeat this Gunpowder Treason chant. It's Guy Fawkes Day! On this day in 1605, a man named Guy Fawkes nearly blew up King James I and his government.

Robert Catesby was one of the conspirators' leaders. A Roman Catholic extremist, he wanted to avenge the anti-Catholic laws of England. He enlisted at least 11 other people to help him carry out his plans. The most famous of these was Guy Fawkes, a soldier who had been serving in Flanders. The group rented a house next to Parliament and tunneled into a cellar beneath the House of Lords. There, Fawkes and the other conspirators stacked 36 barrels of gunpowder, covered with iron bars and firewood. All that remained was to set the gunpowder off. The date selected for the explosion was November 5, when King James himself was scheduled to appear for the opening of Parliament. The conspirators hoped that the massive explosion would kill James and the members of Parliament, and in turn set off a Catholic uprising throughout Britain.

Although the plan required secrecy, word got out. Since the conspirators needed more money to finance the planned uprising, they invited several wealthy men to join them. One of these men, Sir Francis Tresham, revealed the plot to his brother-in-law Lord Monteagle, through a letter warning him not to attend Parliament. Monteagle had the cellar searched. On November 5, 1605, Fawkes was captured, and what came to be known as the Gunpowder Plot was ended. Ironically, the Gunpowder Plot, which was conceived to help the plight of persecuted Roman Catholics, actually caused Roman Catholic persecution to be more vigorous and bitter in England.

The conspirators were tried and convicted. On January 31, 1606, Fawkes and seven of the other conspirators were beheaded. Of the 11 conspirators, Guy Fawkes—because he intended to light the fuse—is the most remembered. A year after the gunpowder was discovered, Parliament enacted a law establishing November 5 as a day of public thanksgiving. To this day, children make effigies of Guy Fawkes. The "Guys" are then burned in bonfires, and fireworks fill the skies.

REVIEWING THE PROFILE

Directions: Answer the following questions on a separate sheet of paper.

1. What role did Guy Fawkes play in the Gunpowder Plot?

2. What was the purpose of the plot, and what were its results?

3. **Critical Thinking** **Drawing Conclusions.** Why did the Parliament choose November 5 to be a day of thanksgiving?

People in World History Activity 14 — Profile 2

Blaise Pascal (c. 1623–1662)

The heart has its reasons that reason knows not of.

Pensées, Blaise Pascal

While the seventeenth-century European monarchies were fighting each other and opponents of absolutism, the modern Scientific Revolution was beginning. Like the monarchs, many of the early-modern European scientists were concerned about religion. Some obediently followed the church's ideas about knowledge, and some thought religion only hindered understanding the world. Others, like the Frenchman Blaise Pascal, spanned the worlds of religion and science.

Pascal came from a talented family. His sister, Jacqueline, was a literary prodigy. His talents lay in mathematics and natural science, however. By his early twenties, Pascal had published important works in geometry and algebra. Later he helped found probability theory. He also invented a calculating device to help his father, a judge in the local tax court. Though operated by hand, this device is a forerunner of the computer. That's why in 1971, a new programming language was named Pascal.

The severe illness of his father in 1646 made Pascal take religion seriously. For the next nine years, he divided his time between scientific work and the spiritual life. Interested in Galileo's theories, Pascal did experiments on atmospheric pressure. During these he invented the syringe and the hydraulic press. He also formulated Pascal's Law: Pressure is transmitted equally throughout a confined liquid. This law made a fundamental contribution to hydrostatics, the science used to build such things as dams and ships.

On November 23, 1654, Pascal experienced what he referred to as a "night of fire," a conversion experience that began a new life devoted almost exclusively to religion. During this period, Pascal composed his most famous work, the *Pensées* (Thoughts). It advocated a faith based on intuition and the heart's love of God. It is here, as well, that Pascal proposed his famous argument, called Pascal's Wager—to convert intellectually those unmoved by religion and lead them to the full conversion of their hearts. According to Pascal's Wager, if God does not exist, a person loses nothing by believing He does; if God does exist, a person wins eternal life by believing He does. Therefore, believing in God is sensible. Nothing to lose and everything to win—for Pascal that sounded logical.

REVIEWING THE PROFILE

Directions: Answer the following questions on a separate sheet of paper.

1. To what three areas of life did Pascal devote himself?

2. Explain the argument called Pascal's Wager. Whom did Pascal hope to convert with this argument?

3. According to Pascal, what should be the basis of religious faith?

4. **Critical Thinking** Drawing Conclusions. Why might the severe illness of his father have caused Pascal to take religion seriously?

PRIMARY SOURCE READING 14

A Day at the Court of the Sun King

The luxurious and elaborate lifestyle of royal courts in the seventeenth and eighteenth centuries seems almost unbelievable today. The French court, especially during the long reign of Louis XIV, set the style for the rest of Europe. The colorful picture of court life in this selection was written by Louis de Rouvroy, duke of Saint-Simon, a noble whose *Memoirs* are considered a masterpiece of French literature. Saint-Simon's multivolume journals describe court life and personalities in the years 1694–1723, which include the final years of the reign of Louis XIV and the regency that followed.

Guided Reading *In this selection, read to learn what a "typical" day entailed in the life of King Louis XIV.*

At eight o'clock the chief *valet de chambre* [personal servant] on duty, who alone had slept in the royal chamber, and who had dressed himself, awoke the King [Louis XIV]. The chief physician, the chief surgeon, and the nurse (as long as she lived) entered at the same time. . . . At the quarter [8:15], the grand chamberlain was called . . . and those who had what was called the *grandes entrées* [greatest access]. The chamberlain (or chief gentleman) drew back the curtains which had been closed again, and presented the holy water from the vase at the head of the bed. These gentlemen stayed but a moment, and that was the time to speak to the King, if anyone had anything to ask of him; in which case the rest stood aside. . . . Then all passed into the cabinet of the council. A very short religious service being over, the King called [and] they re-entered. The same officer gave him his dressing-gown; immediately after, other privileged courtiers entered, and then everybody, in time to find the King putting on his shoes and stockings, for he did almost everything himself, and with address [attention] and grace. Every other day we saw him shave himself; and he had a little short wig in which he always appeared, even in bed, and on medicine days. . . .

As soon as he was dressed, he prayed to God, at the side of his bed, where all the clergy present knelt, the cardinals without cushions, all the laity [those outside the clergy] remaining standing; and the captain of the guards came to the balustrade during the prayer, after which the King passed into his cabinet. He found there, or

was followed by all who had the entrée, a very numerous company, for it included everybody in any office. He gave orders to each for the day; thus within a half a quarter of an hour it was known what he meant to do; and then all this crowd left directly. . . .

All the Court meantime waited for the King in the gallery. . . . During this pause the King gave audiences when he wished to accord any, spoke with whoever he might wish to speak secretly to, and gave secret interviews to foreign ministers. . . .

The King went to mass, where his musicians always sang an anthem. . . . The King amused himself a little upon returning from mass and asked almost immediately for the council. Then the morning was finished.

On Sunday, and often on Monday, there was a council of state; on Tuesday a finance council; on Wednesday council of state; on Saturday finance council. Rarely were two held in one day or any on Thursday or Friday. . . . Often on the days when there was no council the dinner hour was advanced more or less for the chase [hunt] or promenade. The ordinary hour was one o'clock; if the council still lasted, then the dinner waited and nothing was said to the King.

The dinner was always *au petit couvert*, that is, the King ate by himself in his chamber upon a square table in front of the middle window. It was more or less abundant, for he ordered in the morning whether it was to be "a little," or "very little" service. But even at this last, there were always many dishes, and three courses without counting the fruit. . . .

CHAPTER 14

PRIMARY SOURCE READING 14

Upon leaving the table the King immediately entered his cabinet [private room]. That was the time for distinguished people to speak to him. He stopped at the door a moment to listen, then entered; very rarely did anyone follow him, never without asking him for permission to do so; and for this few had the courage. . . .

The King amused himself by feeding his dogs, and remained with them more or less time, then asked for his wardrobe, changed before the very few distinguished people it pleased the first gentleman of the chamber to admit there, and immediately went out by the back stairs into the court of marble to get into his coach. From the bottom of that staircase to the coach, anyone spoke to him who wished. . . .

As he was but little sensitive to heat or cold, or even to rain, the weather was seldom sufficiently bad to prevent his going abroad. He went out for three objects: stag-hunting, once or more each week; shooting in his parks (and no man handled a gun with more grace or skill), once or twice each week; and walking in his gardens for exercise and to see his workmen. Sometimes he made picnics with ladies, in the forest at Marly or at Fontainbleau [a chateau], and in this last place, promenades with all the Court around the canal, which was a magnificent spectacle. . . .

At ten o'clock his supper was served. . . . This supper was always on a grand scale, the royal household (that is, the sons and daughters of France [the king]) at table, and a large number of courtiers and ladies present, sitting or standing. . . .

The King, wishing to retire, went and fed his dogs; then said good night, passed into his chamber to . . . his bed, where he said his prayers. . . .

INTERPRETING THE READING

Directions *Use information from the reading to answer the following questions. If necessary, use a separate sheet of paper.*

1. What members of the court and household attended the king in the mornings?

_____

_____

2. When did the king attend to government business?

_____

_____

3. What did the king do for entertainment and relaxation?

_____

4. What part did religion play in court life?

_____

Critical Thinking

5. Making Inferences From this account, does the king's life seem enjoyable? Explain your answer.

_____

_____

_____

World Art and Music Activity 14

Rembrandt

In the 1600s, the Netherlands was a newly independent country. Consequently, Dutch artists were not supported by a system of commissions from church and state, as were the artists in older Catholic countries. Instead, artists were dependent on private collectors. There were many wealthy collectors, which encouraged an explosion of artistic talent. The master of all the Dutch artists was Rembrandt, who produced in his lifetime more than 600 paintings, 300 etchings, and 2,000 drawings. Yet he died alone, penniless, and largely unappreciated.

DIRECTIONS: Read the passage below about this Dutch painter, then answer the questions that follow.

Rembrandt van Rijn (1606–1669) was born in Leyden, the son of a miller. He received a classical education at the Latin School and spent one year at the university. He left school at the age of 15 to study art under a local artist. Recognition and fame came early, and Rembrandt was soon sought after to produce portraits and other paintings for collectors. He was also an excellent teacher; in fact, hundreds of works thought to have been painted by Rembrandt are now known to be the work of his students.

One of Rembrandt's specialties was large oil paintings—some of biblical stories, others on historical subjects. These include *The Blinding of Samson, The Return of the Prodigal Son, The Sacrifice of Abraham, Aristotle Contemplating the Bust of Homer,* and *The Night Watch.* Much of his genius was in his use of chiaroscuro, or the play between light and dark. Sometimes in his paintings, light pours in from outside, illuminating the important figures. More often the figures themselves seem to radiate their own light, as in the self-portrait shown here. Also, each face painted by Rembrandt is different—Samson looks wretched; the father forgiving his son is full of tenderness and compassion; the soldiers on night watch are alert. There is also balance and an attention to detail. The emotions portrayed draw the viewer into an intimate relationship with the art. It is not necessary to know the story behind

Rembrandt, *Self-Portrait*

the painting to feel its emotions and share the experience. Rembrandt's appeal is said to lie in his "profound humanity"—the compassion he has for all his subjects.

Rembrandt was the first artist to specialize in self-portraits. And his sense of humanity is evident in the

(continued)

World Art and Music Activity 14

more than 90 paintings he created of himself, spanning his lifetime. They display a scrupulous honesty, portraying Rembrandt at different times and in different states of mind. They never glorify or dramatize; they are never angry or bitter. Instead, they seem to say, "This is who I am. I accept it."

Reviewing the Selection

1. Describe Rembrandt's technique of using light and shadow. What is this technique called?

   _____

   _____

2. What are two types of paintings Rembrandt specialized in, and how are they unique?

   _____

   _____

3. Reread the second paragraph of the passage and look at the self-portrait shown there. Do you agree with the writer's assessment? Explain your answer, using details from the painting to support your opinion.

   _____

   _____

   _____

   _____

   _____

Critical Thinking

4. **Demonstrating Reasoned Judgment** Michelangelo was supported by the exceedingly wealthy Medici government in Florence. Rembrandt was dependent on local art lovers who could afford paintings. Is one way of encouraging art better than the other? Explain.

   _____

   _____

   _____

5. **Predicting Consequences** If Rembrandt had been supported by the church or the state, how might his art have been different?

   _____

   _____

   _____

   _____

CHAPTER 14

Reteaching Activity 14

Crisis and Absolutism in Europe

The monarchs who ruled England, France, Spain, the German states, and Russia from 1550 to 1750 battled to expand their domain and their power. Their struggles laid the foundation for the ensuing territorial strife in Europe.

DIRECTIONS: Complete the following KWL chart to review the information in Chapter 14. A few sample questions have been filled in for you.

Crisis and Absolutism in Europe, 1550–1715		
K What I Already Know	**W** What I Want to Know	**L** What I Learned
Spain	Why did Philip II and other Spanish monarchs have difficulty ruling the Spanish Empire?	
England	How did the Tudor monarchs influence English and European affairs?	
France		
The German States		
Russia		

CHAPTER 14

★ Enrichment Activity **14** ★

Addressing the Troops

By 1558 when Elizabeth Tudor ascended to the throne of England at the age of 25, she could read and write Greek, Latin, French, Italian, Spanish, German, and, of course, English. During the era that was named for her, she was celebrated in many poems and plays. Her own writing reveals the same intelligence and learning that distinguished much of sixteenth-century writing.

Below is the speech that Elizabeth delivered to the English troops assembled at Tilbury in 1588 waiting for the landing of the Spanish Armada.

My loving people,

We have been persuaded by some that are careful of our safety, to take heed how we commit our selves to armed multitudes, for fear of treachery; but I assure you I do not desire to live to distrust my faithful and loving people. Let tyrants fear, I have always so behaved myself that, under God, I have placed my chiefest strength and safeguard in the loyal hearts and good-will of my subjects; and therefore I come amongst you, as you see, at this time, not for my recreation and disport, but being resolved, in the midst and heat of the battle, to live or die amongst you all; to lay down for my God, and for my kingdom, and my people, my honour and my blood, even in the dust. I know I have the body but of a weak and feeble woman; but I have the heart and stomach of a king, and king of England too, and think foul scorn that Parma or Spain, or any prince of Europe, should dare to invade the borders of my realm; to which rather than any dishonour shall grow by me, I myself will take up arms, I myself will be your general, judge, and rewarder of every one of your virtues in the field. I know already, for your forwardness you have deserved rewards and crowns; and We do assure you in the word of a prince, they shall be duly paid you. In the mean time, my lieutenant general shall be in my stead, than whom prince never commanded a more noble or worthy subject; not doubting but by your obedience to my general, by your concord in the camp, and your valour in the field, we shall shortly have a famous victory over those enemies of my God, of my kingdom, and of my people.

—From "Speech to the Troops at Tilbury" by Elizabeth I.

DIRECTIONS: Answer the questions below in the space provided.

1. According to Elizabeth, why is she at Tilbury with the troops? _____
   _____

2. What does Elizabeth's presence at Tilbury with the soldiers tell you about her character?
   _____

3. How would you describe the tone or mood of this speech? _____

4. What effect do you think this speech had on the soldiers? _____
   _____

5. Imagine that Philip II of Spain was addressing his troops as they set off to invade England. How do you think his speech might compare with Elizabeth's? _____

GLENCOE
WORLD HISTORY

Chapter 14
Section Resources

GUIDED READING ACTIVITY 14-1   **124**

GUIDED READING ACTIVITY 14-2   **125**

GUIDED READING ACTIVITY 14-3   **126**

GUIDED READING ACTIVITY 14-4   **127**

SECTIONS

Guided Reading Activity 14-1

Europe in Crisis: The Wars of Religion

DIRECTIONS: Answer the following questions as you read Section 1.

1. What was the chief cause of religious wars that plagued Europe in the sixteenth century?
   _____

2. Who were the Huguenots?
   _____

3. What issues besides religion played a role in the French civil wars?
   _____

4. What event brought the French Wars of Religion to an end?
   _____

5. How did Philip II strengthen his control over Spain?
   _____

6. How did Spain see itself, based on its Catholic heritage?
   _____

7. What happened when Philip tried to crush Calvinism in the Netherlands?
   _____

8. Why has the seventeenth century been called the golden age of the Dutch Republic?
   _____

9. What two notable things happened during the reign of Elizabeth Tudor?
   _____

10. What did Philip II believe would happen if Spanish forces invaded England?
    _____

Guided Reading Activity 14-2

Social Crises, War, and Revolution

DIRECTIONS: Fill in the blanks below as you read Section 2.

From 1560 to 1650, Europe experienced an economic slowdown. Spain's economy, dependent on imported **(1)** _____, was failing. A growing population demanding land and food led to **(2)** _____. Spain's economy was seriously falling by the 1640s due to **(3)** _____ producing less silver, fleets subject to **(4)** _____ attacks, and the loss of Muslim and Jewish **(5)** _____ and **(6)** _____.

During the sixteenth and seventeenth centuries, more than a hundred thousand people were charged with **(7)** _____. Under intense torture, accused witches usually **(8)** _____ to a number of practices. By 1650, people were finding it **(9)** _____ to believe in the old view of a world haunted by evil spirits.

(10) _____ played an important role in the outbreak of the Thirty Years' War, as well as **(11)** _____ and **(12)** _____ motives. The Peace of **(13)** _____ stated that all German states, including the Calvinist ones, could determine their own religion.

At the core of the English Revolution was the struggle between king and **(14)** _____ to determine what role each should play in governing England. James I of England believed kings receive their **(15)** _____ from God and are responsible only to him. Parliament proved victorious due largely to the New Model of Army of **(16)** _____.

Dutch leader William of **(17)** _____ and his wife **(18)** _____ raised an army and invaded England in 1688. With almost no bloodshed, England had undergone a "**(19)** _____." As William and Mary took the English throne, they accepted a Bill of Rights setting forth **(20)** _____ right to make laws and levy taxes.

SECTION 14-2

📖 Guided Reading Activity 14-3

SECTION 14-3

Response to Crisis: Absolutism

DIRECTIONS: Fill in the blanks below as you read Section 3.

I. _____ is a system in which a ruler holds total _____.

   A. In seventeenth-century Europe, absolutism was tied to the divine

   _____. .

   B. The reign of _____ in France is the best example of absolutism.

     1. Cardinal Richelieu strengthened the _____ by limiting rights and spying on the nobles.

     2. Louis XIV called himself the _____.

     3. Louis XIV had complete authority over _____, the

     _____ and _____.

II. _____ and _____ emerged as European powers after the Thirty Years' War.

   A. Prussia was a small territory with no natural _____ for defense.

     1. Frederick William built a large and efficient _____.

     2. In 1701 Frederick William's son _____ officially became king.

   B. The _____ had long served as emperors in the Holy Roman Empire.

     1. In the seventeenth century, they had lost the _____ Empire.

     2. After the defeat of the Turks in 1683, Austria took control of all of

     _____, _____, _____, and

     _____.

III. Ivan IV became the first Russian ruler to take the title of _____, or caesar.

   A. The most prominent member of the _____ dynasty was Peter the Great.

   B. Peter was especially eager to borrow European _____ to modernize the army and navy.

   C. A hard-fought war with _____ enabled the building of St. Petersburg.

Guided Reading Activity 14-4

The World of European Culture

DIRECTIONS: Fill in the blanks below as you read Section 4.

1. _____ in art used elongated figures to show _____, heightened _____, and religious _____.

2. The mood depicted by El Greco reflected well the tensions created by the religious upheavals of the _____.

3. The _____ painting style was known for its use of dramatic effects to arouse the emotions and reflect a search for power.

4. Perhaps the greatest figure of the baroque period was the Italian architect and sculptor _____, who completed St. Peter's _____ in Rome.

5. Of all the Elizabethan _____, none is more famous than _____ .

6. The Globe theater's admission charge of one or two pennies enabled even the _____ to attend.

7. Miguel de Cervantes' novel _____ has been hailed as one of the greatest literary works of all time.

8. Beginning in the 1580s, the standard for playwrights was set by _____, who wrote perhaps 1,500 plays in all.

9. Hobbes called the state "that great _____ to which we owe our peace and defense."

10. Locke believed government should protect the _____ rights of the people. If government betrayed their trust, the people could _____ the government.

11. John Locke's ideas were used to support demands for _____ government, the rule of law and the protection of rights.

SECTION 14-4

GLENCOE
WORLD HISTORY

Chapter 15 Resources
The Muslim Empires, 1450–1800

READING SKILLS ACTIVITY 15
Evaluating   131

HISTORICAL ANALYSIS SKILLS ACTIVITY 15
Examining Trends   132

DIFFERENTIATED INSTRUCTION ACTIVITY 15
A Comparison of Empires   133

ENGLISH LEARNER ACTIVITY 15
The Ottoman Empire   135

CONTENT VOCABULARY ACTIVITY 15
The Muslim Empires, 1450–1800   137

ACADEMIC VOCABULARY ACTIVITY 15
The Ottoman Empire   139

SKILLS REINFORCEMENT ACTIVITY 15
Using Library Resources   141

CRITICAL THINKING SKILLS ACTIVITY 15
Recognizing Bias   142

HISTORY AND GEOGRAPHY ACTIVITY 15
Constantinople   143

MAPPING HISTORY ACTIVITY 15
The Battle of Chaldiran   145

HISTORICAL SIGNIFICANCE ACTIVITY 15
The Monument to Love   146

COOPERATIVE LEARNING ACTIVITY 15
Muslim Empires Time Line   147

HISTORY SIMULATION ACTIVITY 15
Lives in the Past   149

TIME LINE ACTIVITY 15
The Muslim Empires   151

LINKING PAST AND PRESENT ACTIVITY 15
Mosques and Skyscrapers   152

PEOPLE IN WORLD HISTORY ACTIVITY 15
Profile 1: Selim I (1470–1520)   153
Profile 2: Shah Abbas
(c. 1571–1629)   154

PRIMARY SOURCE READING 15
Four Hundred Years of the
East India Company   155

WORLD ART AND MUSIC ACTIVITY 15
Musical Instruments of
Southwest Asia   157

RETEACHING ACTIVITY 15
The Muslim Empires   159

ENRICHMENT ACTIVITY 15
Islam in China   160

Reading Skills Activity 15

Evaluating

LEARNING THE SKILL

In order to be an effective reader, you need to form an opinion about what you read. Your understanding of a topic is strengthened if you think critically about all the information presented in the text on a particular topic before forming your opinion. When you've thought critically and formed objective opinions, you are equipped to evaluate information based on motivations and circumstances. History comes alive when you evaluate the motives and behaviors of the people you read about.

PRACTICING THE SKILL

DIRECTIONS: Read the following passage from page 501 of the textbook about the Mogul ruler Aurangzeb.

> *Aurangzeb is one of the most controversial rulers in the history of India. . . . A man of high principle, he attempted to eliminate many of what he considered to be India's social evils. He forbade the Hindu custom of suttee (cremating a widow on her husband's funeral pyre), and he put a stop to the levying of illegal taxes. He tried to forbid gambling and drinking as well.*
>
> *Aurangzeb was a devout Muslim and adopted a number of measures that reversed the Mogul policies of religious tolerance. For instance, he imposed a tax on non-Muslims. Also, he prohibited the building of new Hindu temples, and he forced Hindus to convert to Islam.*
>
> *Aurangzeb's policies led to Hindu outcries and domestic unrest. He even received criticism from Shias. . . .*

Talk about your reactions to this passage as a class.

1. How did you feel as you were reading this passage?

2. Evaluate the actions described in the above passage. What motivations and points of view do you need to keep in mind? Do you think Aurangzeb or the people reacting to his policies would come to the same conclusions about their actions as you did?

APPLYING THE SKILL

DIRECTIONS: Read "Society and the Role of Women" on page 488 in your textbook. Choose a partner and then choose sides to have a debate on the way women's roles were carried out and perceived by the Ottomans and Moguls. On separate pieces of paper, one of you should write an opinion supporting Ottomans' ideas on women's roles, and the other should write an opinion supporting the Moguls' ideas on women's roles. Then present your statements to each other and discuss how you came up with them. Finally, each person should come up with a rebuttal, or answer, to the other person's statement.

CHAPTER 15

Historical Analysis Skills Activity 15

Examining Trends

CHAPTER 15

LEARNING THE SKILL

Historians can pinpoint what people valued or designated as important during particular periods based on what trends stand out. In modern history, people leave obvious examples of current trends in magazines, advertising, or even a time capsule. Most trends aren't highlighted as blatantly, but can be spotted quickly if you know where to look. For example, examining campaign buttons or bumper stickers from a specific presidential campaign indicates what was considered important to voters at the time. Likewise, an abundance of commercial advertising of low-fat food indicates a particular eating trend.

PRACTICING THE SKILL

DIRECTIONS: Read the following excerpt from Chapter 15 about a trend in Ottoman architecture, and then answer the questions below.

> By far the greatest contribution of the Ottoman Empire to world art was in architecture, especially the magnificent mosques of the last half of the sixteenth century. The Ottoman Turks modeled their mosques on the open floor plan of Constantinople's Byzantine church of Hagia Sophia, creating a prayer hall with an open central area under one large dome.
>
> In the mid-sixteenth century, the greatest of all Ottoman architects, Sinan, began building the first of his 81 mosques. One of Sinan's masterpieces was the Suleymaniye Mosque in Istanbul. Each of his mosques was topped by an imposing dome, and often the entire building was framed with four towers, or minarets.

1. On which time period does this excerpt focus? Which trend is examined?

_____

_____

2. How does this architecture trend characterize this particular period in history?

_____

_____

_____

_____

_____

APPLYING THE SKILL

DIRECTIONS: Imagine that you are an architect designing new buildings based on current trends. What purposes would your buildings serve? What would your buildings tell future historians about the time period we live in?

A Comparison of Empires

The Ottoman dynasty began in the early fourteenth century as the group of Turks expanded and built power. Over the next three hundred years, the Ottoman Empire moved into areas in western Asia, North Africa, and Europe. The Mogul Empire established unity in India though they were not native Indians. Their army was smaller than those of their enemies, but they had an advanced artillery that was able to overpower the enemy.

DIRECTIONS: Using the Venn diagram below, compare and contrast the Ottoman and Mogul Empires' treatment and role of women. On the outside of each circle, list examples that pertain to the specific empire. In the space where the two circles overlap, list commonalities both empires share.

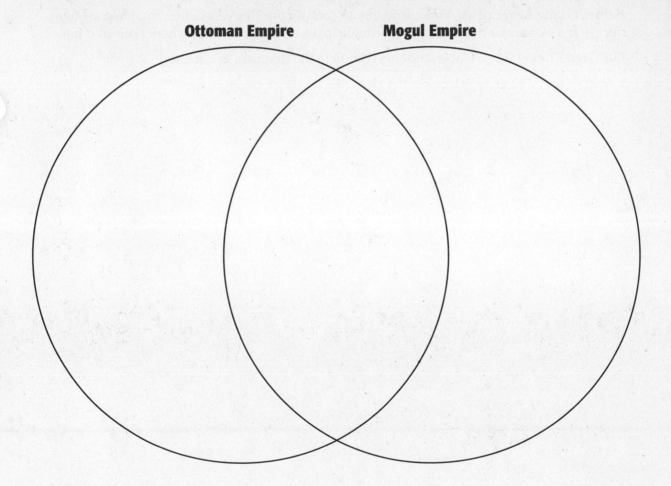

Ottoman Empire   **Mogul Empire**

(continued)

Differentiated Instruction Activity **15**

For the Teacher

TEACHING STRATEGIES FOR DIFFERENT LEARNING STYLES

The following activities are ways the basic lesson can be modified to accommodate students' different learning styles:

English Learners (EL) Review the assignment with students, explaining how to correctly record information in the organizer. Help students to understand they should list commonalities between both empires in the center of the diagram. Direct students' attention to the sections in the chapter they should use to locate information and review any terminology students may not understand.

Advanced Learners (AL) After students have researched the role of women in the empires, ask them to also research the culture of each. Have students choose one empire to present to the class.

Below Grade Level (BL) Assist students in completing the Venn diagram. Help students decide if a statement belongs in individual circles or in the middle where both overlap.

On Grade Level (OL) Have students complete the diagram as directed.

English Learner Activity 15

The Ottoman Empire

✪ A. PRE-READING ACTIVITY: IMPROVING READING COMPREHENSION

Directions: *Before reading "Expansion of the Empire" on page 484, answer the following questions.*

1. In this chapter, you will read about the Ottoman Empire and their observance of religious tolerance. What is religious tolerance? What would be the effects of religious tolerance?

   _____

   _____

   _____

   _____

2. Another word for tolerance is *open-mindedness.* In what ways are you tolerant?

   _____

   _____

   _____

   _____

✪ B. READING COMPREHENSION ACTIVITY: WORDS IN CONTEXT

Directions: *Fill in the blanks with the following words: guilds, pastoral, inherit, merchants, peasants, occupation. Use each word only one. You can check your answers by rereading the section "Society and the Role of Women" on page 488.*

Individuals of the Ottoman Empire were divided by **(1)** _____.
The four main groups of occupations included: peasants, artisans, merchants, and
(2) _____ peoples. **(3)** _____ were leased land by the state
and farmed it. Craft **(4)** _____ were established, and artisans were grouped
according to their craft. **(5)** _____ were the most privileged class in Ottoman
society outside of the ruling class. During this period, women were allowed to own and
(6) _____ property.

CHAPTER 15

(continued)

English Learner Activity 15

✪ C. TEXT ANALYSIS ACTIVITY: IDENTIFYING TRANSITIONAL DEVICES

Language Usage Note: Identifying Transitional Devices

Good writers use transitions to make their writing clear and easy to follow. Transitions have different purposes, such as to signal similarity or contrast, to show time, or to identify examples. Here is a list of some commonly used transitional devices.

To add information: also, furthermore, in addition

To give examples: for example, for instance, such as

To show similarity: like, likewise, similarly, as

To contrast: although, even though, however, in contrast, nevertheless, on the other hand, but, not

Directions: *Circle the transitional devices in the sentences below and identify the purpose of each. Put a ✓ in the appropriate box.*

Sentence	Add Information	Show Contrast	Show Similarity	Give Examples
1. However, in the second half of the seventeenth century, they again went on the offensive.				
2. Like the other Muslim empires in Persia and India, the Ottoman Empire is often labeled a "gunpowder empire."				
3. In some areas, however, such as present-day Bosnia, large numbers of non-Muslims converted to the Islamic faith.				
4. In addition to the ruling class, there were four main occupational groups: peasants, artisans, merchants, and pastoral peoples.				
5. For instance, woman were allowed to own and inherit property.				

CHAPTER 15

Content Vocabulary Activity 15

The Muslim Empires, 1450–1800

DIRECTIONS: Match each term with its definition by writing the correct letter on the blank.

A.	sultan	**F.**	harem	**K.**	suttee
B.	grand vizier	**G.**	ulema	**L.**	minaret
C.	janissary	**H.**	shah	**M.**	mosque
D.	pasha	**I.**	orthodoxy	**N.**	merchants
E.	gunpowder empire	**J.**	zamindar		

_____ **1.** nonreligious political leader of the Ottoman Empire

_____ **2.** most privileged class in Ottoman society outside ruling elite, exempt from government regulations and taxes

_____ **3.** traditional religious beliefs

_____ **4.** local official and landholder collecting and paying taxes on the land under his jurisdiction

_____ **5.** practice of a Hindu widow's cremating herself on her husband's funeral pyre

_____ **6.** group of religious advisers who administered the legal system and schools for educating Muslims

_____ **7.** conquerors who unified regions based on their mastery of firearms

_____ **8.** elite Ottoman warrior who was trained to be efficient and fearless

_____ **9.** official appointed by the central government under the Ottoman rule

_____ **10.** Ottoman chief minister who headed the bureaucracy

_____ **11.** Muslim house of worship

_____ **12.** king (used in Persia)

_____ **13.** private domain of the sultan called "the sacred place"

_____ **14.** tall slender tower attached to a mosque

Academic Vocabulary Activity 15

The Ottoman Empire

A. Word Usage Activity

Using Words in Speech and Writing

DIRECTIONS: Answer the following questions, using all of the underlined words.

1. Into which areas did the Ottoman Empire <u>expand</u>? By the fourteenth century, where had they <u>expanded</u>?

    _____

    _____

2. What was <u>breached</u> allowing Ottoman soldiers to pass into Constantinople? What did Mehmet II say after the <u>breaching</u>?

    _____

    _____

3. <u>Administrators</u> within the Ottoman and Safavid Empires were trained to do what task? What responsibilities do <u>administrators</u> in your school complete?

    _____

    _____

4. What qualities did most of Abbas's <u>successors</u> lack that led to religious orthodoxy?

    _____

    _____

5. Akbar's <u>intelligence</u> helped create the greatest Indian empire since what dynasty? Name another <u>intelligent</u> person you know. How does this individual use his/her <u>intelligence</u> to lead others?

    _____

    _____

6. The Mogul Empire adopted a policy of <u>tolerance</u> in what area? In what specific ways are you <u>tolerant</u> of others?

    _____

    _____

(continued)

Academic Vocabulary Activity 15

B. Word Meaning Activity

Antonyms

DIRECTIONS: Determine which answer is the antonym of the given word. Remember, antonyms are words that have opposite meanings.

1. native
   - **a.** resident.
   - **b.** local
   - **c.** alien

2. integration
   - **a.** combine
   - **b.** segregate
   - **c.** unite

3. tolerant
   - **a.** impatient
   - **b.** open-minded
   - **c.** considerate

4. breach
   - **a.** closed
   - **b.** gap
   - **c.** opening

5. intelligent
   - **a.** smart
   - **b.** ignorant
   - **c.** knowledgeable

6. expand
   - **a.** enlarge
   - **b.** expand
   - **c.** contract

7. elite
   - **a.** exclusive
   - **b.** ordinary
   - **c.** best

8. seclusion
   - **a.** inclusion
   - **b.** retirement
   - **c.** isolation

CHAPTER 15

Skills Reinforcement Activity 15

Using Library Resources

Knowing what kinds of research sources to use when you are looking for information on different types of subjects can help you find what you need more quickly.

DIRECTIONS: Decide which of the library sources listed below you would use to answer each of the following questions. Write the letter of the best resource in the blank. Then complete the activity that follows.

A. encyclopedia: set of books with short articles on many subjects

B. atlas: collection of maps and charts with an alphabetical index

C. almanac: collection of current statistics and facts that is updated annually

D. biographical dictionary: short biographies listed alphabetically

E. catalog: computer or card listing of all of a library's materials; can be searched by subject, author, or title

F. periodical guide: print or computer listing of magazine articles; can be searched by subject, author, or title

---

_____ **1.** What are the differences between Sunni and Shiite Muslims?

_____ **2.** What are the borders of Turkey today?

_____ **3.** What was religion like in the Ottoman world?

_____ **4.** What do present-day historians think about the accomplishments of the Ottoman Empire?

_____ **5.** Why was Aurangzeb a controversial ruler?

_____ **6.** What are the major industries of Turkey and India today?

7. Suppose you are doing a summer internship at your local public television station. Your boss asks you to start collecting information on the Ottoman Empire for a special series that is being developed. The six-part series will feature the people, events, and culture of the Ottoman Empire as well as Turkey today. Using your school or local library, list below at least three specific books or articles you would use to find the information you need. Include more than one type of research source. After each source, explain what kind of information it would provide for the television series.

_____

_____

_____

_____

Critical Thinking Skills Activity 15 | Recognizing Bias

CHAPTER 15

In the following selection, a British historian writes in the nineteenth century about British rule in India, which began in 1757. While reading the selection, recognize the author's bias, or prejudices, about India. Bias can be identified by looking for adjectives, or words that modify nouns. For example, a negative bias of meat might be "Tasty vegetables provide more protein than greasy beef." In this case, the adjective *greasy* tells us that the speaker's bias regarding meat is negative.

DIRECTIONS: Read the selection. Then answer the questions below.

> Remember what India had been for countless ages before the establishment of British rule. Think of its endless wars of race and creed, its savage oppressions, its fierce anarchies, its barbarous customs, and then consider what it is . . . to have conferred upon more than 250 millions of the human race perfect religious freedom, perfect security of life, liberty, and property; to have planted in the midst of these teeming multitudes a strong central government, enlightened by the best knowledge of Western Europe, and steadily occupied in preventing famine, alleviating disease, extirpating savage customs, multiplying the agencies of civilisation and progress. . . .
>
> . . . Whatever misfortunes, whatever humiliations, the future may reserve to us, they cannot deprive England of the glory of having created this mighty empire.
>
> —From a speech by British historian W. E. H. Lecky
> (1838–1903)

1. Give examples of the types of adjectives the author uses to describe Indian civilization. How does he describe British civilization?

   _____

2. What is the author's overall opinion of Indian civilization? Of British civilization?

   _____

   _____

   _____

3. In the following chart, give examples from the textbook of facts or information that may be used to contradict the author's negative bias of Indian history.

Contrasting Opinions	
Author's Opinion of Indian Culture	**Facts or Information to Contradict Opinion**
"barbarous customs"	
"savage oppressions"	
"endless wars of race and creed"	

Copyright © Glencoe/McGraw-Hill, a division of The McGraw-Hill Companies, Inc.

★ HISTORY AND GEOGRAPHY ACTIVITY 15

Constantinople

"One could not believe there was so rich a city in all the world," noted the crusader Villehardouin about the splendor of Constantinople. In its glory from the A.D. 500s to 1000s, this "New Rome" on the Bosporus was dedicated to the Christian religion. What role did Constantinople play in the history of the Byzantine Empire?

The city of Constantinople, a center of trade and education, stood at the crossroads of Europe and Asia. Its citizens were the descendants of various peoples but still considered themselves Romans. Social acceptance depended on knowledge of the Greek language and adherence to the Christian faith. In preserving its Greek and Roman heritage, Constantinople also developed its own distinct culture.

A city of great power and pageantry, Constantinople was home to half a million people. Vessels that crowded its great

The Conquest of Constantinople

Indeed you should know that they gazed well at Constantinople, those who had never seen it; for they could not believe that there could be in all the world a city so rich, when they saw all those tall ramparts and the mighty towers with which it was shut all around, and those rich palaces and those tall churches, of which there were so many that nobody could believe their eyes, had they not seen it, and the length and breadth of the city which was sovereign among all others.

—Villehardouin

The significance of religion in Byzantine culture and the close ties between church and state are depicted in this mosaic. Emperor Constantine IX is shown holding a purse of money; his wife, Zoe, is holding a signed and sealed document confirming the donation to the church, with Christ shown as the recipient.

HISTORY AND GEOGRAPHY ACTIVITY 15 (continued)

harbor filled the city's markets with silks, spices, furs, precious stones, perfumed woods, carved ivory, gold and silver, and enameled jewelry. Within the walls of the fortress city stood magnificent examples of Byzantine architecture, such as the Hippodrome, the Great Palace, and the church of Hagia Sophia.

Life in Constantinople included government regulation of trade and industry, as well as control of banking, insurance, and credit services. The poor were put to work in state bakeries and market gardens. The lives of all citizens also were affected greatly by the close ties between the church and the state.

You can describe a place by naming various physical and human characteristics that give an area its identity. Human characteristics include aspects of a culture—its language, religion, political systems, economic activities, and social structures, for instance. Religion was a distinguishing human characteristic in the Byzantine capital of Constantinople (the present-day city of Istanbul, Turkey). The Christian religion influenced virtually every aspect of life, including art, architecture, and politics. By comparing the human characteristics of a place, such as the economic and religious activities of its people, you can determine significant features of each characteristic.

APPLYING GEOGRAPHY TO HISTORY

DIRECTIONS: Answer the questions below in the space provided.

1. What are the human characteristics of a place?

    _____

2. Describe Constantinople's human characteristics.

    _____

3. What human characteristics make your community distinct from other communities?

    _____

Critical Thinking

4. **Drawing Conclusions** How might the human characteristics of a place affect its relations with other countries?

    _____

    _____

Activity

5. Read a local daily newspaper for one week, noting specific examples of how human characteristics influence or affect community life. At the end of the week, compile a list of the issues that reflect these human characteristics. Share your findings in a classroom discussion.

Mapping History Activity 15

The Battle of Chaldiran

In 1507 Safavid ruler Shah Ismail began raiding Ottoman lands in eastern Asia Minor, antagonizing the Ottomans and making future conflict between the two states inevitable. Tensions reached their height in 1514. The two armies met in August of that year at Chaldiran. The Ottomans, the first Islamic empire to employ artillery in warfare, completely decimated the Safavid cavalry. Ismail withdrew his troops, but the Ottoman Sultan, Selim I, did not pursue him. Following the battle, the Safavid capital was moved from Tabriz to Qazvin. The battle also established the border between the two empires, which remains the border between Turkey and Iran today.

DIRECTIONS: Use the map below to answer the questions that follow.

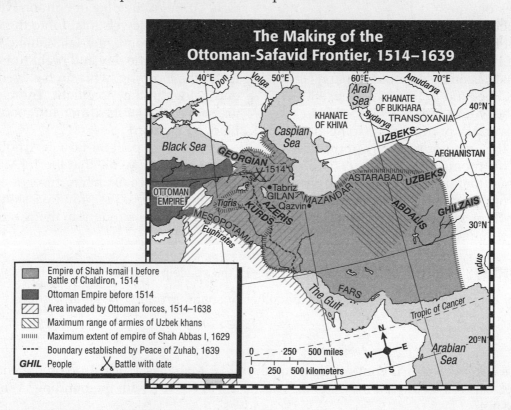

The Making of the
Ottoman-Safavid Frontier, 1514–1639

Legend:
- Empire of Shah Ismail I before Battle of Chaldiron, 1514
- Ottoman Empire before 1514
- Area invaded by Ottoman forces, 1514–1638
- Maximum range of armies of Uzbek khans
- Maximum extent of empire of Shah Abbas I, 1629
- Boundary established by Peace of Zuhab, 1639
- **GHIL** People   Battle with date

1. Why do you think the Safavids moved their capital from Tabriz to Qazvin following the battle at Chaldiran?

_____

2. What army threatened the Safavids from the east?

_____

3. What made defending their territory difficult for the Safavids?

_____

CHAPTER 15

Historical Significance Activity 15

The Monument to Love

India is full of beautiful temples and other architectural splendors, but even in such a setting the Taj Mahal stands out. *Taj Mahal* means "Crown Palace," and indeed it is the crown jewel of India's architectural wonders. In this chapter you learned that it was built by the Emperor Shah Jahan as a tomb for his second wife, Mumtaz Mahal, and as a monument to their deep love for each other. The Indian writer Rabindranath Tagore called the Taj Mahal "a teardrop on the cheek of time."

At his wife's request, Shah Janan promised that he would do four things in the event of her death: first, he would build the Taj Mahal; second, he would remarry; third, he would be kind to their children; and fourth, he would visit the Taj Mahal on the anniversary of her death. To his deep sorrow, the emperor had the opportunity to keep his promises.

It is said that the emperor was so crushed by his wife's death that his hair and beard turned white. He had no problem fulfilling his first promise. He poured his grief into the building that would house his beloved's body and show to the world their passionate devotion to each other. The Taj Mahal expresses what Mumtaz Mahal meant to Shah Jahan.

The architecture reflects this meaning. For example, the rectangular base of the building symbolizes the four sides from which to look at one's beloved. The main gate is like the bridal veil that, when lifted gently, reveals the beauty of the woman's face. Through the play of light on water and the use of jewels inlaid into the white marble of the tomb, the Taj Mahal changes colors during the day and night. It is pinkish in the morning, white in the evening, and golden in the moonlight. These colors are said to depict the different moods of a beloved woman.

The English poet Sir Edwin Arnold said it best when he wrote that the Taj Mahal was "not a piece of architecture, as other buildings are, but the proud passions of an emperor's love wrought in living stones."

DIRECTIONS: Answer the following questions in the space provided.

1. Why do you think Mumtaz Mahal made her husband promise to remarry should she die?

_____

2. Does Rabindranath Tagore's description of the Taj Mahal as a "teardrop on the cheek of time" express well what the emperor was trying to convey with the building? Why or why not?

_____

3. We know that the Taj Mahal symbolizes architecturally what Mumtaz Mahal meant to her husband. Consider the architecture of a famous modern skyscraper, the Chrysler Building in New York City. What does it symbolize?

_____

4. Why could Shah Jahan not keep his fourth promise? Or could he?

_____

★ Cooperative Learning Activity 15 ★  ★

Muslim Empires Time Line

BACKGROUND

The histories of the Ottoman Empire, the Safavid dynasty, and the Mogul Empire provide much of the backdrop to western Asian, Indian, and African civilizations from 1450 to around 1800. The Islamic religion, trade, and arts flourished under these dynasties. Depicting these Islamic empires and their evolving cultures as a series of succeeding time lines will help you obtain a better understanding of how and why Islamic culture developed as a civilization.

GROUP DIRECTIONS

1. Your group will produce a time line representing the rise and fall of three great Islamic empires. The time line will contain three distinct strands, or sequences, one for each of the following:

   • the Ottoman Empire
   • the Safavid dynasty
   • the Mogul Empire

2. Color-code each strand on the time line. Enter dates of significant events for each of the time line periods and draw or attach visuals to illustrate the most significant events or people. In addition to the information on the time lines in your textbook, use other sources to learn more details about each of the empires. Decide as a group which events would be most important to include in each strand and why. Also determine how the strands will overlap by determining through your research the approximate beginning and ending dates of each empire. The time line could be produced on a series of posters, or on butcher paper.

3. Present your time line to the class, ensuring that the class appreciates the parallel histories of the three empires. Display your time line where it can be viewed by the class and other groups.

ORGANIZING THE GROUP

1. **Group Decision Making** As a group, brainstorm the tasks that need to be completed, the work plan, the schedule, and the materials and processes to be used to create the actual time line. Appoint a recorder to take notes on the brainstorming and a leader to guide the discussion. As a group, use the textbook as a reference and agree on the beginning and ending dates for each of the three empires. Assign detailed research on specific events and important places and figures for each of the empires to specific team members. Unlike previous time lines the group may be familiar with, this time line needs to be constructed as three separate but parallel sequences, one for each empire, and each a distinctly visible color.

2. **Individual Work** Use appropriate reference sources to identify the key events for your assigned empire(s). List them in order and decide why each event is

Cooperative Learning Activity 15 (continued)

significant. Also identify possible sources of visual information to include on the time line.

3. **Group Work/Decision Making** Have the individual members share their research with the group. Together decide what information to use and what visuals to include. Create and illustrate the time lines, creating a distinct, color-coded sequence for each empire.

4. **Extended Group Work/Sharing** Invite the class to question the members of the group on the significance of each empire and the events listed within them.

GROUP PROCESS QUESTIONS

- What is the most important thing you learned about the Islamic empires from this activity?

- What problems working with a group did you have?

- How did you solve the problems?

Quick **CHECK** ✔

1. How was creating a time line different from other types of projects?

   _____

   _____

2. Did you have problems working together? If so, how did you solve them?

   _____

   _____

3. How were the tasks organized among group members?

   _____

   _____

   _____

4. What organizational changes would improve a similar Cooperative Learning Activity?

   _____

   _____

   _____

HISTORY SIMULATION ACTIVITY 15

Lives in the Past

Three important Islamic empires—Ottoman, Safavid, and Mogul—existed between 1450 and 1800. Each of these empires had a profound impact on the lives of many people. That impact, however, varied greatly depending on who a person was and where and when he or she lived.

TEACHER MATERIAL

Learning Objective To gain an understanding of three different Islamic empires by "interviewing" people who lived in them.

Activity In small groups, students will prepare and present segments of a television interview show titled "Lives in the Past." Each segment will involve "interviews" with people who lived during one of the Islamic empires. Possible topics include religious practices, government, society, specific leaders, or art and architecture. Students will do additional research when necessary.

Teacher Preparation Make several copies of the next page for each group. Help students locate reference sources including books, magazine articles, and Internet addresses to learn more about a specific topic.

Activity Guidelines

1. Introduce the activity to students by reviewing the important concepts and information from this chapter.

2. Tell students that they will prepare a portion of a television show titled "Lives in the Past." Explain that each segment of the show will include a panel of four people who lived during one of the Islamic empires and two interviewers who will ask them questions. Point out that the objective of the show will be to learn more about what life was like for people living during this time.

3. Have students form groups of five or six. Invite them to choose one of the Islamic empires: the Ottoman, Safavid, or Mogul. Then have each group choose one or more topics to discuss in their segments. Tell students to determine who will play the roles of interviewers and who will be the interviewees. Students should choose three to four panel members and two interviewers.

4. Have groups decide which characters will appear on their panels. For example, one group might choose to interview historical figures from the chapter such as Akbar or Süleyman I. Another group might choose to interview a Safavid farmer or an Ottoman architect.

5. Distribute the planning forms and direct students to divide among group members the tasks involved in preparing and producing their program segment. Tasks include completing the planning form, recording research notes, preparing interview questions, and conducting interviews.

6. Suggest students use the following format for their segments:

   - One of the interviewers announces what the audience is about to see and hear.

   - The two interviewers take turns asking questions. Questions can be directed at one panel member or all of them.

   - Encourage students to ask questions that all the panelists might be able to answer, each from his or her own point of view. Allow time for panelists to respond to the questions. Remind panelists to stay in character.

7. When the panel shows are completed, have groups gather together to discuss the interview. Ask them:
   - What worked well with the interview?
   - What could have been improved?
   - Did the questions encourage panel members to speak? Why or why not?

Lives in the Past—Planning Form

Islamic Empire _____

Topic(s) _____

_____

Panel Members _____

Interviewers _____

Research information:

_____
_____
_____
_____
_____
_____
_____
_____

General plan for panel discussion:

_____
_____
_____
_____
_____
_____
_____

Time Line Activity 15

The Muslim Empires

DIRECTIONS: After 1450, Muslim empires conquered vast territories in eastern Europe, Asia, and Africa. European forces prevented their advance westward and the British established a presence in India. Look at the events on the time line and answer the questions in the space provided.

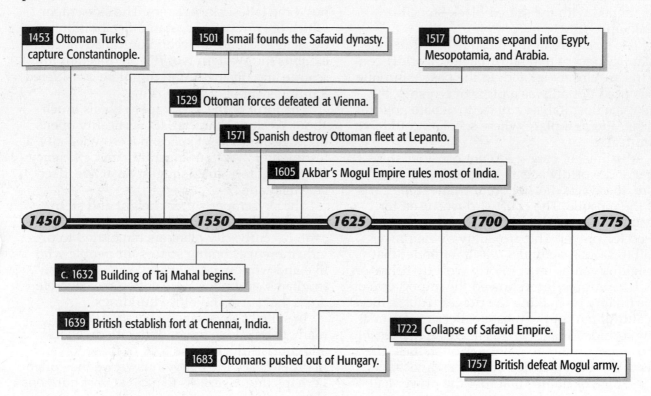

1453 Ottoman Turks capture Constantinople.

1501 Ismail founds the Safavid dynasty.

1517 Ottomans expand into Egypt, Mesopotamia, and Arabia.

1529 Ottoman forces defeated at Vienna.

1571 Spanish destroy Ottoman fleet at Lepanto.

1605 Akbar's Mogul Empire rules most of India.

1450   1550   1625   1700   1775

c. 1632 Building of Taj Mahal begins.

1639 British establish fort at Chennai, India.

1683 Ottomans pushed out of Hungary.

1722 Collapse of Safavid Empire.

1757 British defeat Mogul army.

1. Constantinople was built in 330. How long did it last until captured by the Ottomans?
   _____

2. How long did the Safavid dynasty last? _____

3. Which Muslim empires existed at the same time? _____

4. When were the Ottomans expelled from Hungary? _____

5. Name two prior defeats suffered by Ottoman forces. _____

6. Who founded the Safavid dynasty and when? _____

7. Approximately when was there a significant expansion of Ottoman rule? _____

8. When did construction of an Indian architectural landmark begin? _____

Mosques and Skyscrapers

CHAPTER 15

THEN An examination of mosques that were built in the past can help us understand some important aspects of Islamic culture. The traditional mosque consists of a courtyard surrounded by arcades. The courtyard lies outside a covered hall. One of its walls must be aligned with the sacred Black Stone in Makkah.

The structure of the mosque illustrates the Islamic concept that spiritual and worldly concerns are closely related. In the past, a mosque was used not only as a place of worship, but also as a hospital, as a place to debate political ideas, and as a place where scholars could live and teach.

Muslims, of course, do not consider spiritual and worldly acts to be identical. Therefore, these acts did not occur in the same parts of the mosque. The courtyard was used for secular purposes, and the covered hall was used for prayer. The proximity of the prayer hall to secular activities was a reminder that religious values must inform worldly behavior.

Islamic architects showed the importance of spirituality by making the prayer hall the most beautiful part of the mosque. Because Islamic law forbids Muslim artists to create images, mosques contain no paintings or statues. The beauty of mosques lies in their architecture. The dome or domes that roof the prayer hall sculpt its space into soft curves. Columns add variety to the interior, and arched niches give it mystery. Richly colored tiles with abstract designs adorn the walls and appear to be natural extensions of the mosque's structure.

NOW A look at modern skyscrapers may give insights into the modern Western character. These buildings are the most striking features of cityscapes in the West and in countries influenced by the West. To show their dedication to progress, Western cities compete to build the tallest skyscrapers. The skyscraper, which often functions as an office building, owes its existence to technological advances. It exhibits the Western world's predilection for science and business, and might be considered a fitting symbol of capitalism.

The form of the skyscraper reveals much about Western character. Its verticality opens up huge amounts of space in a crowded city, a testimony to Western ingenuity and efficiency. Sharp, vigorous lines suggest an active, decisive mentality.

The skyscraper's great height and stern design tends to make humans feel insignificant. Recently, city planners have tried to provide more welcoming spaces for people who live and work in cities. Parks with gardens, fountains, and pools now soften the concrete areas that surround office buildings.

In spite of skyscrapers' harsh qualities, many people love them. Both city dwellers and tourists flock to the tops of these towers in order to see the marvelous views they offer. Perhaps this eagerness to gaze at vast horizons shows the Western drive to explore new worlds.

CRITICAL THINKING

Directions: Answer the following questions on a separate sheet of paper.

1. **Drawing conclusions:** Many Middle Eastern countries are theocracies; that is, their rulers are also their religious leaders. What characteristic of the mosque suggests that Muslim countries were originally intended to be theocracies?

2. **Making inferences:** Why is a vertical building an advantage in a crowded city?

3. **Synthesizing information:** Other art forms besides architecture can reveal things about culture. Choose a painter that you like, and discuss what he or she expresses about his or her society. Do research in the library and on the Internet to learn what critics and historians have said about this artist. Write a brief report on your findings.

People in World History Activity 15   Profile 1

Selim I (1470–1520)

Selim I became the ninth sultan of the Ottoman Empire by killing his brothers and forcing his father, Bayezid II, to abdicate. Later Selim killed all possible claimants to the sultanate, including his sons, grandsons, and nephews. However, he did spare his chosen heir, his son, Süleyman I, later known as the Magnificent. For these killings, and for his brutal treatment of enemies in battle, Selim I became known as Selim the Grim.

Sultan Selim I ruled the Ottoman Empire for only eight years (1512–1520), but his reign extended the empire to parts of Persia, Syria, the Hejaz (in present-day Saudi Arabia), and Egypt and raised the Ottomans to leadership of the Muslim world.

At the time of Selim's accession, the Ottoman Empire faced no major problems toward the west, so Selim turned his complete attention to the problems of the east. A major conflict involved the rivalry between Muslim sects. Selim and the Ottomans were officially the defenders of the orthodox Sunni Muslim faith. In the East, the Safavids declared the Shiite Muslim faith the state religion of Persia (Iran). In response, Selim conquered the Safavid rulers of Persia and annexed some of their territory to the Ottoman Empire. Three years later he won Syria and Egypt away from the Mamelukes.

The conquest of Egypt made the Ottoman Empire one of the wealthiest of the sixteenth-century empires. Acquiring Arabia gave the Ottomans control of the holiest places in the world of Islam, the holy cities of Makkah and Madinah. These conquests made the Ottoman Empire the most important Islamic kingdom in the world for the next three decades.

In Cairo, the sharif of Makkah presented Selim with the keys to the holy city, thus symbolically acknowledging Selim's role as the leader of the Islamic world. Selim resurrected and assumed the title of caliph, which made him the spiritual as well as the governmental ruler of the Islamic world. Not yet satisfied with his conquests, Selim was preparing an invasion of Rhodes when he died in 1520. In addition to being a fierce warrior and leader, Selim was a poet and a patron of Islamic art and literature.

CHAPTER 15

REVIEWING THE PROFILE

Directions: Answer the following questions on a separate sheet of paper.

1. How did Selim assure that his son Süleyman would become the next sultan of the Ottoman Empire?

2. How did Selim make the Ottoman Empire one of the wealthiest of its time?

3. Why was Selim I known as Selim the Grim?

4. **Critical Thinking** Determining Cause and Effect. Why do you think Selim's style of ruling was successful in making changes to the Ottoman Empire?

5. **Critical Thinking** Drawing Conclusions. What do you think motivated the sharif of Makkah to acknowledge Selim as leader of the Islamic world?

People in World History Activity 15

Profile 2

Shah Abbas (c. 1571–1629)

When Shah Abbas, the greatest ruler of the Safavid Empire, came to power in 1588, the empire was in trouble. Turks and Uzbeks, the empire's enemies, were encroaching on Persian territory. Abbas needed to expel the Ottoman and Uzbek armies. At this moment, Abbas showed a good mind for strategy. He knew his armies could not win a war against two enemies at once, so he made peace with the Ottoman Empire and planned to go after the Uzbeks.

Abbas had to wait 10 years, however. The reason was he decided to create something novel in the Safavid Empire—a standing army. Abbas had to figure out its structure. For this job, he used the Englishman Sir Robert Sherley. Sherley organized the army into three groups: the slaves, the riflemen, and the artillerymen. All three groups were trained and armed according to European military standards. This training, along with his strategic powers and artillery, gave Abbas victories against the Uzbeks and the Turks. They returned all the Persian land they had seized.

Abbas made Isfahan his capital. It rapidly became one of the most important and beautiful cities in the world. During Abbas's reign, the arts of Persian painting, bookbinding, illuminated manuscripts, and ceramics reached their peak. Architecture flourished.

Carpet weaving first became the important industry it still is today in such countries as Turkey and Iran. Manufacturing and trade thrived. The Portuguese, Dutch, and English were all active commercially with the Safavid Empire.

Shah Abbas had a passion for justice and cared deeply that his subjects were treated well. He would listen to the commoners in order to learn of any of his officials who were being unjust. Typically, such officials were punished severely. He also was more tolerant of other religions than most rulers were. He allowed many Christian groups to build churches and worship.

Abbas did not behave privately as well as he ruled publicly. His fear of conspiracy turned to an obsessive paranoia about being assassinated. He blinded or assassinated anyone whom he suspected. He executed one son, blinded two more, and blinded and imprisoned his father and brothers. Not surprisingly, Abbas died without an heir, one factor that led to the decline and disappearance of the Safavid dynasty after his death.

REVIEWING THE PROFILE

Directions: Answer the following questions on a separate sheet of paper.

1. What problem faced Shah Abbas when he took power?

2. What innovation did Shah Abbas make to handle the problem?

3. What was Shah Abbas's attitude towards his subjects?

4. **Critical Thinking** Cause and Effect. What factors led to Shah Abbas's military victories?

5. **Critical Thinking** Cause and Effect. What caused Shah Abbas to treat his own family so badly?

PRIMARY SOURCE READING 15

Four Hundred Years of the East India Company

The East India Company began as a private trade organization that was later empowered by the British crown. Robert Clive was chief representative of the East India Company and acted on Britain's behalf to ensure and consolidate British power in India.

Guided Reading *In this selection, read to learn about one of the most powerful expansion vehicles of the British Empire.*

The year 2000 marks the 400th anniversary of the founding of the English East India Company, the trading organization that acted as the vehicle for British commercial and imperial expansion in Asia. For over two hundred years, the Company stood like a colossus over trade, commerce and empire, and contemporaries could only marvel at its influence, resources, strength and wealth. Writing at the beginning of the nineteenth century, the political economist David Macpherson was unequivocal in his assessment that the Company was "the most illustrious and most flourishing commercial association that ever existed in any age or country." Today even the most powerful firm pales by comparison in terms of longevity and wide-ranging economic, political and cultural influence. In an era before fast travel and instant communication, the East India Company established a far-flung empire and then set about governing, controlling and exploiting it from a great distance in London. It managed to do this until it was finally rendered obsolete by the tumultuous events surrounding the Indian Mutiny in 1857.

The Company was granted its first charter by Elizabeth I on the last day of 1600, and it had to survive an uncertain first century or so as it sought access to Asian markets and commodities. At home, it was restructured several times, notably between 1698 and 1708 when an 'old' and 'new' East India Company co-existed before merging to form the United Company of Merchants Trading to the East Indies. In the East, the Company came under such pressure from its Dutch rivals during the mid-seventeenth century that it was obliged to shift the main focus of its activities from the Malay archipelago and the Spice Islands to South Asia. Over time, it man-

aged to establish a commercial presence in India centered upon three 'presidencies' established at Madras [Chennai], Bombay and Calcutta. These tenuous footholds were fortified and defended by the Company as it sought to consolidate its position in an often hostile commercial and political world. This in turn gave rise to the growth of a small private army that was eventually to rival the regular British army in terms of size and manpower. The Company's role in India was thus defined by both commercial activity and a military presence: it was considered legitimate to use force in support of trade, and the overseas personnel were organised and deployed accordingly. In the words of one contemporary, it was a "fighting company."

By the mid-eighteenth century, the Company had begun to assert itself over rival European companies and Indian powers alike, and this placed it in a position from which it could begin to carve out an extended territorial and commercial empire for itself. The actions of men such as Robert Clive (1725–74), Warren Hastings (1732–1818) and Charles Cornwallis (1738–1805) helped to transform the Company from trader to sovereign, so that during the second half of the eighteenth century millions of Indians were brought under British rule. As William Playfair put it in 1799:

From a limited body of merchants, the India Company have become the Arbiters of the East.

The Company created the British Raj, and as such it has left a deep and permanent imprint on the history and historiography of India. The story, once almost universally described as the 'rise of British India', not so long ago formed part of the staple reading diet of British schoolchildren and students. In the post-colonial era,

PRIMARY SOURCE READING 15

when imperial history has ceased to be fashionable, the legacies of British India are still hotly debated and contested. It is within this context that the history of the East India Company remains to the fore.

Rather less obvious, perhaps, is the part played by the East India Company in the domestic development of Britain. Indeed, today's casual observer finds few signs of the leading role it once played in the nation's business, commercial, cultural and political life. In terms of architecture, for example, there is little surviving evidence in London of the Company's once-extensive property empire.

The London docklands, home to the East India dock complex, has been reshaped. Although Commercial Road and East India Dock Road—the purpose-built link with the City—survive, the docks themselves have been filled in and redeveloped, leaving only a few poignant reminders of the Company's once formidable presence in the area. To the West, the great fortress-like warehouses built by the Company at Cutler Street were partially demolished and refurbished in controversial circumstances during the late 1970s. There is no trace remaining whatsoever of the Company's headquarters in Leadenhall Street. Charles Dickens once described the "rich" East India House "teeming with suggestions" of eastern delights, but it was unceremoniously pulled down in the 1860s, and in its place today stands the new Lloyd's Building, also a monument to commercial capitalism, but displaying rather different architectural qualities. In recent years, the only obvious local clue to the Indian connection was provided by the East India Arms, a tavern in nearby Lime Street, but that too has now fallen victim to the modern re-naming and re-branding process. As a result, the East India Company is now out of sight and out of mind.

INTERPRETING THE READING

Directions *Use information from the reading to answer the following questions. If necessary, use a separate sheet of paper.*

1. Describe the rationale for the East India Company's military presence in India.

_____

2. How did the company's small private army compare to the regular British army?

_____

3. What evidence is left in London of the company's empire?

_____

Critical Thinking

4. **Summarize** Summarize how the author characterizes the East India Company.

_____

_____

World Art and Music Activity 15

Musical Instruments of Southwest Asia

Music has always played an important part in Southwest Asian cultures. Young village boys from central Turkey duel with one another using sung poetry; devout Muslims in Iran stage musical dramas to celebrate religious holidays; singers in Egyptian coffee houses, accompanied by the sound of the violin, retell epic tales of heroes from ancient times. As different regions of the area became unified under large empires, Southwest Asian musical traditions and instruments were shared and spread, eventually influencing music around the world. Many of the instruments found in the West today are descended from Southwest Asian instruments.

DIRECTIONS: Read the passage below about some of these instruments, and then answer the questions in the space provided.

Persian Musicians (1818), engraving by James Justinian Morier and Theodore H.A. Fielding

Surnaya, *mizmar, sibs,* and *aba*—these are different terms used throughout Southwest Asia to refer to a double-reed instrument from which the oboe is a Western descendant. The earliest evidence of this reed instrument is on Jewish coins of the second century A.D. It was played at weddings and other celebrations. The modern oboe is very similar in structure to its Southwest Asian ancestors. The shape of the instrument, the reed, and the manner of playing are more or less unchanged. The oboe is a long, smooth tube of wood that flares outward from its reed and circular mouthpiece to a wider bell-shaped bottom. A number of holes are drilled into the oboe to control pitch—the more holes left open, the higher the pitch. Modern oboes are made of a hard black wood called ebony, and their key systems are made

(continued)

World Art and Music Activity 15

of silver. The oboe is an important instrument in contemporary Western orchestras, often featured in solo parts because of its unique sound.

Another modern instrument with Southwest Asian roots is the flute. Arabic flutes date back as far as 3000 B.C. The Arabic name for the flute is *qasaba;* in Egypt and in Iran it is known as the *nay.* Southwest Asian flutes have remained essentially the same over time—they are made of cane, and are about 2 feet (60 centimeters) long, with 5 or 6 finger holes to vary the pitch. They are held vertically when played. Wooden flutes derived from the Arabic flute became widely used in Europe in the 1700s. During the 1800s, flutes were greatly adapted. They were made out of metal, not wood, and a more complicated key mechanism was developed. Even the playing style changed. Modern flutes are played horizontally, with the player blowing across an opening rather than into it. Like the

oboe, the flute has been incorporated into contemporary Western orchestras.

String instruments, such as the three-stringed spike fiddle played by the Persian musician in the engraving shown, are an important element of Southwest Asian music and its legacy. For example, the *Gnawa gnbri* is a stringed instrument dating back to ancient Egypt whose descendants include the American banjo. The dulcimer is a type of harp, invented in Persia. Its brass strings are struck with mallets. The first appearance of the dulcimer in western Europe dates to a relief carving done in Spain in A.D. 1184. European immigrants brought the dulcimer to the United States in the 1800s, where a new method of playing developed in which the strings are plucked instead of struck. The plucked dulcimer is still a popular instrument in American folk music today.

Reviewing the Selection

1. List examples that show the importance of music in Southwest Asian cultures.

_____

_____

2. Choose one of the instruments described above and explain how it has or has not changed from its Southwest Asian origins.

_____

_____

_____

_____

Critical Thinking

3. **Identifying Central Issues** Many instruments used in Western music have Southwest Asian roots. Write a paragraph explaining how these instruments crossed over from one culture to another.

_____

_____

_____

_____

Reteaching Activity 15

The Muslim Empires

From 1450 to the 1800s, powerful empires held sway over most of Asia. In the period you have read about, each empire succeeded in diversifying the people under its rule. Politically, these empires centralized many state functions and brought new levels of technical and military efficiency to their states. Culturally, each promoted a mixing of artistic and literary styles.

DIRECTIONS: For each empire listed below, provide examples of cultural and political diversity. Use the headings surrounding each empire as a guide. One example has been done for you.

Copyright © Glencoe/McGraw-Hill, a division of The McGraw-Hill Companies, Inc.

CHAPTER 15

CULTURAL DIVERSITY   **POLITICAL DIVERSITY**

CULTURAL DIVERSITY		POLITICAL DIVERSITY
Ulema	Ottoman Empire	Gunpowder Empire — formed by outside conquerors who unified the regions they conquered
Architecture — magnificent mosques, Sinan		Sultan
Shah Abbas	Safavid Empire	Pyramid System
Textiles		Shah Ismail
Architecture and Painting	Mogul Empire	Babur
Akbar		Government Tolerance

★ Enrichment Activity 15

CHAPTER 15

Islam in China

You have read about the spread of Islam throughout Southwest Asia and the various social and political systems that evolved from it. For example, there are Süleyman's *millets* and the religious advisory board he established known as the ulema.

Chinese Muslims are either descendants of Turkish people from Central Asia or descendants of Chinese converts to Islam. Islam probably reached China along trade routes and grew slowly. When the Mongols overthrew the Song dynasty, they established the Yuan dynasty. This period has been called the golden age " of Islam in China. Under the Yuan dynasty, Muslims received special status, including the right to hold powerful state positions. By 1368, the Mongols had been overthrown, and the Ming dynasty was in power. The Muslims lost their special status and government positions. When the Qing dynasty came to power, the status of Muslims was lower than it had been before. As a result, the Muslims rebelled, most notably in the Panthay Rebellion. This rebellion lasted from 1855 to 1873, when it was finally crushed.

DIRECTIONS: Answer the questions below in the space provided.

1. From what you know of Muslim trade routes, how do you think Islam reached China in the first place? Based on this information, where would you expect Muslim communities to be located? (Review Chapter 3.) _____
_____
_____
_____

2. How can you explain the length of the Panthay Rebellion, based on what you know of the state of the Qing dynasty during the nineteenth century? _____
_____
_____
_____

3. Based on the structure of Chinese dynasties, why would Muslims have been persecuted by the Ming and Qing dynasties? (Hint: Think about the Confucian order system.)
_____
_____
_____

4. How did the Qing and Ming repression of Muslims differ from Akbar's religious policies in India? _____
_____
_____
_____

GLENCOE
WORLD HISTORY

Chapter 15
Section Resources

GUIDED READING ACTIVITY 15-1   162

GUIDED READING ACTIVITY 15-2   163

GUIDED READING ACTIVITY 15-3   164

SECTIONS

Guided Reading Activity 15-1

The Ottoman Empire

DIRECTIONS: Answer the following questions as you read Section 1.

1. What change came over the Osman Turks as the Seljuk Empire began to decline?
   _____

2. What happened after the Ottomans recruited janissaries from the local Christian population of the Balkans?
   _____

3. What did Mehmet II say when he saw the ruin he had inflicted on the city of Constantinople?
   _____

4. What three things did Sultan Selim I declare himself to be after taking control of Mesopotamia?
   _____

5. Name the three responsibilities of a pasha appointed by the central government of the Ottomans.
   _____

6. Why was the Ottoman empire labeled a "gunpowder empire"?
   _____

7. In what two ways was the sultan the supreme authority in the Ottoman system?
   _____

8. How did a sultan communicate his desires to the grand vizier?
   _____

9. What was the new Muslim name for the city of Constantinople?
   _____

10. What was the greatest contribution of the Ottoman Empire to the world of art?
    _____

11. What was the status of women in Ottoman society?
    _____

Guided Reading Activity 15-2

The Rule of the Safavids

DIRECTIONS: Fill in the blanks below as you read Section 2.

Unlike many of their Islamic neighbors who were **(1)** _____ Muslims, the Safavids became ardent **(2)** _____. Shah Ismail used his forces to seize much of **(3)** _____ and **(4)** _____ in 1501. He founded the Safavid dynasty. After the death of Shah **(5)** _____ in 1629, the Safavid dynasty gradually lost its vigor. In the early eighteenth century, during the reign of Shah Hussein, **(6)** _____ peoples invaded and seized the capital of Isfahan. Persia then sank into a long period of **(7)** _____ and **(8)** _____ anarchy.

Strong-minded shahs firmly controlled the **(9)** _____ of the landed aristocracy. In addition, appointment to serious positions in the **(10)** _____ was based on **(11)** _____ rather than **(12)** _____. For example, Shah Abbas hired a number of foreigners from neighboring countries for positions in his **(13)** _____.

The Safavid shahs played an active role in **(14)** _____ and manufacturing. Most goods in the empire traveled by **(15)** _____ or **(16)** _____ caravans. The **(17)** _____ were kept fairly clear of thieves and bandits. Hemmed in by the sea power of the **(18)** _____ to the south and the land power of the **(19)** _____ to the west, the Safavids found trade with **(20)** _____ difficult.

Knowledge of **(21)** _____, medicine, and **(22)** _____ under the Safavids was equal to that of other societies in the region. Persia witnessed an extraordinary **(23)** _____ of the arts during the reign of Shah Abbas from 1588 to 1629. Much of the original city of **(24)** _____ still stands and is a gem of modern-day Iran.

SECTION 15-2

Guided Reading Activity 15-3

SECTION 15-3

The Grandeur of the Moguls

DIRECTIONS: Fill in the blanks below as you read Section 3.

I. In 1500 the Indian _____ was divided into a number of Hindu and Muslim kingdoms.

    A. The founder of the _____ dynasty was Babur, descended from Timur Lenk.

    B. Babur captured _____ and established his power in the plains of North India.

II. By 1605 _____ had brought Mogul rule to most of India.

    A. Akbar was known for the _____ character of his rule.

        1. A Muslim, he adopted a policy of religious _____.

        2. Akbar took a _____ princess as one of his wives.

    B. Overall, the Akbar Era was a time of _____ by the standards of the day.

III. Shah Jahan's rule was marred by his failure to deal with _____ problems.

    A. His son Aurangzeb had his brother put to death and _____ his father.

    B. In 1739 Delhi was sacked by the _____, who left it in ashes.

IV. The arrival of the _____ hastened the decline of the Mogul Empire.

    A. The British overcame _____ competition through the genius of Sir Robert Clive.

    B. Indian guerrilla fighters continued to _____ the British.

V. The Moguls were foreign _____ ruling a largely _____ population.

    A. Many Hindus adopted the Islamic practice of _____ women.

    B. The Mogul era saw the emergence of a _____ landed nobility.

    C. The _____ is widely considered to be the most beautiful building in India.

GLENCOE
WORLD HISTORY

Chapter 16 Resources
The East Asian World, 1400–1800

READING SKILLS ACTIVITY 16
Connecting   167

HISTORICAL ANALYSIS SKILLS ACTIVITY 16
Connecting Ideas   168

DIFFERENTIATED INSTRUCTION
ACTIVITY 16
Japanese Classes Emerge Under
the Tokugawa   169

ENGLISH LEARNER ACTIVITY 16
China at Its Height   171

CONTENT VOCABULARY ACTIVITY 16
The East Asian World, 1400–1800   173

ACADEMIC VOCABULARY ACTIVITY 16
The East Asian World   175

SKILLS REINFORCEMENT ACTIVITY 16
Using E-mail   177

CRITICAL THINKING SKILLS ACTIVITY 16
Recognizing a Stereotype   178

HISTORY AND GEOGRAPHY ACTIVITY 16
In the Shogun's Grip   179

MAPPING HISTORY ACTIVITY 16
Toyotomi Hideyoshi   181

HISTORICAL SIGNIFICANCE ACTIVITY 16
Do Not Disturb   182

COOPERATIVE LEARNING ACTIVITY 16
The East Asian World Trivia Game   183

HISTORY SIMULATION ACTIVITY 16
Empire Bingo   185

TIME LINE ACTIVITY 16
The East Asian World   187

LINKING PAST AND PRESENT ACTIVITY 16
Chinese Medicine   188

PEOPLE IN WORLD HISTORY ACTIVITY 16
Profile 1: Wan-Li (1563–1620)   189
Profile 2: Toyotomi Hideyoshi
(c. 1536/37–1598)   190

PRIMARY SOURCE READING 16
Laws Governing the Military
Households   191

WORLD ART AND MUSIC ACTIVITY 16
Japanese Wash Drawings   193

RETEACHING ACTIVITY 16
The East Asian World   195

ENRICHMENT ACTIVITY 16
History Reflected in Art   196

Reading Skills Activity 16

Connecting

LEARNING THE SKILL

When you make connections to any type of text that you read, the text becomes more personal. As a result, you are more likely to remember the information. As you read, ask yourself, "Does this subject relate to my life? If so, how?" You might also ask yourself, "How does this text connect to something that I have already read about?" This way of thinking helps you connect the text to other learning experiences. Finally, you can ask yourself, "How does this text relate to the world around me?" When you think in this way, you are connecting the text to what is happening in today's world. Ask yourself these questions as you read so that you can better comprehend the information.

PRACTICING THE SKILL

DIRECTIONS: Read the following paragraphs from page 517 of your textbook and create a list of questions that describe how the information connects to yourself, to other texts, and to the world around you.

> *Chinese society was organized around the family. The family was expected to provide for its members' needs, including the education of children, support of unmarried daughters, and care of the elderly. At the same time, all family members were expected to sacrifice their individual needs to benefit the family as a whole. This expectation was based on Confucian ideals.*
>
> *The ideal family unit in Qing China was the extended family, in which as many as three or four generations lived under the same roof. When sons married, they brought their wives to live with them in the family home. Unmarried daughters also remained in the house, as did parents and grandparents. Chinese society held the elderly in high regard. Aging parents knew they would be cared for in their home by their children.*

1. Connects to my life: _____

_____

2. Connects to text read earlier:_____

_____

3. Connects to world today: _____

_____

APPLYING THE SKILL

DIRECTIONS: Choose a paragraph from Chapter 16 and list three ways that you can make connections to it (text-to-self, text-to-text, and text-to-world). In one or two sentences on a separate sheet of paper, identify which type of connection helps you best remember the information.

Historical Analysis Skills Activity 16

Connecting Ideas

CHAPTER 16

LEARNING THE SKILL

Historians search the past for the origins of the thoughts and technologies that enrich our world today. Ideas were spread throughout history by conquest and trade, gradually changing over time as each culture built upon what came before. In this way, we can trace our own thoughts about values, family, justice, and religion as they progressed from the beginning of recorded history.

PRACTICING THE SKILL

DIRECTIONS: In the space provided, match each historical event with the result it brought about.

Event

1. _____ China's Ming rulers promoted an efficient government bureaucracy and school system.

2. _____ New crops were introduced under China's Ming rulers.

3. _____ Chinese innovations in paper manufacturing encouraged the growth of printing.

4. _____ Traditional Ming art objects had less domestic demand by the end of the Ming Dynasty.

5. _____ In Japan, the Tokugawa began a new focus on trade and industry.

6. _____ Korea was called the "Hermit Kingdom" because of its isolationism.

7. _____ Muslim merchants wanted to join the growing spice trade in southeast Asia.

8. _____ Mainland states in southeast Asia valued political unity and strength than non-mainland states.

Result

A. Banking flourished and a merchant class emerged in Edo.

B. The country developed its own unique alphabet, called Hangul.

C. The country's food production was greatly increased.

D. Jingdezhen potters increased shipments of porcelain to foreign markets such as Europe.

E. European traders were more successful at gaining power in the spice trade in non-mainland states.

F. The country's trade and manufacturing flourished.

G. An Islamic trade network grew as Muslims moved into the Malay Peninsula and the Indonesian archipelago.

H. A new form of literature, the realistic novel, arose and evolved.

APPLYING THE SKILL

DIRECTIONS: Suppose the United States were to change from a representative democracy to a Javanese style of kingship. Do you think that this would be a desirable change in our system? Write a one-page essay relating your thoughts on a separate sheet of paper. Be sure to describe both positive and negative aspects of such a change.

Differentiated Instruction Activity 16

Japanese Classes Emerge Under the Tokugawa

As one of the largest cities in the world, Edo had a population of over one million by 1750. During this time, Japan's class system became strict, and there were four main classes below the emperor and imperial court families: warriors, peasants, artisans, and merchants. Individuals could not marry outside their class. Women's rights were restricted and broad authority went to the male heads of households.

DIRECTIONS: Use your textbook, library resources, and the chart below to compare the four different classes under the Tokugawa and women's roles in each. Think about our society today. Is it divided into classes? If so, what are they? If not, how would you describe it? Present and defend your position in a two-page essay.

Warriors	Peasants	Artisans	Merchants
Role of Women	**Role of Women**	**Role of Women**	**Role of Women**

CHAPTER 16

(continued)

Differentiated Instruction Activity 16

For the Teacher

TEACHING STRATEGIES FOR DIFFERENT LEARNING STYLES

The following activities are ways the basic lesson can be modified to accommodate students' different learning styles:

English Learners (EL) Provide students with a partially completed chart, with one section filled in for each column. Students should work in pairs to complete the organizer. Have students discuss their position on our society or talk about the distinctions between class distinctions in their culture.

Advanced Learners (AL) After students have completed the chart, have them complete a similar chart to compare the classes within China around the 1800s. Have students present their research comparing the Chinese and Japanese.

Below Grade Level (BL) Photocopy appropriate sections of the text for students to use to complete this activity. Read the text together. Have students highlight information about each class in a different colored highlighter. Help students record the information they highlighted in the chart.

On Grade Level (OL) Have students complete the assignment as instructed. Students can share their essay with a partner.

English Learner Activity 16

China at Its Height

⭐ PRE-READING ACTIVITY: IMPROVING READING COMPREHENSION

Directions: *Before reading "The Ming Dynasty" on pages 510–512, answer the following questions.*

1. The title of this chapter is "China at Its Height." What do you anticipate to read about in this chapter?

    _____

    _____

2. China flourished under the reign of the Ming Dynasty. What is a dynasty? In what ways are countries flourishing today?

    _____

    _____

⭐ B. WORD BUILDING ACTIVITY: ADJECTIVES ENDING IN *–ED* AND *–ING*

Word Usage Note: <u>Participial Adjectives –ed and -ing</u>

Many adjectives can be formed from verbs by adding –ing or –ed/-en/-t. The –ing adjective is active and describes the person or object that is doing something or causing the situation (an *interesting* teacher, a *developing* country). The –ed/ed/t adjective is passive and describes a condition (an *excited* student) or a person or object that receives the action (the *tired* worker, the *polluted* water).

Study these examples:
1. Ecology is the study of the relationship between living things and their environment.
2. Nations have been enacting recycling programs.
3. It took years for the burned and blackened forests to grow back.

Directions: *Read the sentences and identify correct adjectives by writing **C** for correct and **I** for incorrect. You can check your answers by rereading "The Voyages of Zeng He" and "First Contacts with the West."*

1. _____ Young Le built large monuments, strengthened the Great Wall, and restored Chinese rule over Vietnam.

2. _____ Some of them held the Confucian view that traded activities were unworthy and that being a merchant was an inferior occupation.

3. _____ Many of them were highly educated men who brought along instruments, such as clocks, that impressed Chinese officials and made them more receptive to Western ideas.

(continued)

English Learner Activity 16

CHAPTER 16

✪ C. WORD BUILDING ACTIVITY: DEFINITIONS

Directions: *Choose the best definition for each word. You can check your answers by rereading "Chinese Art and Literature" on page 519.*

1. **corrupt**

    a. true **b.** highly regarded **c.** wicked

2. **immense**

    a. huge **b.** slight **c.** urgent

3. **innovation**

    a. unoriginal **b.** new ideas **c.** highly regarded

4. **admire**

    a. approve of **b.** loathe **c.** unoriginal

5. **expansion**

    a. look forward **b.** decrease **c.** development or growth

6. **realistic**

    a. unoriginal **b.** based on facts **c.** made up

7. **disintegration**

    a. put together **b.** separate into parts **c.** decrease

8. **commoner**

    a. common people **b.** highly regarded **c.** slight

Content Vocabulary Activity 16

The East Asian World, 1400–1800

DIRECTIONS: Select and write the term that best completes each sentence.

1. Heads of families who ruled over peasants in fifteenth-century Japan were known as _____ (samurai/daimyo).

2. The Qing organized the Manchus into separate military units known as _____ (banners/shogunates), the chief fighting force of the empire.

3. Despite the growth in trade and manufacturing, China did not develop the kind of _____ (shamanism/commercial capitalism)—private business based on profit—that was emerging in Europe.

4. Artists from both the Qing and Ming eras produced beautiful blue-and-white _____ (mandarins/porcelain).

5. Hereditary military dictators of Japan, the _____ (shoguns/daimyo), ruled Japan until 1868.

6. A tribe or collection of families known as a _____ (clan/yurt) provided a built-in welfare system because wealthier families looked after poor relatives.

7. When the Tokugawa rulers set out to establish control of the feudal system, the state was divided into about 250 separate territories called _____ (khans/hans), or domains.

8. During the "Great Peace" brought by Tokugawa rule, the _____ (mandarins/samurai) gradually ceased to be a warrior class.

9. The shogunate controlled the daimyo by a _____ (hostage system/meritocracy), where the family of the daimyo had to move from their homeland to Edo in the event of the daimyo's absence.

10. The Tokugawa enacted severe laws to regulate the places of residence, the dress, and hairstyles of Japan's outcasts, the _____ (eta/yasa).

11. All men in China faced execution if they did not wear a _____ (queue/Manchu), a pigtail.

12. The _____ (Ming/Wu) dynasty began when Ming Hong Wu overthrew the Mongol dynasty.

13. The _____ (Manchu/Qing) dynasty was controlled by the farming and hunting people who lived in Manchuria.

14. The _____ (Imperial City/Golden Lotus), a walled compound containing apartments, offices, banquet halls, and gardens, was home to China's emperors.

CHAPTER 16

Academic Vocabulary Activity 16

The East Asian World

Key Words

Academic Vocabulary	Words with Multiple Meanings	Content Vocabulary
centralized	revive	queue
flourish		banners
inferior		
isolation		
nomadic		
preserve		
revolt		
subordinate		
traditionalist		

A. Vocabulary in Context

Word Meaning

DIRECTIONS: Answer the following true and false questions. Mark **T** for true and **F** for false. If the statement is false, rewrite it using the underlined vocabulary word to make it true.

1. _____ During the Ming dynasty, the Chinese made peace with <u>nomadic</u> tribes.

_____

2. _____ <u>Traditionalists</u> in the bureaucracy during Yong Le's reign were not surprised by the enormous profits made by Zeng He's voyages.

_____

3. _____ The Chinese believed trade and manufacturing was <u>inferior</u> to farming.

_____

4. _____ Chinese society respected women and thought men to be <u>subordinate</u> to their wives.

_____

5. _____ Secondary education <u>flourished</u> during the Tokugawa era.

_____

6. _____ The social systems in Japan and Korea were <u>restrictive</u>.

_____

(continued)

Academic Vocabulary Activity 16

B. Word Usage Activity
Identifying Word Forms
DIRECTIONS: Determine whether the words in the chart below are in noun, verb, or adjective form. Put check marks (✓) in the appropriate columns. Remember, some words can be more than one form.

Word	Noun	Verb	Adjective
1. centralized			
2. revolt			
3. sacred			
4. preserve			
5. inferior			
6. nomadic			

C. Word Meaning Activity
Defining Vocabulary Words
DIRECTIONS: Choose the definition of each vocabulary word.

1. inferior

   a. high regard   **b.** lower rank   **c.** conclude

2. restrict

   a. confine   **b.** free reign   **c.** bring back

3. preserve

   a. dictatorial   **b.** unguarded   **c.** protect and maintain

4. subordinate

   a. superior   **b.** assistance   **c.** inferior

5. traditionalist

   a. vogue   **b.** trendy   **c.** respect for tradition

6. centralized

   a. concentrated   **b.** spread out   **c.** commander

Skills Reinforcement Activity 16

Using E-mail

You can use a computer to communicate directly with another computer user through e-mail, or electronic mail. Although many e-mail programs offer a variety of features, most allow you to perform these basic functions: composing and sending messages, responding to an incoming message, forwarding a message, organizing e-mail into folders, and saving and deleting messages.

DIRECTIONS: Send an e-mail to your teacher reflecting on one aspect of Chinese culture from your text. Copy the e-mail to yourself. Then answer the questions below in the space provided.

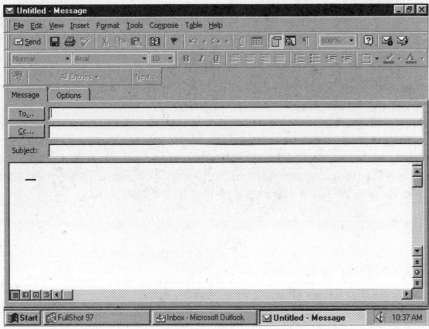

1. What do you enter in the "To" portion of the message header?

   _____

2. How do you move the cursor to the "Subject" text box?

   _____

3. Why is it unnecessary to identify yourself in the body of your message?

   _____

4. How do you send your message?

   _____

5. Check the message you sent by looking in your "In" mailbox. What information was automatically supplied in the header portion?

   _____

CHAPTER 16

Critical Thinking Skills Activity 16 | Recognizing a Stereotype

Stereotypes are oversimplified opinions or generalizations held by one group about all the members of another group. The Act of Seclusion passed in 1636 resulted in near-total isolation of the Japanese islands from Western influence. In 1853 Commodore Matthew Perry of the U.S. Navy broke 200 years of Japanese isolation by landing a small fleet at Edo Bay near Tokyo. Before Perry's visit, only the Dutch had been allowed to trade with the Japanese at a small port near Nagasaki.

DIRECTIONS: Read the following passage by Hirata Atsutane describing Japanese views of the Dutch. Then answer the questions below.

> As everybody knows who has seen one, the Dutch are taller than other people, have fair complexions, big noses, and white stars in their eyes. By nature they are very light-hearted and often laugh. They are seldom angry, a fact which does not accord with their appearance and is a seeming sign of weakness. They shave their beards, cut their nails, and are not dirty. . . . Their clothing is extremely beautiful and ornamented with gold and silver.
>
> Their eyes are really just like those of a dog. They are long from the waist downward, and the slenderness of their legs makes them resemble animals. Moreover, apparently because the backs of their feet do not reach to the ground, they fasten wooden heels to their shoes, which makes them look all the more like dogs. . . . none of them lives very long. For a Dutchman to reach 50 years is as rare as for a Japanese to live to be over 100.

1. Is Atsutane's overall attitude toward the Dutch negative or positive? What words or phrases in the text point to his biases?

   _____

   _____

2. Atsutane was a nationalist who believed Japan was superior to all other nations. How would his portrayal of the Dutch strengthen such beliefs?

   _____

   _____

3. The Japanese and the Chinese both called Westerners "barbarians." Look up in a dictionary the etymology, or the origin, of the word *barbarian* and explain why this term might be easily applied to members of an unfamiliar culture.

   _____

4. Do you think it is possible ever to achieve a totally unbiased view of another culture or group? If not, what are some ways to minimize stereotypical views of others?

   _____

   _____

★ HISTORY AND GEOGRAPHY ACTIVITY 16

In the Shogun's Grip

Hideyoshi, the warlord who had united all Japan, stopped his horse and gestured toward the head of Edo Bay. "Make your capital there," he said to Tokugawa Ieyasu. How did the rich Edo region fit into Ieyasu's plans to rule the region himself one day?

Ieyasu crushed the power of the Hideyoshi family in 1600. Soon he ruled from Edo as shogun, supreme military commander. Edo, at first a little fishing village on the bay, grew rapidly into a city of 500,000 inhabitants centered on a circular fortress two miles in diameter. It commanded the broad Kanto Plain, the richest farm region in rocky Japan. Tokugawa shoguns continued to add territory until they directly controlled as much as a third

Laws Governing Daimyo, 1615

Great lords, the lesser lords, and officials should immediately expel from their domains any among their retainers or henchmen who have been charged with treason or murder.

Henceforth no outsider, none but the inhabitants of a particular domain, shall be permitted to reside in that domain. . . . Immediate report should be made of . . . factional conspiracies being formed in neighboring domains.

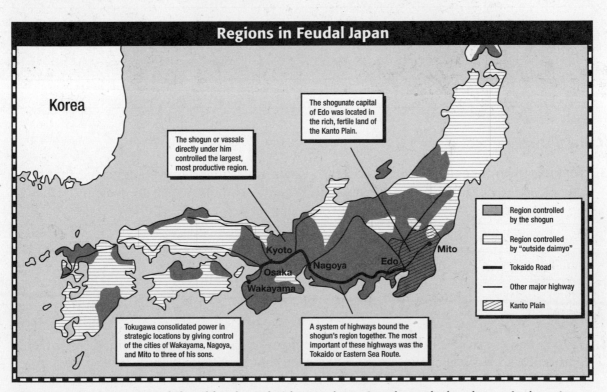

Regions in Feudal Japan

Korea

The shogunate capital of Edo was located in the rich, fertile land of the Kanto Plain.

The shogun or vassals directly under him controlled the largest, most productive region.

Kyoto
Osaka
Wakayama
Nagoya
Edo
Mito

Tokugawa consolidated power in strategic locations by giving control of the cities of Wakayama, Nagoya, and Mito to three of his sons.

A system of highways bound the shogun's region together. The most important of these highways was the Tokaido or Eastern Sea Route.

- ▨ Region controlled by the shogun
- ▤ Region controlled by "outside daimyo"
- ▬ Tokaido Road
- ── Other major highway
- ▥ Kanto Plain

The vast Edo region was defined by the Tokaido Road running through the shogun's domains. The road served as a visual manifestation of the extent of the shogun's power.

HISTORY AND GEOGRAPHY ACTIVITY 16 (continued)

of Japan's people and a third or more of its agricultural wealth. Even the emperor's capital, Kyoto, belonged to the shoguns.

The shogun gave other daimyo control only in their own domains. He also issued strict laws to keep the daimyo in the shogun region isolated and weak.

Because any feature, either natural or human-made, can define a region, it is no surprise that regions can take almost any shape or size. Political features defined regions of feudal Japan. Hundreds of daimyo held domains of varying sizes.

Some of these political units also could belong to a far larger and more powerful region controlled by the shogun. The Tokugawa shogunate controlled a major portion of Japan. The policy of the shogunate was to centralize shogun power and keep daimyo power fragmented. The smaller domains of the daimyo were essentially individual regions, cut off from one another so that they could never combine against the shogun. So successful was this scheme that the Tokugawa shogunate lasted until 1868.

APPLYING GEOGRAPHY TO HISTORY

DIRECTIONS: Answer the questions below in the space provided.

1. Why do regions vary in size?

_____

_____

2. Explain how both the size and the location of the region held by the shogun helped him control the daimyo.

_____

_____

Critical Thinking

3. **Making Inferences** A commentary on the laws governing daimyo suggested that the customs of each domain should be secret. What do you think was the reason for this?

_____

_____

_____

Activity

4. As you can see from the example of feudal Japan, regions are often defined by power and politics. Regions can interact with one another to change history. With others in your class, discuss examples of regions you have studied that were in conflict with one another.

Mapping History Activity 16

Toyotomi Hideyoshi

One of the most significant figures in Japanese history is Toyotomi Hideyoshi. Hideyoshi's predecessor and mentor, Oda Nobunaga, attempted to unify Japan. Upon succeeding Nobunaga, Hideyoshi was left to forge a new administrative organization to guarantee unification. By 1590 he had established a national structure that allowed various regional daimyo to remain independent and yet still cooperate with one another.

DIRECTIONS: The map below shows Hideyoshi's activity in achieving unity in Japan, as well as his efforts to seize more territory. Use the map to answer the questions and complete the activity that follows.

1. What other domain shared territory in Japan with Oda Nobunaga, and then Toyotomi Hideyoshi, prior to 1589?

   _____

   _____

   _____

2. By what means did Hideyoshi achieve his success in unifying Japan?

   _____

   _____

   _____

   _____

3. What was the result of Hideyoshi's two attempts to conquer China through Korea?

   _____

   _____

   _____

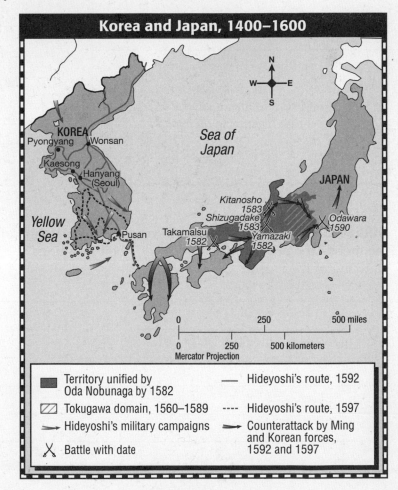

4. The Korean navy dealt the final blow to Hideyoshi's plan to conquer Korea by completely disrupting Japanese supply lines. On the map, circle the battle or counterattack where this most likely took place.

Historical Significance Activity 16

CHAPTER 16

Do Not Disturb

History is not only about big events. It is also about the arts and culture. The creation of Western drama in ancient Greece and the symphony in modern Europe, for example, mean as much to human history as any battle, royal power struggle, or scientific discovery. So does the creation and tradition of haiku poetry.

Haiku is a seventeenth-century Japanese poetry form that tries to capture in 17 syllables the essence of a moment, perception, or realization, often by connecting the natural world to human nature. Haiku's charm lies in the reverent mood the poems generally have, a mood that says to allow things to be as they are. In Chapter 16 you learned that the greatest haiku poet was Basho. Here are two more of his poems.

Clouds appear
And bring to men a chance to rest
From looking at the moon.

Temple bells die out.
The fragrant blossoms remain.
A perfect evening!

DIRECTIONS: In the space below, write an interpretation of these poems. Be sure to discuss the moods the poems bring out in you, their meanings, their imagery, and Basho's understanding of the world.

_____

_____

_____

_____

_____

_____

_____

_____

_____

★ Cooperative Learning Activity 16 ★

The East Asian World Trivia Game

BACKGROUND

The peoples of East Asia, specifically China, Japan, and Korea, developed sophisticated cultures and civilizations between 1400 and 1800, even as they tried to exclude expansionist European nations from their shores. Yet few people in the West appreciated the accomplishments of these great nations and peoples during this time period. In this activity, you will work in groups to create a trivia game based on East Asian cultures and then compete in the East Asian Trivia Game championship.

GROUP DIRECTIONS

1. Use Chapter 16 of your textbook and library resources or the Internet to collect facts about famous people, events, and accomplishments of the countries of East Asia between 1400 and 1800. Make notes about what you find and record your sources.

2. Use your facts to write questions and answers for a history game. You also will need to know these facts to answer questions during the game.

3. Create an original trivia game about East Asia.

4. The following categories should be used. Add any others that your group thinks are appropriate. Use the list in planning your research and creating your game.

The Ming dynasty   The Qing dynasty
Western impact on East Asia   Daily life in China
Chinese cultural developments   The Tokugawa dynasty
Tokugawa culture   The Yi dynasty in Korea
Economic and social changes in Japan

ORGANIZING THE GROUP

1. **Decision Making** As a group, appoint a recorder to take notes on the brainstorming session and then distribute copies to all group members. Decide which topic each member will research. Brainstorm the kinds of events, people, and accomplishments that you will look for in your research.

2. **Individual Work** Conduct research to find out as much as possible about your assigned topic. Write questions and answers on note cards—questions on one side, answers on the other. Label your card as to the category assigned and include complete source information.

3. **Group Work/Decision Making** Meet with your group and share your research with them. Take turns asking each other your questions and checking that the answers given are correct. Make corrections and clarifications as needed. Combine your group's cards with those of the other teams.

Cooperative Learning Activity 16 (continued)

4. **Additional Group Work** Half the class should color code the cards. Use one color per category. For example, color blue the top of each card that contains questions and answers about the Ming dynasty. That way, you can easily find each category. The other half of the group should make two cubes from Styrofoam or some other material. On each face of each cube, write the name of one topic from the list on page 183. One cube provides 6 faces, so 2 cubes provide 12 faces, one for each topic and three extras for options such as "Miss a Turn," "Roll Again," or "Bonus Points, Roll Again." You are now ready to play your game.

5. **Group Sharing** Organize the class into two teams. (There is no need to keep the original groups together.) Take turns rolling the cube. Pick a card from the category rolled. The team that rolled the cube must answer the question or lose a point. Team members may collaborate on the answer. If the team that picked the card cannot answer correctly, the other team can earn a point by answering correctly. Score one point for each correct answer. Keep track of the teams' scores and give the winning team a small prize.

GROUP PROCESS QUESTIONS

- What is the most important thing you learned about East Asia from this activity?
- What part of the project did you enjoy most?
- What problems did you have?
- How did you solve the problems?
- How was it helpful to work with others?

Quick **CHECK** ✔

1. Was the goal of the assignment clear at all times?

_____

2. How was designing a trivia game different from other types of projects?

_____

3. How did the game teams work together to answer the questions?

_____

_____

4. Were you satisfied with your work on this project? Why or why not?

_____

_____

HISTORY SIMULATION ACTIVITY 16

Empire Bingo

From A.D. 1400 to 1700, East Asian empires arose in China and Japan to become powerful political forces within their regions. At the same time, these empires experienced great cultural advances.

TEACHER MATERIAL

Learning Objective To become familiar with basic facts about the East Asian empires of China and Japan.

Activity Three groups prepare questions with one-word (or one-name) answers for a game based on information from this chapter. Groups compete in a class game of Empire Bingo.

Teacher Preparation Make one copy of the game card for each group. Have on hand the following supplies: three sheets of paper for the questions and answers and paper clips for groups to use as game markers.

Activity Guidelines

1. Explain to students that they are to develop 24 questions and answers for a game called Empire Bingo based on facts from this chapter.

2. Organize the class into three groups to develop the question-and-answer sheets. Assign one section of this chapter to each group. Give each group a sheet of paper and ask the groups to designate a recorder.

3. Explain that each group must work together to brainstorm eight questions that require one-word (or one-name) answers. Sample question: What was the Chinese name of the founder of the Ming dynasty, which brought stability and a new era of greatness to China? *(Ming Hong Wu)* The recorder writes the

questions and answers on the paper. Allow about 10 minutes for this part of the activity. Then collect the question-and-answer sheets.

4. Next, give each group a game card. As you call out the answers, students should write them on any space of the game card. There will be one free space on each card, and it can be anywhere. Allow another 10 minutes for this part of the activity. When this is completed, supply each group with some paper clips and Bingo can begin.

5. Ask one student to serve as quizmaster. The person who will serve as quizmaster reads each question, and players place a clip on the proper answer on the card. Remind students that the free space on the card automatically gets a clip. When a group has covered answers on five spaces that spell BINGO (the answers do not have to be all in the same row), they call out BINGO! In their group, students should repeat the question for each of their answers. The winning team earns 1 point.

6. A student from the winning team becomes the next quizmaster. He or she mixes up the questions and begins a new game. At the end of the class period, the team with the most points wins.

HISTORY SIMULATION ACTIVITY 16

HANDOUT MATERIAL

Empire Bingo—Game Card

Empire

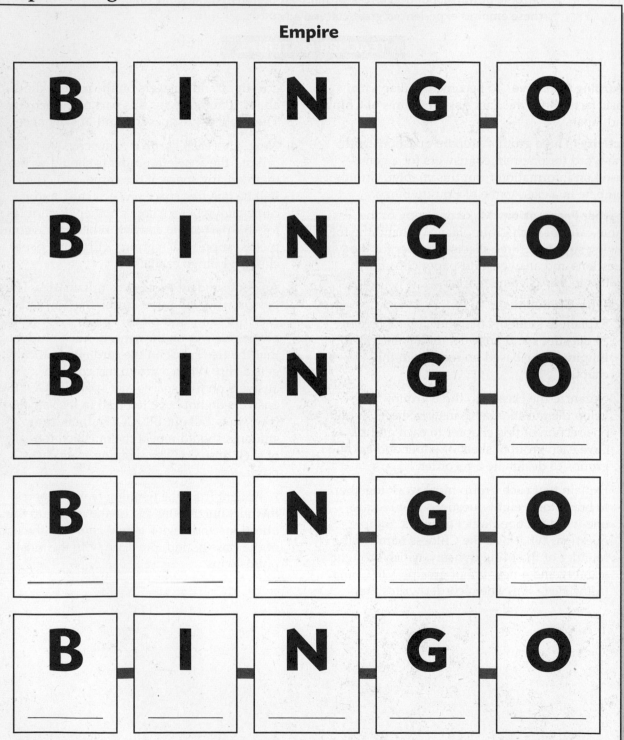

Time Line Activity 16

The East Asian World

DIRECTIONS: The empires you have read about in Chapter 16 all faced both internal and external challenges to their stability and ways of life. Each attempt at change was met in a unique way by the empires involved. The time line below shows some changes that took place in Asian empires. Read the time line. Then answer the questions that follow.

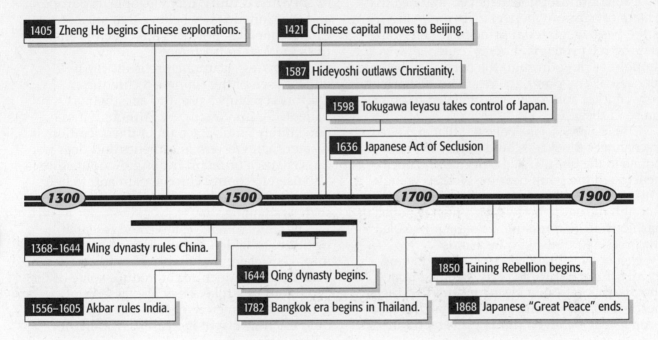

1405	Zheng He begins Chinese explorations.
1421	Chinese capital moves to Beijing.
1587	Hideyoshi outlaws Christianity.
1598	Tokugawa Ieyasu takes control of Japan.
1636	Japanese Act of Seclusion
1368–1644	Ming dynasty rules China.
1644	Qing dynasty begins.
1850	Taining Rebellion begins.
1556–1605	Akbar rules India.
1782	Bangkok era begins in Thailand.
1868	Japanese "Great Peace" ends.

1300   1500   1700   1900

1. What happened early in the fifteenth century that showed the Ming dynasty's interest in expansion?

_____

2. How long did Japan enjoy the "Great Peace" from the start of Tokugawa rule?

_____

3. How long did the Ming dynasty last?

_____

4. What dynasty followed the Ming dynasty?

_____

5. What event took place in Japan after unification began?

Linking Past and Present Activity 16

Chinese Medicine

THEN Traditional Chinese medical treatments are thousands of years old. They include acupuncture, acupressure, herbs, and *qigong* (a combination of physical exercise and meditation). These medical treatments are based on concepts found in Daoism.

Daoist philosophers believed that health is a state of harmony between yin and yang. Yin is the passive, material principle in life. Yang is its active principle. Energy, called *qi*, was thought to flow through the body. If *qi* became blocked at any point, the resultant disharmony between yin and yang was believed to be the cause of disease.

Chinese physicians believed that *qi* flowed in channels. Blockage could occur at various points in the body. Using a needle, the doctor penetrated the point near the blocked energy. This permitted the energy to flow freely through the entire body, which then regained its harmony. In acupressure, a masseur kneaded the pressure points with his hands.

Qigong was practiced to keep *qi* flowing evenly throughout the body. People learned the discipline from a *qigong* master and then performed it by themselves. Those who practiced *qigong* believed that it prevented illness as well as cured it.

Another important idea in traditional Chinese medicine was the belief that the body contained five fundamental elements—earth, fire, water, wood, and metal. These elements took the form of active states rather than of matter. Sickness occurred if any one of these states predominated over the others. Doctors prescribed various herbs and diets to keep these states in balance.

NOW From the late nineteenth century to the early twentieth century, Western medicine replaced traditional medicine in China. When the Communists gained control of the Chinese government, traditional Chinese medicine steadily regained its status. Today, in the twenty-first century, many people in Europe and the United States believe that ancient Chinese medical practices are effective alternatives to Western treatments.

In the West, acupuncture is the most widely used of the Chinese techniques. Doctors sometimes use it to anesthetize patients for minor surgery. Although it may not entirely numb the pain of the operation, it is safer than Western anesthetics and does not cause nausea or retard healing. Acupuncture is also used to control chronic pain and to help people rid themselves of addictive behavior such as smoking.

The Chinese have established research institutes to widen the application of acupuncture. They claim that their research has shown that scalp acupuncture can reduce some of the symptoms of stroke. They also assert that using an acupuncture needle charged with a mild electric current increases its ability to relieve pain.

Many people take Chinese herbs instead of the drugs prescribed by Western doctors. So far, there has been no concrete evidence that Chinese medications are better.

Qigong, however, has a better track record. People have found that its meditative and physical exercises can calm and energize them, as well as keep them flexible.

CRITICAL THINKING

Directions: Answer the following questions on a separate sheet of paper.

1. **Making comparisons:** How are acupuncture and acupressure alike? How are they different?
2. **Making inferences:** How do you think Chinese scientists study procedures such as acupuncture and acupressure?
3. **Synthesizing information:** Daoist philosophy claims that the balance of forces is necessary for the health of living systems. What branch of science also makes the same claim? Do research in the library and on the Internet to learn more about this branch of science. Identify natural phenomena that can get out of balance.

> ## People in World History Activity 16 | Profile 1

Wan-Li (1563–1620)

The Ming dynasty (1368–1644) is remembered as a time of peace and prosperity in Chinese history. Farming flourished. Trade expanded. Artists, writers, and artisans created works that are still revered today. Beijing was built. To many people, then and now, the Ming dynasty seemed a golden age.

The end of this dynasty, then, is of special interest. What caused its fall? One of the last Ming emperors, known as Wan-Li, played a pivotal role in the end of the Ming dynasty. Although he did not cause the dynasty's downfall, his weak rule at a crucial time doubtless contributed to the end of an era.

Wan-Li became emperor in 1573, when he was only 10 years old. By all accounts, he was a sweet boy who cared little for the power and responsibility that fell upon him. His father, who shortly before his death had named him emperor, entrusted the boy's care to two ministers: Kau-kung and Chang-chu. Wan-Li allowed these two officials to wield the real power. Chang-chu eventually managed to get Kau-kung dismissed, and so functioned as the virtual emperor of China. Apparently, when Wan-Li reached the age of 18, Chang-chu was willing to relinquish his authority to the rightful ruler. Wan-Li, however, refused. He did not wish to be burdened with leadership, and gladly left it with Chang-chu. Chang-chu remained in control until 1582, when he died. Soon after his death, it was revealed that he had privately enriched himself at public expense. This was a great disgrace to the emperor.

The duties of emperor now thrust upon him, Wan-Li was fortunate to confront few major problems at first. Then, in 1587 a great flood drowned people, ruined farms, and caused a famine. Wan-Li did virtually nothing, and a court official upbraided him for drunkenness, a generally bad temper, and self-indulgence. This situation—serious problems in the country and weak responses from the emperor—became a hallmark of Wan-Li's reign. Hard times were made worse by the high taxes Wan-Li extracted to pay for the lavish lifestyles of the ruling class. Wan-Li's rule was seriously damaged by invading forces and internal rebellion. Both situations were resolved, but public opinion finally forced Wan-Li to appoint his eldest son as heir.

Meanwhile, the Manchu people were moving southward, and by 1644 they would set up the Qing dynasty.

REVIEWING THE PROFILE

Directions: Answer the following questions on a separate sheet of paper.

1. What challenges did Wan-Li face as emperor?
2. **Critical Thinking** **Identifying Alternatives.** How might Chinese history have been different if Wan-Li had been a more effective emperor?

CHAPTER 16

> ## People in World History Activity 16
Profile 2

Toyotomi Hideyoshi (c. 1536/37–1598)

Toyotomi Hideyoshi was one of Japan's most important lords, who served as imperial minister from 1585 to 1598. He completed the unification of Japan begun by the great Japanese leader Oda Nobunaga after centuries of feudalism.

Hideyoshi's life is a rags to riches story. He was a peasant's son who became a foot soldier in Nobunaga's army. Because of his tact, intelligence, and courage, he was promoted to samurai. Hideyoshi fought in many of Nobunaga's battles in central Japan. By overthrowing two daimyo, he became a lord himself.

Nobunaga ordered Hideyoshi to subjugate western Japan. Later Hideyoshi tried to conquer the whole of Japan, but could not defeat the powerful daimyo Tokugawa Ieyasu. The two lords formed an alliance. Hideyoshi then made peace with another of his major adversaries. Eventually he became head of an alliance of daimyo that formed a government of national unification.

Hideyoshi instituted a number of government policies. He destroyed castles to reduce the number of strongholds throughout Japan, and he ordered a sword hunt to confiscate weapons from the peasants.

He introduced what was called *shi-no-ko-sho*, a policy that strictly recognized class distinctions. The policy separated warriors, farmers, craftspeople, and merchants. By requiring different groups to live in the country or city, and permitting each class to live in different areas of a town if necessary, the policy created order in a still-feudal society. Hideyoshi also did land surveys to clarify ownership and taxes, promoted transportation, and developed mineral resources to make coins. The currency was to help encourage trade.

In part to use the tens of thousands of samurai newly under his control, Hideyoshi turned his attention to conquering Korea. He wanted to control China eventually. He failed twice to conquer Korea because Japan lacked the forces. After Hideyoshi's death, Tokugawa Ieyasu founded the Tokugawa shogunate. Ieyasu followed Hideyoshi's policies of national unification, which became the foundation of the peaceful Tokugawa period.

Because of his poor beginnings, Hideyoshi never had a formal education. He educated himself and understood the importance of culture, however. He was a skillful poet and actor in No plays. He studied the tea ceremony and often held tea ceremonies to demonstrate his skill.

REVIEWING THE PROFILE

Directions: Answer the following questions on a separate sheet of paper.

1. What important work of Oda Nobunaga's did Hideyoshi complete?

2. **Critical Thinking** Evaluating Information. Give reasons based on democratic principles against the policy of *shi-no-ko-sho*. Then consider why at the time, the policy might have been necessary. If needed, do further research on the ways that Hideyoshi's policies enforced class distinctions.

PRIMARY SOURCE READING 16

Laws Governing the Military Households

The establishment of the Tokugawa shogunate after the Battle of Sekigahara in 1600 paved the way for far-reaching reforms that centralized the Japanese state and brought previously independent feudal daimyo more under the control of the shogun. One of the ways in which this was done was by establishing codes of proper behavior for the daimyo, both at home and at the shogun's court.

Guided Reading *In this selection, read to learn proper behavior for Japanese nobles during the Tokugawa shogunate.*

The arts of peace and war, including archery and horsemanship, should be pursued single-mindedly.

From of old the rule has been to practice "the arts of peace on the left hand, and the arts of war on the right"; both must be mastered. Archery and horsemanship are indispensable to military men. Though arms are called instruments of evil, there are times when they must be resorted to. In peacetime we should not be oblivious to the danger of war. Should we not, then, prepare ourselves for it?

Drinking parties and wanton revelry should be avoided.

In the codes that have come down to us this kind of dissipation has been severely proscribed. Sexual indulgence and habitual gambling lead to the downfall of a state.

Offenders against the law should not be harbored or hidden in any domain.

Law is the basis of social order. Reason may be violated in the name of the law, but law may not be violated in the name of reason. Those who break the law deserve heavy punishment.

Great lords (daimyō), the lesser lords, and officials should immediately expel from their domains any among their retainers or henchmen who have been charged with treason or murder.

Wild and wicked men may become weapons for overturning the state and destroying the people. How can they be allowed to go free?

Henceforth no outsider, none but the inhabitants of a particular domain, shall be permitted to reside in that domain.

Each domain has its own ways. If a man discloses the secrets of one's own country to another domain or if the secrets of the other domain are disclosed to one's own, that will sow the seeds of deceit and sycophancy [insincere flattery].

Whenever it is intended to make repairs on a castle of one of the feudal domains, the [shogunate] authorities should be notified. The construction of any new castles is to be halted and stringently prohibited.

"Big castles are a danger to the state." Walls and moats are the cause of great disorders.

Immediate report should be made of innovations which are being planned or of factional conspiracies being formed in neighboring domains.

"Men all incline toward partisanship; few are wise and impartial. There are some who refuse to obey their masters, and others who feud with their neighbors." Why, instead of abiding by the established order, do they wantonly embark upon new schemes?

Do not enter into marriage privately [without notifying the shogunate authorities].

Marriage follows the principle of harmony between yin and yang, and must not be entered into lightly. In the *Book of Changes*, under the thirty-eighth hexagram (*k'uei*), it says, "Marriage should not be contracted out of enmity [against another]. Marriages intended to effect an alliance with enemies [of the state] will turn out badly." The Peach Blossom ode in *The Book of Poetry* also says that "When men and women are proper in their relationships and marriage is arranged at

PRIMARY SOURCE READING 16

the correct time; then throughout the land there will be no loose women." To form an alliance by marriage is the root of treason. . . .

The samurai of the various domains shall lead a frugal and simple life.

When the rich make a display of their wealth, the poor are humiliated and envious. Nothing engenders corruption so much as this, and therefore it must be strictly curbed.

The lords of the domains should select officials with a capacity for public administration.

Good government depends on getting the right men. Due attention should be given to their merits and faults; rewards and punishments must be properly meted out. If a domain has able men, it flourishes; if it lacks able men it is doomed to perish. This is the clear admonition of the wise men of old.

The purport of the foregoing should be conscientiously observed.

INTERPRETING THE READING

Directions *Use information from the reading to answer the following questions. If necessary, use a separate sheet of paper.*

1. Why are daimyo forbidden to drink or gamble?

_____

2. If a daimyo wishes to make any extensions or repairs to his castle, what must he do first and why?

_____

_____

3. Which principle should be followed when one person wants to marry another person according to the rules above?

_____

4. According to the selection, samurai should not depend on extensive wealth or property to live. What reasons are given in support of this view?

_____

_____

Critical Thinking

5. Drawing Conclusions Which group of people benefits the most from these laws? Which group of people benefits the least? Explain your answers.

_____

_____

6. Identifying Alternatives According to the selection, "good government depends on getting the right men." In your view, how can this best be accomplished in a society?

_____

_____

World Art and Music Activity 16

Japanese Wash Drawings

Landscapes were a favorite subject of Japanese artists. The Zen Buddhist emphasis on humanity's harmony with its surroundings and humanity's relative unimportance in comparison to the universe appears to have influenced this trend, which continued into the 1800s. Pictured below is a typical Japanese landscape of the early 1500s. The details are few, the presentation is simple, and the mood is calm.

DIRECTIONS: Read the passage below. Then answer the questions in the space provided.

Soāmi Kangaku Shinso, *Landscape of the Four Seasons,* Japanese, ink on paper (c. early 1500s)

In the 1100s, a new sect of Buddhism called Zen was introduced into Japan. With its emphasis on inner peace, the unimportance of humans in comparison to their surroundings, and the undesirability of conflict, Zen appealed to many Japanese as an antidote to the civil wars and military rule that battered the country from the 1100s through the later 1500s.

A cultural atmosphere pervaded scholarly Zen monasteries. Many monks were skilled poets and painters. Japanese monks often traveled to China, bringing Chinese cultural developments back to Japan. One such artistic innovation was the monochromatic wash drawing. The Japanese brought this technique to Japan during the 1200s, but it was not until the mid-1300s that the study of this style became widespread. By the 1400s, it was solidly established in the mainstream of Japanese art and is still used today.

To create a wash drawing, an artist first dampens the paper and stretches it to dry. This prevents the wet inks and water used in making the picture from warping the paper. The artist then applies the ink to the paper with pens and brushes of a variety of sizes. Artists often make their own tools so that they always have exactly what they need to create particular images. Some brushes are as narrow as a single eyelash. Pens are made of bamboo.

(continued)

CHAPTER 16

World Art and Music Activity 16

Monochromatic means "having one color." In the case of Japanese wash drawings, it refers to black ink on white paper. Because ink is a single tone, artists cannot create shading using lighter or darker lines or areas in a drawing. Thus, they invented a technique called wash to create gray tones, adding a softness and subtlety to the inked lines. Sōami Kangaku Shinso used this technique to create the subtle tones of the mountain peaks and hilltops in *Landscape of the Four Seasons.* The artist drew a line in ink, then shaded an area by dipping the pen or brush in water and causing the ink line to bleed into that area. The higher the proportion of water to ink, the lighter the gray would be.

Landscape of the Four Seasons is mounted on a screen, which folds along the vertical dark lines. It probably served a decorative and functional purpose in an ordinary household or in a monastery. This type of decorative art became common in Japan during the 1400s and has remained so to this day.

Reviewing the Selection

1. Describe the process of making a monochromatic wash drawing.

   _____

   _____

2. How did this process come to Japan?

   _____

   _____

   _____

Critical Thinking

3. **Making Inferences** How might the philosophies of Zen Buddhism have influenced the creation and style of *Landscape of the Four Seasons*?

   _____

   _____

   _____

4. **Making Comparisons** Compare *Landscape of the Four Seasons* to other landscape representations with which you are familiar. How is nature portrayed?

   _____

   _____

   _____

   _____

   _____

Reteaching Activity 16

The East Asian World

Major events can affect a region's people and culture in many ways. Sometimes allies come in peace, other times conquering armies force their rule upon unwilling native peoples. Trade, when allowed, also can be an important vehicle for spreading a culture's values as well as its material goods.

DIRECTIONS: Read the events listed in the following chart. Then fill in the effects of these events on East Asia.

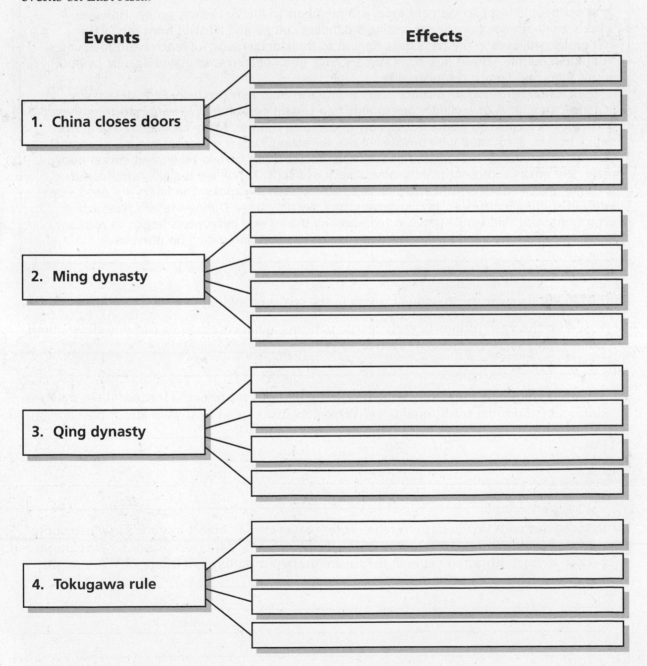

Events   **Effects**

1. **China closes doors**

2. **Ming dynasty**

3. **Qing dynasty**

4. **Tokugawa rule**

★ Enrichment Activity 16

History Reflected in Art

Besides being appreciated for their beauty, works of art often reflect the social conditions under which they were produced. For historians of ancient or endangered cultures, artwork can provide valuable clues to people's traditions, lifestyles, and environments, especially in the absence of forms of writing.

Most people living in Vietnam today are members of the Viet ethnic group. However, a small ethnic minority, possessing a different culture and lifestyle from the larger Viet group, still lives in the highlands. Known as the Montagnards, a French word meaning "mountain people," these migratory farmers have often been discriminated against by both ethnic Viets and French colonists alike.

The Montagnards weave distinct patterns into the cloth they produce. Each design (for instance, an animal or a plant) corresponds to a certain part of their lives. By studying these patterns, historians can gain a better view of complex cultures. Many Montagnard patterns depict images associated with processing rice for eating. Others represent natural phenomena such as colorful bird feathers, the beak of the toucan, water buffalo teeth, and cricket body parts. Still others represent plant products such as kapok. Kapok are the silky strands surrounding the seeds of Southeast Asian trees also known as kapoks. The fibers are used extensively in stuffing mattresses, life preservers, and sleeping bags. During the late twentieth century, Montagnard textile patterns representing planes and helicopters began to appear. These were accompanied by designs that mimic guns and men riding on horseback.

DIRECTIONS: Answer the questions below in the space provided.

1. Based on the descriptions of early textile patterns, what conclusions can you draw about the Montagnards' traditional lifestyle? _____

_____

2. What do you think the late twentieth-century patterns represent? How are these patterns different from more traditional ones? What conclusions can be drawn about the changes in the Montagnards' lives during the twentieth century? _____

_____

_____

_____

3. Create your own textile pattern representing an everyday object in your life. Then show it to classmates and see if they can guess the object your pattern represents. Why might people living a hundred years in the future find your patterns of interest? What might they learn from your pattern? _____

_____

_____

_____

WORLD HISTORY

Chapter 16

Section Resources

GUIDED READING ACTIVITY 16-1   198

GUIDED READING ACTIVITY 16-2   199

GUIDED READING ACTIVITY 16-3   200

GUIDED READING ACTIVITY 16-4   201

SECTIONS

Guided Reading Activity 16-1

China at Its Height

DIRECTIONS: Answer the following questions as you read Section 1.

1. How far did the Chinese empire extend under the Ming emperors?

   _____

2. What was the beneficial effect of building the Grand Canal?

   _____

3. What animal brought from East Africa especially fascinated the Chinese emperor?

   _____

4. What was significant about the arrival of a Portuguese fleet off the coast of China in 1514?

   _____

5. How did both Chinese and Europeans benefit from their early cultural exchanges?

   _____

   _____

6. What happened to the last Ming emperor?

   _____

7. What did the Manchu rulers order to make it easier to identify rebel forces?

   _____

8. How did the Qing deal with the problem of being ethnically and culturally different from the Chinese population?

   _____

   _____

9. Who was perhaps the greatest emperor in Chinese history?

   _____

10. What led to unrest in rural areas during the rule of Qianlong?

    _____

11. When a British mission visited Beijing in 1793 seeking more liberal trade policies, how did Emperor Qianlong reply?

    _____

    _____

Guided Reading Activity 16-2

Chinese Society and Culture

DIRECTIONS: Fill in the blanks below as you read Section 2.

Between 1500 and 1800, China remained a mostly **(1)** _____ society. However, the Chinese **(2)** _____ was changing. A long period of peace under the Qing dynasty and improvements in the food supply led to a large increase in **(3)** _____. Despite the growth in trade and manufacturing, China did not develop the kind of commercial **(4)** _____ that was emerging in Europe.

Chinese society was organized around the **(5)** _____. The ideal family unit in Qing China was the extended family, with as many as three or four **(6)** _____ living under the same roof. Beyond the extended family was the **(7)** _____, consisting of dozens or even hundreds of related families. Women who had bound feet were more **(8)** _____ than those who did not.

A new form of literature, the **(9)** _____, arose during the Ming dynasty. *The* **(10)** _____ *Lotus* depicts the corrupt life of a wealthy landlord in the late Ming period who cruelly manipulates those around him for sex, money, and power. **(11)** _____, by Cao Xuegin, is generally considered even today to be China's most distinguished popular novel.

The most outstanding example of Ming dynasty architecture is the **(12)** _____ in Beijing. The Imperial City includes a maze of private apartments and offices, as well as stately halls for **(13)** _____ audiences and banquets and spacious gardens. Perhaps the most famous of all the arts of the Ming Era was blue-and-white **(14)** _____.
(15) _____ admired the beauty of this porcelain and collected it in great quantities.

SECTION 16-2

Guided Reading Activity 16-3

Tokugawa Japan and Korea

DIRECTIONS: Fill in the blanks below as you read Section 3.

SECTION 16-3

I. The process of Japanese _____ began in the late-sixteenth century.

    A. Three _____ political figures brought this about.

        1. Oda Nobunaga seized _____ and placed the shogun under his control.

        2. Toyotomi Hideyoshi located his capital at _____.

        3. In 1598 Tokugawa Ieyasu completed the restoration of _____ authority.

    B. The first _____ began to arrive as Japan was being unified.

        1. _____ traders landed on the islands in 1543.

        2. The first Jesuit missionary, _____, arrived in 1549.

II. The Tokugawa rulers set out to establish control of the _____ system of Japan.

    A. Tokugawa rule brought about a long period known as the _____.

    B. Trade and _____ began to flourish as never before.

    C. When _____ conditions became desperate, some peasants revolted.

    D. During this era, the _____ system became rigid.

        1. Distinctions were set among _____, peasants, artisans, and merchants.

        2. Below these were Japan's outcasts, the _____.

III. In the Tokugawa Era, a new set of _____ values began to appear.

    A. Ihara Saikaku's greatest _____ was *Five Women Who Loved Love.*

    B. Entertainment in the cities gave rise in the theater to _____.

    C. _____ competed to erect the most magnificent mansions.

IV. The Yi dynasty in _____ began in 1892.

    A. A Japanese force invaded Korea in the late _____ century.

    B. Korean rulers sought to limit contact with _____ countries.

    C. Korea earned the name the _____.

Guided Reading Activity 16-4

Spice Trade in Southeast Asia

DIRECTIONS: Fill in the blanks below as you read Section 4.

1. In 1500 mainland Southeast Asia was a relatively _____ region.

2. On the Malay Peninsula and the Indonesian Archipelago, Muslim merchants were attracted to the growing _____ trade.

3. The political system in Southeast Asian states evolved into four styles of monarchy: _____, _____, _____, and Vietnamese emperors.

4. In the Buddhist model, the king was considered _____ to other human beings and served as the link between human society and the _____.

5. The Javanese style of kingship was rooted in the political tradition of _____.

6. The Islamic sultan was a defender of the faith and staffed his _____ mainly with aristocrats.

7. The Vietnamese emperor ruled according to the teachings of _____.

8. Since ancient times, _____ had been highly valued and their sources eagerly sought.

9. The purpose of the voyage of Vasco da Gama to Calicut in 1498 was twofold: _____ and _____.

10. The situation changed with the arrival of the _____ and _____ traders, who were better financed than the Portuguese.

SECTION 16-4

Chapter 17 Resources
Revolution and Enlightenment, 1550–1800

READING SKILLS ACTIVITY 17

Synthesizing   205

HISTORICAL ANALYSIS SKILLS ACTIVITY 17

Understanding Chronology   206

DIFFERENTIATED INSTRUCTION ACTIVITY 17

Creating a Rational Society   207

ENGLISH LEARNER ACTIVITY 17

Revolution and Enlightenment   209

CONTENT VOCABULARY ACTIVITY 17

Revolution and Enlightenment,
1550–1800   211

ACADEMIC VOCABULARY ACTIVITY 17

Revolution and Enlightenment   213

SKILLS REINFORCEMENT ACTIVITY 17

Outlining   215

CRITICAL THINKING SKILLS ACTIVITY 17

Identifying Central Issues   216

HISTORY AND GEOGRAPHY ACTIVITY 17

Where Is the World?   217

MAPPING HISTORY ACTIVITY 17

The Age of Revolution   219

HISTORICAL SIGNIFICANCE ACTIVITY 17

The First Amendment   220

COOPERATIVE LEARNING ACTIVITY 17

Ideas That Changed the World   221

HISTORY SIMULATION ACTIVITY 17

Science on Trial   223

TIME LINE ACTIVITY 17

Revolution and Enlightenment   225

LINKING PAST AND PRESENT ACTIVITY 17

Leeuwenhoek and Modern Biology   226

PEOPLE IN WORLD HISTORY ACTIVITY 17

Profile 1: Nicholas Copernicus
(1473–1543)   227
Profile 2: Adam Smith (1723–1790)   228

PRIMARY SOURCE READING 17

Of the *Encyclopedia*   229

WORLD ART AND MUSIC ACTIVITY 17

John Singleton Copley   231

RETEACHING ACTIVITY 17

Revolution and Enlightenment   233

ENRICHMENT ACTIVITY 17

The Commotion Galileo Caused   234

Reading Skills Activity 17

Synthesizing

LEARNING THE SKILL

Synthesizing is a critical skill to practice. Synthesizing is a process of making connections between bits of knowledge to draw conclusions about their relationships or to discover overarching themes. Piecing together information from different places in a textbook—or even completely different books—and relating them to each other helps you build your knowledge exponentially.

PRACTICING THE SKILL

DIRECTIONS: Read the following quotations from two Enlightenment philosophers on the subject of women. Using what you know from your reading of the chapter, describe on a separate sheet how Wollstonecraft's response to Rousseau was a natural outcome of Enlightenment ideas.

It is the part of the one to be active and strong, and of the other to be passive and weak. Accept
this principle; and it follows in the second place that woman is intended to please man.

—Jean-Jacques Rousseau, *Emile* (1762)

Though, to reason on Rousseau's ground, if man did attain a degree of perfection of mind when his body arrived at maturity, it might be proper, in order to make a man and his wife one, that she should rely entirely on his understanding; and the graceful ivy, clasping the oak that supported it, would form a whole in which strength and beauty would be equally conspicuous. But, alas! husbands, as well as their helpmates, are often only overgrown children; nay, thanks to early debauchery, scarcely men in their outward form—and if the blind lead the blind, one need not come from heaven to tell us the con-sequence.

—Mary Wollstonecraft, *A Vindication of the Rights of Woman* (1792)

APPLYING THE SKILL

DIRECTIONS: The Declaration of Independence and the Bill of Rights to the U.S. Constitution are both documents that synthesize ideas from the Enlightenment in order to create something new. Find a copy of each document on the Internet or in your classroom resources, and print it out. Working in pairs, identify the specific features of these documents that are linked to Enlightenment ideas; underline these ideas and note on the page their connection to specific ideas or philosophers described in your textbook. When you are finished, join with another pair to compare your findings, then answer the question: Why should U.S. citizens understand the Enlightenment?

Historical Analysis Skills Activity 17

Understanding Chronology

LEARNING THE SKILL

As you study history, it is important to consider how echoes of the past are still heard today. Historians can trace many of the ideas that shape our world to specific decisions made and events that occurred decades, even centuries ago. The world we live in has inherited, for good or ill, the legacies of those who came before us.

PRACTICING THE SKILL

DIRECTIONS: Read the following excerpt from Jean Jacques Rousseau's *On Social Contract* (1762), published during The Enlightenment. Answer the questions that follow on a separate sheet of paper.

> *Since no individual has natural authority over his fellow man . . . agreements remain the basis of all legitimate authority among men. If a private individual . . . can make himself the slave of a master, why could not an entire people . . . make itself the subject of a king? . . . It will be said that the despot guarantees his subjects civil tranquility. That may be, but what do they gain by that, if the wars which his ambition brings upon them . . . devastate them more than their own dissensions . . . Living in dungeons is also tranquil: is that enough to make them appealing?*

1. What comparison did Rousseau see between having a king and slavery?

2. What assumptions can you make about how Rousseau felt about the idea of a monarchy? Explain.

3. Why might this essay have been controversial when published?

4. In what way was American politics influenced by views such as Rousseau's?

APPLYING THE SKILL

DIRECTIONS: Imagine that your school recently held an election for student council. Using the English Bill of Rights, the writings of the Enlightenment philosophes, and the American Bill of Rights as models, draft a Bill of Rights for the students in your school, outlining the rights you would expect your student council and school administrators to respect. Be sure to set realistic goals.

Differentiated Instruction Activity 17

Creating a Rational Society

Enlightenment thinkers were so impressed by the Scientific Revolution that they set out to apply scientific thinking to the study of society. In particular, Enlightenment thinkers relied on the inductive method of reasoning rather than the deductive method that traditional philosophers had used. In *deductive reasoning*, conclusions are based on assertions. An example might be:

> **Assertion 1:** All cats have whiskers.
> **Assertion 2:** "Mittens" is a cat.
> **Conclusion:** "Mittens" has whiskers.

This kind of structured argument is called a *syllogism.*

Inductive reasoning is different because it draws conclusions from data and observations. An example might be:

> **Observation 1:** Mary was late for work and her clothes were wrinkled.
> **Observation from prior experience:** Mary is usually well-dressed.
> **Likely Conclusion:** Mary overslept.

Both kinds of reasoning can be flawed. Inductive reasoning is often flawed because it relies on too few observations or too little data. Still, it is often more scientific because it is based on experience. This is why Enlightenment thinkers preferred it to the deductive method, which used assertion and strict logic.

DIRECTIONS: Go back and scan Chapter 17 for ideas and beliefs of the philosophes about human nature, government, and religious toleration. Then practice creating syllogisms that reflect these ideas. Here is an example:

> **Assertion 1:** Governments that allow freedom of religion should be supported.
> **Assertion 2:** My government does not allow me to practice my religion.
> **Conclusion:** I should not support my government.

Then create examples of inductive reasoning that reflect the same topic:

> **Observation:** My religious leader was put in jail.
> **Observation:** The governor of my state proclaimed my religion was backward.
> **Observation:** I am not allowed to miss school for my religious holidays.
> **Conclusion:** The government is against my religion.

CHAPTER 17

(continued)

Differentiated Instruction Activity 17

For the Teacher

TEACHING STRATEGIES FOR DIFFERENT LEARNING STYLES

The following activities are ways the basic lesson can be modified to accommodate students' different learning styles:

English Learners (EL) EL students will benefit from the use of a graphic organizer to clarify the concepts. Create an organizer like the one below for deductive reasoning. Students could replicate graphic organizers to accompany their activities.

Deductive Reasoning

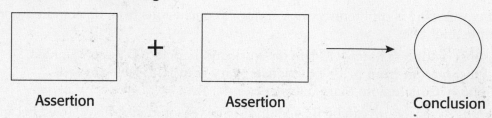

Assertion   Assertion   Conclusion

Advanced Learners (AL) Explain to students that the conclusions of deductive reasoning should be evaluated as sound or not. For example, in some Enlightenment works, the following argument was made:

> **Premise:** All human beings are rational and can thus be educated.
> **Premise:** Women are not rational.
> **Conclusion:** Women cannot be educated.

We can call this an unsound conclusion. Unsound conclusions result from one or both premises being questionable or false. Sometimes these are called *logical fallacies*. Have students complete the activity and also create a list of four more syllogisms based on their reading of Chapter 17. At least one should have more than two premises.

Below Grade Level (BL) Explain terms that might be unfamiliar, such as *deductive reasoning, argument, logic, assertion,* and *syllogism*. Lead students through the deductive and inductive reasoning processes. Then help them develop examples of inductive reasoning from their daily lives before beginning the activity.

On Grade Level (OL) Have students complete the activity as presented.

English Learner Activity 17

Revolution and Enlightenment

⭐ A. PRE-READING ACTIVITY: IMPROVING READING COMPREHENSION

Directions: *Before reading "Causes of the Scientific Revolution" on pages 538–539, answer the following questions.*

1. This chapter is about the development of democratic ideals and the Enlightenment. What are democratic ideals? How do they differ from those of a monarchy?

   _____

   _____

   _____

   _____

2. Many nations discussed in this chapter fought civil wars. What is a civil war? Has your nation ever had a civil war? If so, when?

   _____

   _____

   _____

   _____

   _____

⭐ B. PRE-READING ACTIVITY: READING COMPREHENSION

Directions: *Before reading this chapter, study the words and their definitions below.*

accountable (adj.): answerable; responsible; obligated
assert (v.): to state firmly; claim; stress
attribute (v.): to give credit to; assign; refer
divine (adj.): holy or sacred
eternal (adj.): forever; always; everlasting
monarch (n.): a ruler who reigns for life, such a king, queen, prince, or emperor
resolve (v.): to figure out or successfully conclude
solely (adv.): only; alone; entirely

CHAPTER 17

(continued)

English Learner Activity 17

⊠ C. READING COMPREHENSION ACTIVITY: SENTENCE COMPLETION

Directions: *Check your understanding of the section "The Impact of the Enlightenment" by filling in the blanks with one of the following words:* **accountable, assert, attribute, divine, eternal, monarch, resolve, solely.** *You may need to add -ed endings to some words.*

1. During the sixteenth and seventeenth centuries, most European countries were governed by absolute rulers who _____ that their power came directly from God.

2. Many thought that the _____ should have special privileges because he was born to be king.

3. Members of the monarchy did not believe that they had to explain their actions or be _____ to the people they ruled.

4. This belief was called the _____ right of kings, and it allowed them to do whatever they wanted without an explanation.

5. If an individual questioned a monarch's actions, he was considered a religious sinner who would face everlasting or _____ punishment from God.

6. Louis the XIV, called the Sun King of France, was convinced that he deserved to reign _____ by himself.

7. The statement "I am the state" has been _____ to him because he saw no need for people to participate in government.

8. It took hundreds of years for people to _____ the conflicts and violence that resulted from the attempts to place limits on a monarch's power.

⊠ D. WORD BUILDING ACTIVITY: FORMING AGENT NOUNS FROM ACTION VERBS

Word Usage Note: Forming Agent Nouns from Action Verbs

Adding the suffix *–er, -or,* or *–ist* to a verb sometimes creates an agent noun that is used to describe a person's job or profession. For example, adding *–er* to the noun *labor* creates the job title *laborer.*

Directions: *Fill in the chart with the titles of the jobs that people do.*

Description of the Job	Job Title
1. a person who studies society by using reason	
2. a person who writes for a newspaper	
3. a person who teaches college	
4. a person who works for social reform	
5. a person who studies the economy	

Content Vocabulary Activity 17

Revolution and Enlightenment, 1550–1800

DIRECTIONS: Match each term with its definition by writing the correct letter on the blank.

A. geocentric	**F.** scientific method	**K.** Bill of Rights
B. philosophe	**G.** natural law	**L.** heliocentric
C. separation of powers	**H.** rationalism	**M.** social contract
D. federal system	**I.** deism	**N.** salon
E. ellipses	**J.** enlightened absolutism	

_____ **1.** religious philosophy based on reason and natural law

_____ **2.** reliance on reason as the best guide for belief and action

_____ **3.** oval paths in which planets move around the Sun

_____ **4.** system by which rulers tried to govern by Enlightenment principles while maintaining their royal powers

_____ **5.** universal moral law that Enlightenment thinkers believed could be understood through reason

_____ **6.** social gathering in which ideas of the Enlightenment were discussed

_____ **7.** relating to a reference system based at the center of the Sun

_____ **8.** intellectual thinker in the Age of Enlightenment

_____ **9.** power shared between the national government and the state governments

_____ **10.** derived from the natural rights proposed by eighteenth-century philosophers

_____ **11.** entire society agrees to be governed by its general will

_____ **12.** executive legislative and judicial branches of the government limit and control each other in a system of checks and balances

_____ **13.** places Earth at the center of the universe

_____ **14.** means of attaining knowledge by repeated observation and experimentation

CHAPTER 17

Academic Vocabulary Activity 17

Revolution and Enlightenment

Key Words

Academic Vocabulary	Words with Multiple Meanings	Content Vocabulary
affect	right	enlightenment
concept		
correspondence		
derive		
evidence		
hypothetical		
nature		

A. Word Family Activity

Word Chart

DIRECTIONS: Fill in the chart below by providing the missing word forms.

Remember: A noun is a word that names a person, place, thing, or idea. Examples include *Isaac Newton, France, power,* and *nature.* A verb is a word that is used to describe an action, experience, or state of being. Examples include *pass, affect,* and *be.* An adjective is a word that describes a noun. Examples include *glorious, mutual,* and *hypothetical.*

Verb	Noun	Adjective
1. affect	affect	affected
2.	concept	
3. derive		
4.		hypothetical

(continued)

CHAPTER 17

ABC Academic Vocabulary Activity 17

B. Word Usage Activity
Understanding Words with Multiple Meanings

Word Usage Note: <u>Words with Multiple Meanings</u>

Some words like *right* have multiple meanings:

a. (n.) something that is due or owed by nature, the government, or the law

b. (adj.) true, correct

c. (adj.) most appropriate or fitting for a particular occasion

d. (n.) legal permission to print or use a story, article, movie, etc.

e. (n.) a direction or side (as opposed to left)

We also use *right* in the following expressions: to know the difference between *right* and wrong/to stand on the side of *right/to* be the *right*-hand man

DIRECTIONS: Write the letter for the best definition of the word *right* in the sentences below.

1. _____ The divine <u>right</u> of kings allowed monarchs to do what they wanted to do.

2. _____ No one could question whether their actions were <u>right</u> or wrong.

3. _____ In the picture, the king is sitting to the <u>right</u>, not the left, of the queen.

4. _____ The Puritans did not feel it was <u>right</u> to play organ music during church services.

5. _____ Film producers need to correspond with writers to get the <u>rights</u> to a story.

C. Word Usage Activity
Understanding Definitions

Word Origins: *resolve*

The word *resolve* comes from the Latin *resolvere* (re- + *solvere*), meaning to *untie*. It has several meanings.

a. (n.) purpose, will power, determination

b. (v.) to settle an argument or solve a problem

c. (v.) to make a firm decision

Even though the Stamp Act was repealed in 1766, the cause of the dispute was not *resolved*.

We also use *resolve* in the following expressions: to *resolve* issues/problems/disputes.

DIRECTIONS: Write the letter for the best definition of *resolve* in the sentences below.

1. _____ Louis XIV <u>resolved</u> to use the divine right of kings.

2. _____ French citizens could not <u>resolve</u> the problems that were facing them.

3. _____ Later, in 1789 they would have the <u>resolve</u> to revolt against the monarchy.

Skills Reinforcement Activity 17

Outlining

Outlining helps you organize information for writing. An informal outline is similar to taking notes—you write words and phrases that help you to remember main ideas. In contrast, a formal outline has a standard format. To formally outline information, first read the text to identify the main ideas. Label these with Roman numerals. Next, write subtopics under each main idea. Label these with capital letters. Then write supporting details for each subtopic, and label these with Arabic numerals. Each level should have at least two entries and should be indented from the level above. All entries should use the same grammatical form, whether phrases or complete sentences.

DIRECTIONS: Use the informal notes below and material from Section 4 of your text to create a formal outline for the American Revolution. Write the main ideas on the lines below. Use these main ideas to create your outline. Use a separate sheet of paper to complete your outline.

Seven Years' War results in need for British revenues

Stamp Act is imposed, 1765

Stamp Act is opposed and repealed, 1766

First Continental Congress, Philadelphia, 1774

Battle of Lexington and Concord, 1775

Second Continental Congress forms an army—George Washington, commander in chief

Approves Declaration of Independence, 1776—beginning of American Revolution

French supply arms and money; grant diplomatic recognition

Spain and Dutch Republic also enter war

General Cornwallis surrenders at Yorktown; British end the war

Treaty of Paris, 1783—grants independence and western territory from Appalachians to Mississippi River

I. _____

II. _____

III. _____

IV. _____

V. _____

Critical Thinking Skills Activity 17 | Identifying Central Issues

You can better remember information presented in a reading by identifying the central issues the writer examines. The central issues are the main points or ideas the writer presents and supports with details. Turn to the key events listed on the opening page of Chapter 17 of your textbook. These events suggest the central issues of Chapter 17: the immediate impact and long-term effects of the scientific revolution.

DIRECTIONS: Read the following excerpt from Jean-Jacques Rousseau's *Treatise on the Social Compact: or, the Principles of Political Law*. Then answer the questions that follow.

Man is born free, and yet is universally enslaved. At the same time an individual frequently conceives himself to be the lord and master over others, though only more eminently deprived of liberty. Whence can this change arise? Are there any means by which it may be rendered lawful? The former question I cannot answer, though I imagine myself capable of resolving the latter.

If I took into consideration only the existence and effects of power, I should say, So long as a people are compelled to obey, they do well to be obedient; but, as soon as they are in a capacity to resist, they do better to throw off the yoke of restraint: for, in recovering their liberty on the same plea by which they lost it, either they have a just right to reassume it, or those could have none who deprive them of it. But there is an inviolable right founded on the very nature of society, which serves as the basis of all others. Man doth not derive this right, however, immediately from nature; it is founded on mutual convention.

1. What human right is the central issue of the first paragraph?

   _____

2. What question does Rousseau attempt to answer in the second paragraph?

   _____

   _____

3. What advice does Rousseau give to the those who are under the "yoke of restraint"?

   _____

   _____

4. Read the cover story in a weekly newsmagazine. On a separate sheet of paper, identify the central issues in the story. If you have difficulty, review the story's beginning. Journalists usually introduce the central issues in the first one or two paragraphs, known as the "lead."

★ HISTORY AND GEOGRAPHY ACTIVITY 17

Where Is the World?

In 1543 Polish astronomer Nicholas Copernicus lay dying when his friends placed the first bound copy of his book, *On the Revolutions of the Heavenly Spheres*, in his frail hands. Copernicus stared at the book and then at his friends and said nothing. No one knew if Copernicus realized what he held. Who could have known that the ideas in the book would forever change people's thinking about the universe?

During the time of Copernicus, European ideas about the universe had come from the teachings of ancient Greeks—teachings that had been formulated nearly 1,400 years earlier. The Greek astronomer Ptolemy had taught that Earth stood still at the center of the universe and that all other spheres revolved around it. The Catholic Church reinforced this view. According to the Church, Earth, where humans lived, was the greatest planet in God's universe; all other planets revolved around it.

Copernicus's studies of the movement of planets led him to challenge this theory. He came to believe that the Sun, not Earth,

---

Copernicus's Universe

In the middle of everything is the Sun. For in this most beautiful temple, who would place this lamp in another or better position than that from which it can light up the whole thing at the same time? . . . Thus indeed, as though seated on a royal throne, the Sun rules the family of planets revolving around it.

—Nicholas Copernicus, in *On the Revolutions of the Heavenly Spheres*, 1543

This diagram illustrates Copernicus's radical new view of the universe.

HISTORY AND GEOGRAPHY ACTIVITY 17 (continued)

was at the center of the universe. All the planets, including Earth, revolved around the Sun.

Yet Copernicus was afraid to publish his ideas lest he be branded a heretic and punished by the Church. He continued his studies in isolation.

With the publication of his ideas at his death, Copernicus launched later scientists into new investigations about the universe. No longer tied to the Church's view and to outdated teachings, astronomers such as Galileo and Kepler would prove that Copernicus was indeed right—Earth and the other planets revolved around the Sun. These new ideas and a growing interest in the natural world marked the beginning of the Scientific Revolution that transformed people's thinking in the 1600s.

As you have learned, location can be described by compass directions or in terms of relation to other landmarks. You can, for example, tell someone your house is two blocks to the east of where you are now standing. Or, depending on the person's familiarity with the area, you may say that your home is just around the corner from Town Hall. Often the description of a location reflects the point of view of a person or a group. In Copernicus's day, the description of the location of Earth and the universe itself reflected the views held by the Roman Catholic Church and by Greek teachings that were thousands of years old.

Today we find that the descriptions of many locations continue to reflect the viewpoints of particular groups and individuals.

APPLYING GEOGRAPHY TO HISTORY

DIRECTIONS: Answer the questions below on a separate sheet of paper.

1. Why might people give different descriptions of the location of a place?

2. Why did the Catholic Church believe that Earth stood in the middle of the universe?

Critical Thinking

3. **Recognizing Ideologies** How do institutions today mold the way people think about places in the world? Use examples from your own experience with institutions such as the government, schools, and church organizations to explain your answer.

Activity

4. As a class, conduct a survey. Ask five people to describe the location of these places: Mexico, Russia, Ethiopia, Switzerland, and China. Compare your findings. What do the descriptions of the locations tell you about the perspectives of the direction-givers?

Mapping History Activity 17

The Age of Revolution

Between 1500 and 1830, a revolution in scientific thinking spread across Europe. This Scientific Revolution affected politics, religion, philosophy, and the arts.

DIRECTIONS: The map below of present-day Europe shows places where significant developments in the Scientific Revolution and the Age of Enlightenment occurred. Use the map to answer the questions and complete the activity that follows.

1. Identify three nations shown on the map that did not exist in the Age of Enlightenment.

   _____

   _____

   _____

   _____

2. Identify three or more cities on the map that existed when the Scientific Revolution began, around 1500.

   _____

   _____

   _____

   _____

   _____

Present-Day Europe

SWEDEN
IRELAND
UNITED KINGDOM
DENMARK
London
NETHERLANDS
Berlin
Warsaw
BELGIUM
POLAND
GERMANY
Paris
LUXEMBOURG
CZECH REPUBLIC
Kraków
ATLANTIC OCEAN
FRANCE
SWITZER-LAND
SLOVAKIA
AUSTRIA
HUNGARY
SLOVENIA
CROATIA
SPAIN
BOSNIA-HERZEGOVINA
YUGO-SLAVIA
Madrid
ITALY
Rome
MONTE-NEGRO
ALBANIA
Mediterranean Sea
GREECE

10°W 0° 10°E 20°E
50°N
40°N

N
W   E
S

0   150   300 miles
0   150   300 kilometers
Azimuthal Equal-Area Projection

CHAPTER 17

3. On the map, mark and label the city or country where the following developments in the Scientific Revolution and the Age of Enlightenment occurred:

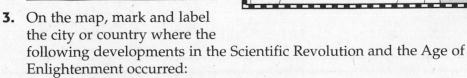

   Copernicus begins his scientific career;

   Galileo stands trial for his heretical ideas;

   Charles II establishes the Royal Society;

   Madame de Pompadour draws together enlightened thinkers in salons.

Historical Significance Activity 17

The First Amendment

The basic freedoms enjoyed by Americans for more than 200 years—freedom of speech, freedom of the press, freedom of religion, and freedom of assembly—come from the Bill of Rights, which became part of the Constitution in 1791. These freedoms are such a basic part of American life that sometimes we take them for granted. Yet billions of people in countries around the world do not enjoy the freedoms that Americans have considered sacred for more than 200 years.

The Bill of Rights contains ten amendments to the Constitution. The First Amendment reads as follows:

> Congress shall make no law respecting an establishment of religion, or prohibiting the free exercise thereof; or abridging the freedom of speech or of the press; or the right of the people peaceably to assemble, and to petition the government for a redress of grievances.

DIRECTIONS: In the space below, describe the story from your life that best expresses the meaning of the First Amendment to you.

_____

_____

_____

_____

_____

_____

_____

_____

_____

_____

_____

_____

_____

_____

_____

_____

★ **Cooperative Learning Activity 17** ★

Ideas That Changed the World

BACKGROUND

Artistic and conceptual creations, discoveries, and revelations marked the Age of Enlightenment. These ideas and discoveries changed people's views of the universe and their role in it. Exclusive reliance on ancient authorities gave way to new forms of inquiry. New political, scientific, philosophical, and artistic theories emerged and established the basis of a modern worldview based on rationalism and secularism. By focusing on some of these ideas that changed the world, you will better appreciate the energy and momentum that fueled the Age of Enlightenment and the Scientific Revolution from 1550 to 1800.

GROUP DIRECTIONS

1. This activity combines research skills with computer skills. You and your group will conduct research and then prepare a multimedia slide show about a leading figure of the Age of Enlightenment.

2. Use your textbook and library resources or the Internet to learn about key individuals of the Enlightenment.

3. Use a software presentation tool such as PowerPoint® with its bank of clip art to create slides for each Enlightenment figure and list his or her accomplishments, personal data, and impact on the age. The information should define why his or her contribution was significant.

4. Use your multimedia slides as the basis of oral presentations to the class on each person showcased.

5. Choose from the following individuals or present your group's suggested figure to your teacher for approval:

Isaac Newton	Jean-Jacques Rousseau
Maria Winkelman	Mary Wollstonecraft
René Descartes	Adam Smith
Blaise Pascal	Johann Sebastian Bach
Francis Bacon	George Frederick Handel
Montesquieu	Wolfgang Amadeus Mozart
Voltaire	Galileo Galilei
Denis Diderot	John Wesley

ORGANIZING THE GROUP

1. **Decision Making** Decide in your groups which person to study. Your teacher may reassign topics if a large number of groups choose the same individual, depending on research resource availability.

2. **Group Work/Decision Making** Meet with your group and brainstorm the kinds of information and clip art you want to include in your multimedia slide show and oral presentation. Be sure to include some personal data on the individual

Cooperative Learning Activity 17 (continued)

and explain, not just what the accomplishments were, but also their importance in the Age of Enlightenment. Discuss how you will prepare your presentation. Then divide up the tasks for creating your multimedia presentation.

3. **Individual Work** Research your assigned topics or conduct general research about the person, noting all sources used. Select appropriate pictures and graphics. Prepare your assigned parts of the presentation.

4. **Additional Group Work** Share your research with the group. Together, organize your group's information and illustrations into a slide show and oral presentation. If none of your own group members are familiar with software such as PowerPoint®, students from other groups or classes may be able to provide a quick tutorial. Decide who will design, create, and present each part of the report so that all members have a role in the presentation.

5. **Group Sharing** Groups should take turns making their presentations to the rest of the class. Together, discuss the similarities and differences among these "enlightened" individuals.

GROUP PROCESS QUESTIONS

- What is the most important thing you learned about the individual you researched from this activity? What was "enlightened" about her or his contribution?

- What part of the project did you enjoy most?

- If you did a multimedia presentation, what special problems did this form of report pose for the group?

- How did you solve the problems?

- How was it helpful to work with others?

Quick CHECK ✓

1. Was the goal of the assignment clear at all times?

_____

2. Did you have problems working well together? If so, how did you solve them?

_____

3. Was your group's presentation as good as you thought it would be? How could it be improved?

_____

_____

HISTORY SIMULATION ACTIVITY 17

Science on Trial

During the Scientific Revolution, Galileo and others made the assertion that the planets revolved around the Sun. In spite of scientific evidence that supported this view, the Inquisition of the Catholic Church condemned Galileo and his ideas as heresy. After a trial, Galileo was forced to recant his idea, though many think he did so only under extreme pressure.

TEACHER MATERIAL

Learning Objective To understand the divisions that existed between scientists of the Enlightenment and the Catholic Church.

Activity Groups of students will role-play a trial of Galileo by the Church. Students will take the parts of Galileo, three members of the Church, and a jury. Each side will present its arguments, and then the jury will decide which has made the best case.

Teacher Preparation Provide several copies of the next page to each group. Help students locate reference sources including books, magazine articles, and Internet addresses related to history or science.

Activity Guidelines

1. Introduce the activity by reviewing important points about Galileo's ideas. Include some of the background information found in the Chapter Preview and Section 1 of this chapter. Then discuss how Galileo's ideas conflicted with those of the Catholic Church.

2. Organize students into groups of 10 to 12 each. Explain that each group will conduct a mock trial of Galileo. Group members will play the following roles: Church members who will defend the position of the Catholic Church, Galileo, and jury members who will judge the case.

3. Distribute the planning forms and direct students to divide among group members the roles that each will play. Have Church members and Galileo research information that they can use to argue their case. Have members of the jury conduct general research about the dispute.

4. As students conduct their research, have them use the planning form and additional sheets of paper if necessary to record the points they will make during the trial. Those supporting Galileo should be well versed about his ideas and the scientific principles upon which he based his conclusions. Those supporting the Church should thoroughly understand the Church's position and why Galileo's ideas threatened it.

5. When students have completed their research, discuss with them how the trial will be conducted. Point out that at an Inquisition trial, there was no jury and that defendants had no rights. Explain that they will not follow this style in order to allow the arguments of both sides to be heard. Students work together to agree on an order of presentation and cross-examination.

6. When both sides have finished presenting their arguments, have the jury discuss the case and come to a verdict by voting. Then have the jury report its decision.

7. After the trial, have the groups come together to discuss what they have learned. Ask students:
   - What new information did you learn about Galileo and his ideas about the solar system?
   - What new information did you learn about why the Church was so strongly opposed to Galileo's ideas?
   - Why is a jury an important part of a trial? How did having a jury make this trial different from Galileo's experience with the Inquisition?

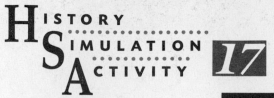

Science on Trial—Planning Form

Galileo _____

Church Members _____

_____

Jury Members _____

_____

Research Notes:

Information about Galileo:

_____
_____
_____
_____
_____
_____

Information about the Church:

_____
_____
_____
_____
_____

Most important points to make:

_____
_____
_____
_____

Time Line Activity 17

Revolution and Enlightenment

DIRECTIONS: During the Scientific Revolution, ideas changed the world. Look at the events listed on the time line. Write each event in the box next to the field of study it affected. Then describe the significance of the event. Events may be placed in more than one box.

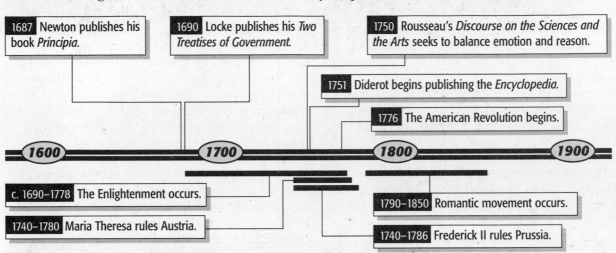

1687 Newton publishes his book *Principia*.

1690 Locke publishes his *Two Treatises of Government*.

1750 Rousseau's *Discourse on the Sciences and the Arts* seeks to balance emotion and reason.

1751 Diderot begins publishing the *Encyclopedia*.

1776 The American Revolution begins.

1600   1700   1800   1900

c. 1690–1778 The Enlightenment occurs.

1740–1780 Maria Theresa rules Austria.

1790–1850 Romantic movement occurs.

1740–1786 Frederick II rules Prussia.

Significance of Historical Events

Field	Event	Significance
Science/Mathematics		
Government/Politics		
Philosophy/Religion		
The Arts		

Leeuwenhoek and Modern Biology

THEN Because many things are impossible to see with the unaided eye, people who lived before and during the Middle Ages had mistaken concepts about material reality. They could not see the eggs that fleas and lice laid. Therefore, they believed that such vermin sprang from nonliving matter. Since the germs that cause diseases are even tinier than insect eggs, they supposed that a mysterious vapor brought plague.

Antonie van Leeuwenhoek (1632–1723) did not change these mistaken ideas during his lifetime. However, he did make discoveries that eventually helped to correct them. Leeuwenhoek was a fabric merchant who experimented with the microscope, which had been invented around 1595. Two scientists, Robert Hooke of England and Jan Swammerdam of the Netherlands, had made microscopes and used them before Leeuwenhoek. Hooke's book, *Micrographia*, turned Leeuwenhoek's attention to the microscopic world.

Leeuwenhoek developed a lens that magnified objects to appear 200 times larger. He used the lens on ordinary things, such as pond water and the tartar from his own teeth. In these, he discovered fabulous creatures that he called animalcules. He was the first to observe such things as bacteria, sperm cells, blood cells, rotifers, and nematodes. Leeuwenhoek's work led to the understanding of the composition of blood and the development of ways to control diseases caused by microbes.

NOW Biology is the science most deeply indebted to Leeuwenhoek's discoveries. Its principle tool remains the microscope. This instrument has, of course, advanced far beyond the simple device used in the sixteenth century. Stereoscopic microscopes allow scientists to dissect extremely small specimens by showing these specimens in three dimensions. Electron microscopes magnify images of objects over one million times. With these and other new instruments and techniques, modern biologists are probing even more deeply into the mysteries of life. Some of the more recent—and most exciting—medical discoveries follow.

Some of biology's most exciting advances have been in genetics, or the study of genes. Genes determine the essence and appearance of living organisms. Scientists have learned to manipulate them to modify living organisms. For example, scientists can change the genetic structures of plants to make them more resistant to disease.

The manipulation of genes has led to a process called cloning. In 1997 Ian Wilmut, a Scottish scientist, cloned a sheep; that is, he reproduced a sheep from one cell of the animal. Biologists hope that cloning will lead to creating animals whose organs can be used to replace damaged human organs.

In 1999 members of the Human Genome Project decoded virtually all the genetic information in a human cell. This knowledge will enable doctors and scientists to help people in a number of ways. For example, a doctor could identify whether a patient has a gene that makes that person susceptible to a particular disease.

CRITICAL THINKING

Directions: Answer the following questions on a separate sheet of paper.

1. **Drawing conclusions:** Why do you think Leeuwenhoek was interested in the microscope?
2. **Making inferences:** Why might it be helpful for people to learn that they have a gene that makes them susceptible to a disease?
3. **Extending prior knowledge:** How do you think Leeuwenhoek's work led to the control of disease? Do research in the library and on the Internet to learn about scientists who fought microbes. Write a brief report of your findings.

> ## People in World History Activity 17 — Profile 1

Nicholas Copernicus (1473–1543)

In the early 1500s, most people believed Ptolemy's theory of the universe. More than 1,000 years earlier, the Greek astronomer had concluded that Earth was the center of the universe. According to Ptolemy, Earth was stationary, and all the other planets moved around it in complicated paths, or orbits. Copernicus, however, dared to disagree with his theory.

Born in Toruń, Poland, Copernicus began his studies at the University of Kraków. His uncle was a prelate, a powerful church official. When Copernicus was 24, his uncle used his influence to have him appointed a canon, an official of the cathedral in Frombork, Poland. Copernicus used the income from this position to finance his studies in mathematics, astronomy, and medicine in Italy. When he was 33, he earned a doctorate from the University of Ferrara. Then he returned to Poland and his position as church canon.

While finishing his formal education, Copernicus became aware of serious problems within the Ptolemaic theory. Most significantly, Ptolemy's theory of the planets' movement in the galaxy seemed too complicated. Looking for a way to make sense of this defective logic, Copernicus began to review other theories of the universe.

After years of careful study, Copernicus came to believe that the Sun is stationary and located near the center of the universe. Further, he theorized that Earth is a planet like all the other planets in the sky. As a result, Earth must move like the other planets. Copernicus believed Earth to be in the third planetary orbit around the Sun.

Disturbing fixed ideas about the universe was a dangerous thing. Copernicus's theory of the universe not only challenged Ptolmey's theory, but it also refuted the Church's view of the universe. If Copernicus's theory became known, he could have been severely punished. Copernicus, however, was careful, and he shared his ideas only with those people with whom he could trust his life. Nonetheless, news of his thesis spread rapidly. Copernicus's masterpiece, *On The Revolutions of the Heavenly Spheres*, was published right before his death in 1543. For his achievements, Copernicus is considered the founder of modern astronomy.

CHAPTER 17

REVIEWING THE PROFILE

Directions: Answer the following questions on a separate sheet of paper.

1. How was Copernicus's theory of the universe different from Ptolemy's theory?

2. **Critical Thinking** Determining Cause and Effect. Why would the Church have been angered by Copernicus's theory?

3. **Critical Thinking** Recognizing Ideologies. Why do you think people in Copernicus's time reacted so negatively to his ideas?

> ## People in World History Activity 17
>
> ### Profile 2

Adam Smith (1723–1790)

How can social order and human progress be possible in a society where people follow their own self-interests? This is the problem that Adam Smith set out to solve.

Smith argued that people's personal interests lead to progress and order. To make money, people make things that other people want to buy. People spend money for the things they want the most. Buying and selling creates social harmony. Smith claimed that all this would happen without control, as if by an "invisible hand." This belief came to be called laissez-faire economics, the policy that a government should impose the fewest possible restrictions on prices and trade. *Laissez-faire* is a French phrase meaning "let do" or "leave them alone." As a result of his work with freedom and order, economic process, and a unified social theory, Adam Smith is considered the founder of modern economics.

Smith was born in Kirkcaldy, Scotland, to a distinguished family. His father was an important lawyer and public official; his mother was a member of the upper class. His college education was the best that could be had: first at Scotland's University of Glasgow and then at England's Oxford University. Smith left Oxford when he was 23 years old. Two years later, he became a professor at the University of Edinburgh, where he taught literature, law, and philosophy. In 1751, he was made a professor of logic at the University of Glasgow. Later that year Smith accepted a post as professor in moral philosophy.

At Glasgow, Smith wrote his first book, *The Theory of Moral Sentiment* (1759). He then was hired to tutor the Duke of Buccleuch. While accompanying the young duke on a tour of France, Smith began his most important book, *The Wealth of Nations*.

When Smith returned to England in 1766, the young duke's stepfather provided him with a regular income. Freed from the need to earn a living, Smith was able to leave teaching and spend the next decade writing and studying. He published the first edition of *The Wealth of Nations* in 1776 and revised it five times during his life. The book became a major influence on economic policy in the early nineteenth century.

REVIEWING THE PROFILE

Directions: Answer the following questions on a separate sheet of paper.

1. What social dilemma did Smith address in *The Wealth of Nations*?

2. What is laissez-faire economics?

3. **Critical Thinking** Recognizing Bias. What assumptions about human nature did Adam Smith make?

4. **Critical Thinking** Identifying Alternatives. What might be the advantage of a government that controls trade—"hands-on" as opposed to Smith's "laissez-faire" ideal?

PRIMARY SOURCE READING 17

Of the *Encyclopedia*

Voltaire was one of the most influential philosophers of the Enlightenment. A man with a sharp tongue and an even sharper pen, he was twice imprisoned in the Bastille for his comments. He spent two years in England, where he was impressed by England's greater freedom of thought. Back in France, he wrote philosophy and satire and, through the influence of Madame de Pompadour, was made a member of the French Academy.

In the passage below, Voltaire ridicules French responses to Diderot's *Encyclopedia*, to which Voltaire himself was a contributor.

Guided Reading *In this selection, read to learn why Diderot's* Encyclopedia *was banned in France and why it should not have been.*

A servant of Louis XV told me that while his master, the king, was dining one day at Trianon with a small group, the conversation turned first on hunting and then on gun powder. Someone said that the best powder is made with equal parts of saltpeter, sulphur and coal. The Duke de La Vallière, who knew better, argued that to make good gun powder all you needed was one part of sulphur and one of coal to five parts of saltpeter that had been well filtered, well evaporated, and well crystallized.

"It is funny," said the Duke de Nivernois, "that we amuse ourselves daily by killing partridges in the park at Versailles, and sometimes by killing men or by being killed ourselves at the frontier, without knowing exactly with what we kill."

"Alas! We are reduced to that state for most things of this world," answered Madame de Pompadour; "I do not know what the rouge I put on my cheeks is made of, and I should be very much embarrassed if someone asked me how the silk hose I am wearing is made."

"It is a pity," the Duke de La Vallière then said, "that His Majesty confiscated our encyclopedic dictionaries, each of which cost us a hundred gold pieces: there we would quickly find the answer to all our questions."

The king justified the confiscation: he had been warned that the twenty-one folio volumes that were found on all the ladies' dressing tables were the most dangerous thing in the world for the French kingdom; and he wanted to know for himself if this were true before allowing anyone to read this work. At the end of the dinner he sent three of his servants for a copy, each of whom returned carrying seven volumes with great difficulty.

They saw at the article "Powder" that the Duke de La Vallière was right; and soon Madame de Pompadour learned the difference between the old Spanish rouge that the ladies of Madrid used to color their cheeks, and the rouge of Parisian ladies. She learned that Greek and Roman ladies were painted with purple that came from seashells, and that consequently our scarlet was the purple of the ancients; she learned that there was more saffron in Spanish rouge, and more cochineal in the French.

She saw how her stockings were manufactured; and the operation of this process delighted her with wonder. "Oh, the fine book!" she exclaimed. "Sire, did you confiscate this storehouse of useful things so as to possess it alone and be the only wise man of your kingdom?"

They all jumped at the volumes like the daughters of Lycomedes at Ulysses' jewels; every one found at once what he was looking for. Those who had lawsuits were surprised to find there the judgment of their cases. The king read all the rights of the crown. "But really," he said, "I don't know why I was told so many bad things about this work."

"Well, don't you see, Sire," said the Duke de Nivernois, "it's because it is very good? Men do not attack the mediocre and the dull of whatever sort. If women try to ridicule a new comer, it is

PRIMARY SOURCE READING 17

certain that she is prettier than they."

All the while the others kept leafing through the pages, and the Count de C . . . said aloud: "Sire, you are too fortunate that there should be under your reign men capable of knowing the arts and of transmitting them to posterity. Everything is here, from how to make a pin to how to make and direct your canons; from the infinitely small to the infinitely great. Thank God for having made men born in your kingdom who have thus served the entire universe. Other nations must either buy the *Encyclopedia* or copy it. Take all my property if you like; but give me back my *Encyclopedia*."

"Yet they say," replied the king, "that there are many faults in this so necessary and so admirable work."

"Sire," rejoined the Count de C . . . , "there were two spoiled sauces at your dinner; we did not eat them, and we ate very well. Would you like to have the whole dinner thrown out the window because of these two sauces?"

The king felt the strength of reason; every one recovered his property: it was a happy day.

Envy and ignorance did not hold themselves beaten; these two immortal sisters continued their outcries, their schemes, their persecutions: ignorance is very learned in these matters.

What happened? Foreigners brought out four editions of this French work, banned in France, and made about eighteen hundred thousand gold pieces.

Frenchmen, try henceforth to understand your interests better.

INTERPRETING THE READING

Directions *Use information from the reading to answer the following questions. If necessary, use a separate sheet of paper.*

1. Why did King Louis XV ban Diderot's *Encyclopedia*?

_____

2. After King Louis XV read the rights of the crown, he stated, "I don't know why I was told so many bad things about this work." Give three reasons why his guests argued not to ban the *Encyclopedia*.

_____

_____

3. What did Voltaire mean by "Envy and ignorance did not hold themselves beaten"?

_____

Critical Thinking

4. Synthesizing Information In one of Voltaire's letters, he states, "Twenty *in-folio* volumes will never cause a revolution; it's the little portable 30 cent books which are to be feared." Discuss why a smaller, less expensive book could have a greater effect on peoples' ideas and beliefs and how it might lead people to revolt against their country.

_____

_____

CHAPTER 17

World Art and Music Activity 17

John Singleton Copley

John Singleton Copley (1738–1815) had two artistic careers. He spent most of the first half of his life in prerevolutionary Boston as a respected portrait painter. At the peak of his fame, he moved to London, where he painted large historical paintings.

DIRECTIONS: Read the passage below about this expatriate artist. Then answer the questions in the space provided.

John Singleton Copley, *The Copley Family,* oil on canvas (1776–1777)

Copley was born in Boston in 1738. As a young boy, he was already drawing and painting. His stepfather was an engraver who exposed the young Copley to prints of English paintings and taught him to engrave and paint. At age 13 he was forced to go to work to help support his family, and so he became a printer and engraver.

It was common at the time for an artist to study and copy the work of other artists. At first, the works available to Copley were not very accomplished, so

(continued)

World Art and Music Activity 17

neither were his copies. As he painted more and more portraits of real people, however, he gradually improved and began to acquire a style of his own. Most portrait painters of the time emphasized their subjects' clothes and jewels. Copley did this as well, but he was more interested in their faces and the aspects of character to be found there. Not only did he paint an individual's appearance, but Copley's paintings also conveyed aspects of the subject's personality.

The family portrait on page 231 is an interesting combination of Copley's early and mature styles. The stiff pose and expressionless face of the child in the center suggest a wooden doll, appealing to the viewer only for her pretty dress. The other three children, however, are rendered like real children—falling all over their parents, laughing and active. Their personalities are captured as clearly as they would be in a modern snapshot.

Copley's most famous portrait is of Paul Revere. The silversmith poses in his shirtsleeves, holding one of his teapots. This relaxed informality is not a Copley

characteristic: he must have seen something unique in Revere. Although Revere is relaxed, his face is intelligent, thoughtful, and alert.

In 1774 Copley left for England. Copley had long wanted to visit Europe; he felt that Europe was the center of the art world at that time, and he wanted to experience all that it had to offer. He quickly gained fame in London and wealthy men and women commissioned many portraits. In between portrait commissions, he worked on larger works featuring groups of people and historical scenes, such as *The Death of Chatham.* This canvas details the earl of Chatham suffering from a fatal stroke while addressing the House of Lords. More than 50 nobles surround the dying prime minister, and each individual is unique and detailed, down to silver shoe buckles. This elevates the work from historical fact to emotional reality.

It has been said that John Singleton Copley was more concerned with painting truth than beauty. In fact, he did both.

Reviewing the Selection

1. What kind of art was Copley known for in America?

_____

_____

2. How was his work in England different?

_____

_____

Critical Thinking

3. **Making Generalizations** What people or institutions supported Copley's art? What do you think this says about colonial Boston?

_____

_____

4. **Determining Cause and Effect** Artists often try to explore problems through painting. These can be the artist's own personal concerns, central issues in society, or aesthetic concerns. Copley' greatest talent was showing the person behind the face. What—if any—problems do you think this attempted to solve?

_____

_____

Reteaching Activity 17

Revolution and Enlightenment

In the Age of Enlightenment, innovative ideas in astronomy, physics, mathematics, medicine, chemistry, and philosophy changed the way people viewed the physical and social world. New theories and beliefs based on the scientific method and on reason replaced old beliefs based on magic, mysticism, and ancient writings.

DIRECTIONS: The outline below lists fields that changed tremendously in the Age of Enlightenment and people who initiated or contributed to these changes. In the space provided, record the discoveries, contributions, or ideas of these individuals.

I. Astronomy, Physics, and Mathematics

    A. Copernicus _____

    B. Kepler _____

    C. Galileo _____

    D. Newton _____

II. Biology

    A. Vesalius _____

    B. Harvey _____

III. Chemistry

    A. Boyle _____

    B. Lavoisier _____

IV. Government

    A. Rousseau _____

    B. Montesquieu _____

V. Literature

    A. Voltaire _____

    B. Diderot _____

★ Enrichment Activity 17

The Commotion Galileo Caused

In Chapter 17, you read about the reaction of the Catholic Church to Galileo's ideas, which conflicted with Church teachings. Galileo's hypothesis that Earth was not the center of the universe threatened to undermine the religious world-view that pervaded every aspect of European society. Read the excerpt below from Bertolt Brecht's play *Galileo*.

Around the corner from the market place a BALLAD SINGER *and his* WIFE, *who is costumed to represent the earth in a skeleton globe made of thin bands of brass, are holding the attention of a sprinkling of representative citizens, some in masquerade, who were on their way to see the carnival procession. From the market place the noise of an impatient crowd.*

BALLAD SINGER (*accompanied by his* WIFE *on the guitar):*
When the Almighty made the universe
He made the earth and then he made the sun.
Then round the earth he bade the sun to turn—
That's in the Bible, Genesis, Chapter One.
And from that time all beings here below
Were in obedient circles meant to go:
    Around the pope the cardinals
    Around the cardinals the bishops
    Around the bishops the secretaries
    Around the secretaries the aldermen
    Around the aldermen the craftsmen
    Around the craftsmen the servants
    Around the servants the dogs, the chickens, and the beggars.

A conspicuous reveller—henceforth called the SPINNER—*has slowly caught on and is exhibiting his idea of spinning around. He does not lose dignity, he faints with mock grace.*

BALLAD SINGER:
Up stood the learned Galileo
Glanced briefly at the sun
And said: "Almighty God was wrong
In Genesis, Chapter One!"
    Now that was rash, my friends, it is no matter small:
    For heresy will spread today like foul diseases.
    Change Holy Writ, forsooth? What will be left at all?
    Why: each of us would say and do just what he pleases!

—From *Galileo,* by Bertolt Brecht, translated by Charles Laughton, edited by Eric Bentley, copyright © 1940 by Arvid Englind, copyright © 1952 by Bertolt Brecht, copyright © 1966 by Eric Bentley.

DIRECTIONS: Answer the questions below in the space provided.

1. Write a one-sentence summary of the message the Ballad Singer tries to convey. _____

   _____

   _____

2. Write your own ballad, poem, or short play about either Copernicus or Diderot and the persecution either man faced for expressing his views. If necessary, use a separate sheet of paper. _____

   _____

   _____

   _____

GLENCOE
WORLD HISTORY

Chapter 17
Section Resources

GUIDED READING ACTIVITY 17-1   236

GUIDED READING ACTIVITY 17-2   237

GUIDED READING ACTIVITY 17-3   238

GUIDED READING ACTIVITY 17-4   239

SECTIONS

📖 Guided Reading Activity 17-1

SECTION 17-1

The Scientific Revolution

DIRECTIONS: Answer the following questions as you read Section 1.

1. What did the writings of Ptolemy and Archimedes make obvious?

   _____

   _____

2. What new invention helped to spread new scientific ideas quickly and easily?

   _____

3. Where is Earth placed in the universe according to the Ptolemaic system?

   _____

4. Contrary to Ptolemy, what did Copernicus argue concerning the construction of the universe?

   _____

5. What discoveries did Galileo make using a telescope?

   _____

6. Why did the Church order Galileo to abandon the Copernican idea of the nature of the universe?

   _____

   _____

7. What did Isaac Newton define in his first book, *The Principia*?

   _____

8. What did William Harvey's observations and experiments show?

   _____

9. What field of science in Germany provided opportunities for women?

   _____

10. What did René Descartes emphasize and assert?

    _____

    _____

11. Who developed the scientific method?

    _____

Guided Reading Activity 17-2

The Enlightenment

DIRECTIONS: Fill in the blanks below as you read Section 2.

The **(1)** _____ was an eighteenth-century philosophical movement of intellectuals who were greatly impressed with the achievements of the **(2)** _____ Revolution. **(3)** _____, natural law, hope, and **(4)** _____ were common words to the thinkers of the Enlightenment.

Montesquieu's analysis of the system of checks and **(5)** _____ through separation of powers was his most lasting contribution to political thought. Voltaire was especially well-known for his criticism of **(6)** _____ and his strong belief in religious toleration. Diderot's most famous contribution to the Enlightenment was the **(7)** _____, or *Classified Dictionary of the Sciences, Arts, and the Trades.*

The **(8)** _____, a French group, were interested in identifying the natural economic laws that governed human society. They believed the state should not interrupt the free play of natural economic forces by imposing government **(9)** _____ on the economy. This doctrine became known as **(10)** _____, meaning "to let do."

Jean-Jacques Rousseau argued for a social **(11)** _____ between the government and the people. Through a social contract, an entire society agrees to be **(12)** _____ by its general will. The English writer Mary **(13)** _____ advanced the strongest statement for the rights of women.

Many Enlightenment philosophes **(14)** _____ the Christian churches. But many people also sought a deeper personal **(15)** _____ to God. **(16)** _____ proved that the need for spiritual experience had not been eliminated by the eighteenth-century search for reason.

SECTION 17-2

Guided Reading Activity 17-3

The Impact of the Enlightenment

DIRECTIONS: Fill in the blanks below as you read Section 3.

I. Enlightenment thought influenced European _____ in the eighteenth century.

   A. Frederick II of _____ was well-versed in the ideas of the Enlightenment.

   B. Joseph II of Austria said, "Philosophy is the _____ of my empire."

   C. Catherine II of Russia said Diderot's _____ theories "would have turned everything in my kingdom upside down."

II. The philosophes _____ war as a foolish waste of life and resources.

   A. In 1740 a major war broke out in connection with the succession to the _____ throne.

   B. The _____ Years' War had three major areas of conflict: Europe, India, and North America.

   C. The struggle between Britain and France in the rest of the world, known as the _____, was fought in India and North America.

III. The Enlightenment brought important changes in art, _____, and literature.

   A. By the 1730s, a new artistic style known as _____ had spread over Europe.

   B. Eighteenth-century Europe produced some of the world's most enduring _____.

      1. Johann Sebastian _____ was one of the greatest composers of all time.

      2. Wolfgang Amadeus _____ was a true child prodigy of the age.

   C. European _____ began to choose realistic social themes over the past century's focus on heroic deeds and the supernatural.

Guided Reading Activity 17-4

The American Revolution

DIRECTIONS: Fill in the blanks below as you read Section 4.

1. The United Kingdom of _____ came into existence in 1707, when the governments of England and Scotland were united.

2. By 1757 Britain controlled _____ English colonies on the eastern coast of the present United States.

3. After the Seven Years' War, British leaders wanted to get new _____ from the colonies.

4. In 1765 Parliament imposed the _____, which required legal documents to carry a stamp showing that a tax had been paid to _____.

5. Fighting finally erupted between colonists and the British army in April 1775 in _____ and _____.

6. On July 4, 1776, the Second Continental Congress approved the _____.

7. When General Cornwallis was forced to surrender to the American and French forces at _____, the British decided to end the war.

8. The _____, signed in 1783, recognized the _____ of the American colonies and granted American control of territory to the _____ River.

9. The proposed Constitution created a _____ system, in which the national and state governments shared power.

10. The _____ guaranteed freedom of religion, speech, press, the right to bear arms, and trial by jury.

SECTION 17-4

Chapter 18 Resources

The French Revolution and Napoleon, 1789–1815

READING SKILLS ACTIVITY 18
Identifying Complex Causation 243

HISTORICAL ANALYSIS SKILLS ACTIVITY 18
Interpreting History 244

DIFFERENTIATED INSTRUCTION ACTIVITY 18
What Is Government? 245

ENGLISH LEARNER ACTIVITY 18
The French Revolution and Napoleon 247

CONTENT VOCABULARY ACTIVITY 18
The French Revolution and Napoleon, 1789–1815 249

ACADEMIC VOCABULARY ACTIVITY 18
The French Revolution and Napoleon 251

SKILLS REINFORCEMENT ACTIVITY 18
Interpreting Graphs 253

CRITICAL THINKING SKILLS ACTIVITY 18
Analyzing Information 254

HISTORY AND GEOGRAPHY ACTIVITY 18
A Doomed March to Russia 255

MAPPING HISTORY ACTIVITY 18
The French Revolution 257

HISTORICAL SIGNIFICANCE ACTIVITY 18
Three Ways Napoleon Changed the World 258

COOPERATIVE LEARNING ACTIVITY 18
Stages of Change in France 259

HISTORY SIMULATION ACTIVITY 18
Unrest in Blaat 261

TIME LINE ACTIVITY 18
The French Revolution and Napoleon 263

LINKING PAST AND PRESENT ACTIVITY 18
Legacy of Colonialism: Class and Tribal Conflict 264

PEOPLE IN WORLD HISTORY ACTIVITY 18
Profile 1: Marie Antoinette (1755–1793) 265
Profile 2: Maximilien François Marie Isidore de Robespierre (1758–1794) 266

PRIMARY SOURCE READING 18
Declaration of the Rights of Man and of the Citizen 267

WORLD ART AND MUSIC ACTIVITY 18
Jacques-Louis David 269

RETEACHING ACTIVITY 18
The French Revolution and Napoleon 271

ENRICHMENT ACTIVITY 18
The *Levée en Masse* 272

Reading Skills Activity 18

Copyright © Glencoe/McGraw-Hill, a division of The McGraw-Hill Companies, Inc.

CHAPTER 18

Identifying Complex Causation

LEARNING THE SKILL

Historians try to make sense of historical events by finding the series of events that led up to a crucial moment. They show a number of causes, called complex causation, leading to a particular effect or event. Together these things have a cumulative effect—they add up to a result that is highly significant. When you read a text, notice whether an author presents multiple reasons for a specific outcome. When you finish reading, ask yourself a focus question that will help identify the various events that led to the final result.

PRACTICING THE SKILL

DIRECTIONS: Identifying complex causation is made easier by using a graphic organizer such as a fishbone diagram as you read. Read the following paragraph. Using this information as well as your textbook, write down in the diagram below five reasons that French revolutionaries identified the destruction of the Bastille prison as the first act of the French Revolution.

With bread prices at record levels in July 1789, and news that the king had banished a financial minister who was sympathetic to the Third Estate, hungry mobs of people attacked the gates of Paris where grain convoys entered the city. They raided every possible source of arms, ending up at the Bastille prison. The Bastille, built around 1370, was converted into a prison in the 17th century by Charles VI, housing mainly political prisoners, but also religious prisoners, "seditious" writers, and young boisterous men held at the request of their families. For example, Voltaire was incarcerated at the Bastille for a brief time for writing against the king. The prison began to acquire a poor reputation when it became the main prison for those taken under lettres de cachet, orders from the king that could put someone in jail or other confinement without a trial. Wealthy aristocrats sometimes bought these letters to get rid of enemies.

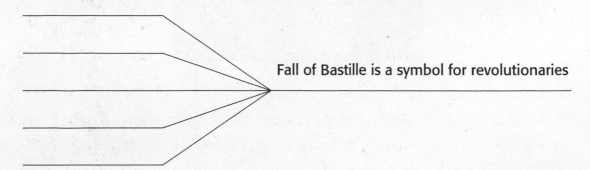

Fall of Bastille is a symbol for revolutionaries

APPLYING THE SKILL

DIRECTIONS: On a separate sheet of paper, use a fishbone diagram to identify the complex causation of Napoleon's rise to power in 1799. Be sure to identify the historical conditions as well as Napoleon's accomplishments and actions.

Historical Analysis Skills Activity 18

Interpreting History

LEARNING THE SKILL

Historians know that reports of events are not necessarily reliable accounts of what actually happened, even if told by an eyewitness. Those who record and write about episodes in history are often biased—that is, they favor one point of view or interpretation of events over another. While reading historical sources, it is important to view them with a critical eye.

PRACTICING THE SKILL

DIRECTIONS: Jacques-Louis David (1748–1825) was a French artist. Sympathetic to the goals of the French Revolution, and later Napoleon Bonaparte, he would eventually rise to the position of Napoleon's official portraitist. Examine David's painting "Napoleon at St. Bernard" (1800), and answer the questions that follow on a separate sheet of paper.

1. Briefly describe the scene portrayed in the painting.

2. Do you believe that the artist is trying to portray Napoleon as a heroic figure? Explain.

3. Is there evidence in the painting of the artist's bias in favor of or against Napoleon? Explain.

APPLYING THE SKILL

DIRECTIONS: Using your local newspaper or Internet sources, find an article containing a first-hand account of a recent news event that occurred anywhere in the world. On a separate sheet of paper, briefly summarize the article and describe whether you found any evidence of bias in the reporting. Be sure to explain your conclusion.

Differentiated Instruction Activity 18

What Is Government?

Enlightenment thinkers argued for freedom of thought and equality before the law. Their arguments sparked new ways of thinking that eventually led to the French Revolution. Jean-Jacques Rousseau was the most progressive of the Enlightenment thinkers. He believed that politics and morality should not be separated. He wrote about government in *The Social Contract* (1763):

The only will dominating government . . . should be the general will or the law. The government's power is only the public power vested in it. As soon as [government] attempts to let any act come from itself completely independently, it starts to lose its intermediary role. If the time should ever come when the [government] has a particular will of its own stronger than that of the sovereign and makes use of the public power which is in its hands to carry out its own particular will—when there are thus two sovereigns, one in law and one in fact—at that moment the social union will disappear and the body politic will be dissolved.

It is sometimes difficult to understand the ideas of earlier times because of how they are written. One way to clarify your understanding of older documents is to rewrite the sentences in contemporary language.

DIRECTIONS: Rewrite Rousseau's paragraph above in your own language and style. As you do so, try to preserve Rousseau's persuasive tone.

_____

_____

_____

_____

_____

_____

_____

_____

_____

_____

_____

CHAPTER 18

(continued)

Differentiated Instruction Activity 18

For the Teacher

TEACHING STRATEGIES FOR DIFFERENT LEARNING STYLES

The following activities are ways the basic lesson can be modified to accommodate students' different learning styles:

English Learners (EL) Explain the terms *vested, intermediary, sovereign,* and *body politic* as used by Rousseau. Ask students to identify specific parts of the passage they find confusing and then help them understand those parts.

Advanced Learners (AL) Besides completing the basic lesson, advanced learners might write a similar passage that reflects an opposing philosophy of government. Lead a discussion with students about the philosophy of government, and ask students which philosophy they support—Rousseau's or the opposing philosophy.

Below Grade Level (BL) Before starting the activity, ask students to write down any terms that are unfamiliar. Explain these terms to students, and have them write a definition for each term so that they can refer to it during the activity.

On Grade Level (OL) Have students complete the activity as presented.

English Learner Activity 18

The French Revolution and Napoleon

★ A. PRE-READING ACTIVITY: IMPROVING READING COMPREHENSION

Directions: *Before reading about Napoleon on pages 596–603, answer the following questions.*

1. In this passage, we discover the qualities that led Napoleon to become Emperor of France. What qualities do you think are important for a leader to have?

    _____

    _____

    _____

    _____

    _____

    _____

2. This time period in France led to some of the most revolutionary changes in the nation's history. What changes have taken place in the United States that you might consider significant or revolutionary?

    _____

    _____

    _____

    _____

    _____

    _____

    _____

★ B. PRE-READING ACTIVITY: READING COMPREHENSION

Directions: *Before reading about Napoleon, study the words and their definitions below.*

beneficial (adj.): good
cease (v.): to stop
dominate (v.): to control someone or something
knowledge (n.): information and understanding gained through learning or experience
lead (v.): to go in front of a group
nobility (n.): people of the highest social class who use special titles with names
preservation (n.): the act of keeping something or someone safe
supreme (adj.): having the highest or most important position of power, or influence

CHAPTER 18

(continued)

English Learner Activity 18

★ C. READING COMPREHENSION ACTIVITY: TRUE/FALSE

Directions: *After you read about Napoleon, complete the exercise below. Three of the answers are true. Circle the letter of the answer that is false.*

1. Napoleon Bonaparte was
    a. Corsican.
    c. of Florentine nobility.
    b. the son of a lawyer.
    d. educated at a military school in Italy.

2. Napoleon was not well liked by his fellow officers because he was
    a. short.
    c. had little money.
    b. spoke with an Italian accent.
    d. very shy.

3. In 1796 Napoleon was made commander of the French armies in Italy, where he won battles by using
    a. honesty.
    c. deception.
    b. speed.
    d. surprise.

4. Napoleon won the confidence of his men with his
    a. energy.
    c. charm.
    b. anger.
    d. ability to make quick decisions.

5. These qualities, combined with his _____, enabled Napoloen to influence people and win their firm support.
    a. keen intelligence
    c. supreme confidence
    b. ease with words
    d. Italian accent

★ D. WORD BUILDING ACTIVITY: SYNONYMS OR ANTONYMS

Directions: *Label the following pairs of words as synonyms (S) or antonyms (A). Remember that synonyms are words with similar meanings, while antonyms are words with opposite meanings.*

1. _____ beneficial / helpful

2. _____ cease / finish

3. _____ knowledge / foolishness

4. _____ nobility / peasantry

5. _____ preservation / loss

Content Vocabulary Activity 18

The French Revolution and Napoleon, 1789–1815

DIRECTIONS: Select and write the term that best completes each sentence.

1. Before the revolution, French society was divided into three _____ (estates/émigrés).

2. Members of the First and Second Estates were exempt from the _____ (tithe/*taille*), a tax on nonprivileged subjects and lands that tended to weigh most heavily on the peasants.

3. French peasants fiercely resented having to pay _____ (duties, estates) for the use of village facilities such as the flour mill or the wine press.

4. The _____ (bourgeoisie/émigrés), or French middle class, supported the revolution.

5. The Third Estate in France came together for a meeting to discuss their government reforms. Finding their assigned meeting hall locked, they moved to a nearby venue. It was here that the _____ (Tennis Court Oath/unicameral legislature), an agreement that they would remain assembled until a constitution had been written, was made.

6. The Constitution of 1791 set up a limited _____ (dictatorship/monarchy) where there was still a king, but a Legislative Assembly would make the laws.

7. During the French Revolution, many radical members of the Paris Commune wore long trousers instead of knee-length breeches and called themselves _____ (*sans-culottes*/reactionaries).

8. The 1793 execution of King Louis XVI pushed the French Revolution into a new stage called _____ (radicalism/liberalism), the political orientation of those who favor revolutionary change in government and society.

9. In order to meet both the domestic and foreign crisis, the National Convention in 1793 gave broad powers to a special committee known as the _____ (plebiscites/Committee of Public Safety), dominated at first by Georges Danton, then by Maximilien Robespierre.

10. The popular general Napoleon Bonaparte seized control of France in a _____ (bourgeoisie/coup d'état).

11. In 1799 Napoleon held absolute power in a new government called the _____ (consulate/unicameral legislature).

12. In other European countries, strong feelings of _____ (nationalism/liberalism), or the cultural identity of a people based on common language, religion, and national symbols, helped to stir revolts against Napoleon.

Academic Vocabulary Activity 18

The French Revolution and Napoleon

Key Words

Academic Words	Words with Multiple Meanings	Content Vocabulary
administrative	order	factions
arbitrary		nationalism
benefit		
consume		
demonstration		
domestic		
exclusion		
expand		
finances		

A. Word Family Activity

Word Chart

> Remember: A *noun* is a word that names a person, place, thing, or idea. Examples include *king, tax, revolution,* and *assumption.* A *verb* is a word that is used to describe an action, experience, or state of being. Examples include *revolt, restore,* and *possess.* An *adjective* is a word that describes a noun. Examples include *active, crucial,* and *reliable.*

DIRECTIONS: Fill in the chart below by providing the missing word forms. Follow the example given.

Noun	Verb	Adjective
arbitration	arbitrate	arbitrary
		administrative
	benefit	
		demonstrative
		exclusive
		expansive

CHAPTER 18

(continued)

Academic Vocabulary Activity 18

B. Word Meaning Activity

Vocabulary in Context

DIRECTIONS: Knowing the words below will help you to understand the reading passages in Chapter 3. Using the context clues, circle the best definition for each underlined word:

1. The Declaration of the Rights of Man and the Citizen was <u>beneficial</u> to the French people.
   a. unimportant   **b.** harmful   **c.** helpful

2. One of the underlying causes of the French Revolution was the poor <u>financial</u> climate brought about by severe food shortages and unemployment.
   a. economic   **b.** noble   **c.** loyal

3. In the eighteenth century, people's wages did not increase as fast as the prices for goods, so many <u>consumers</u> were unable to purchase what they wanted.
   a. buyers of goods   **b.** sellers of goods   **c.** producers of goods

4. In the spring of 1792, defeats in war, coupled with economic shortages at home, led to new political <u>demonstrations</u> by people who organized to fight against the monarchy.
   a. religions   **b.** protests   **c.** families

5. Marie Antoinette's extravagance seemed ignorant, irresponsible, and <u>arbitrary</u>; the people felt that she had no understanding of or compassion for their misery and hunger.
   a. without money   **b.** without help   **c.** without thought

6. The <u>expansion</u> of the French Republic was weakened by King Louis XVI, who did not wish to see it succeed and prosper.
   a. growth   **b.** failure   **c.** limitation

7. After the Revolution, all of the organizational and <u>administrative</u> powers of the Catholic Church were controlled by the French government.
   a. executive   **b.** religious   **c.** educational

8. Although they had agreed to abolish the monarchy and form the French Republic, members of the convention soon split into <u>factions</u> over the fate of the king.
   a. easy compromises   **b.** loud laughter   **c.** conflicting groups

9. The new French army was the creation of a people's government, and its existence fueled strong feelings of pride that developed into modern <u>nationalism</u>.
   a. patriotism   **b.** extravagance   **c.** technology

✎ Skills Reinforcement Activity 18

Interpreting Graphs

Graphs can show a great deal of information in a single, easy-to-read format. To interpret a graph, follow these steps:

First, read the title. Then read the captions and text. Finally, determine the relationships among all sections of the graph.

DIRECTIONS: The graph below illustrates an important aspect of the situation in France just prior to the revolution. Read the graph. Then answer the questions that follow on a separate sheet of paper.

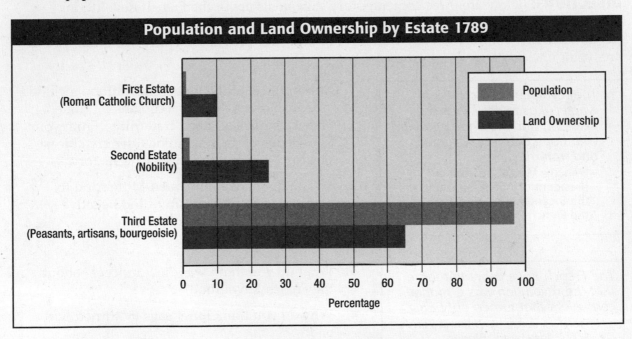

Population and Land Ownership by Estate 1789

First Estate (Roman Catholic Church)

Second Estate (Nobility)

Third Estate (Peasants, artisans, bourgeoisie)

Population

Land Ownership

Percentage

1. What does the horizontal axis of the graph represent?

2. **a.** What percentage of the French population comprised the First Estate?
   b. What percentage of land did they own?

3. **a.** What percentage of the French population comprised the Second Estate?
   b. What percentage of land did they own?

4. **a.** Determine the percentage of the French population that comprised the Third Estate. Write the value on the graph.
   b. Determine the percentage of land owned by the Third Estate. Write the value on the graph.

5. Why was land a good measure of wealth at this time?

6. Which estate had the greatest land ownership in proportion to its population?

7. **a.** How was the relationship between population and land ownership fundamentally different in the Third Estate?
   b. How might this fact have helped lead to the revolution?

Critical Thinking Skills Activity 18 | Analyzing Information

To the French people today, the Revolution of 1789 remains a lively topic of discussion and debate. No one disputes that it was a watershed in French—and human—history. In fact, historians generally agree that 1789 marks the beginning of the modern era. Yet the true meaning and legacy of the French Revolution continue to be debated. To sort through the many opinions about the French Revolution, or any historical event, you need to analyze information. Analyzing information means studying it carefully in order to learn as much as possible about what is being presented.

DIRECTIONS: Below are three contemporary statements about the French Revolution. Answer the questions beside each statement to help you analyze it. Use a separate sheet of paper. Then answer the final two questions in the space provided, which will guide you in analyzing the quotations as a group.

> *The revolution is a complex whole, like life itself, with the inspiring and the unacceptable, with hope and fear, violence and fraternity.*
> —François Mitterrand, former president of France, speaking at the Bicentennial Celebration of the French Revolution

1. Mitterrand said the French Revolution included "the inspiring," "the unacceptable," "hope," "fear," "violence," and "fraternity." From your knowledge of the revolution, identify at least one historical fact that fits each category.

2. What might have motivated Mitterrand to emphasize both the positive and negative aspects of the revolution?

> *The French have come to realize that the revolution was a magnificent event that turned out badly.*
> —François Furet, historian at Paris's Ecole des Hautes Etudes

3. What do you think was "magnificent" about the French Revolution?

4. Why do you think Furet says it "turned out badly"?

> *One of my ancestors stormed the Bastille, and I feel both thrilled and proud to be French whenever I walk past the place where it once stood.*
> —Jacques Delmas, a lawyer from Reims

5. What is the source of Jacques Delmas's pride?

6. Do you think he would agree with Furet's statement? Why or why not?

7. Which of the three statements is the most positive about the revolution? The most negative? Explain your choices.

_____

8. Which one do you think best summarizes the revolution? Why?

_____

★ HISTORY AND GEOGRAPHY ACTIVITY 18

CHAPTER 18

A Doomed March to Russia

Napoleon gathered troops from all quarters of his European empire in his quest to conquer the Russian Empire. By June 1812, his Grand Army, numbering over 600,000 men, began to march east across the vast, level Russian plain. Yet six months later, these same troops were making a desperate escape from Russia—having lost more than 500,000 men. What caused this panicked retreat and massive loss of life?

Napoleon had underestimated the Russian troops and his most bitter rival, the fierce Russian winter. To resist Napoleon, the Russians used a new strategy. Instead of meeting the French in open battle, the Russian army retreated slowly, drawing the French army deeper and deeper into Russia.

In September, Napoleon's forces finally reached Moscow, which the Russians had evacuated. The day after the French entered

The Grand Army's Retreat

The strongest threw into the river those who were weaker, and . . . trampled underfoot all the sick whom they found in their way. . . . Others, hoping to save themselves by swimming, were frozen in the middle of the river, or perished by placing themselves on pieces of ice, which sunk to the bottom. Thousands and thousands . . . were lost.

—French officer's account

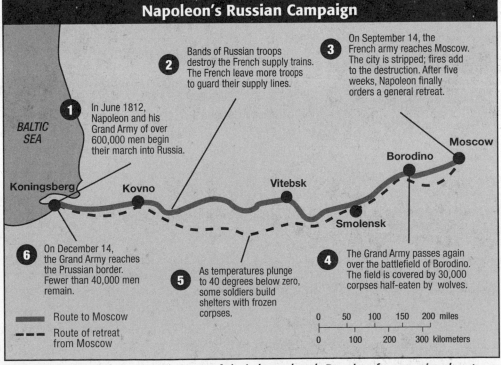

Napoleon's Russian Campaign

1 In June 1812, Napoleon and his Grand Army of over 600,000 men begin their march into Russia.

2 Bands of Russian troops destroy the French supply trains. The French leave more troops to guard their supply lines.

3 On September 14, the French army reaches Moscow. The city is stripped; fires add to the destruction. After five weeks, Napoleon finally orders a general retreat.

4 The Grand Army passes again over the battlefield of Borodino. The field is covered by 30,000 corpses half-eaten by wolves.

5 As temperatures plunge to 40 degrees below zero, some soldiers build shelters with frozen corpses.

6 On December 14, the Grand Army reaches the Prussian border. Fewer than 40,000 men remain.

BALTIC SEA

Koningsberg • Kovno • Vitebsk • Smolensk • Borodino • Moscow

Route to Moscow
Route of retreat from Moscow

0   50   100   150   200 miles
0   100   200   300 kilometers

With the help of the severe winter of their homeland, Russian forces wiped out 80 percent of the Grand Army by the time it returned to Poland.

HISTORY AND GEOGRAPHY ACTIVITY 18 (continued)

Moscow, a huge fire, probably started by Russian patriots, destroyed the city. With the Russian winter looming, Napoleon faced a difficult decision. He could either chase the Russian army farther to the east or turn back to the west.

Napoleon waited too long to make his decision to retreat. Bitter cold and driving snow plagued the Grand Army as it crossed the vast Russian plain once again. Temperatures plunged and Russians began attacking French forces without mercy.

Throughout history, people have moved from one location to another to fulfill specific needs. Sometimes the movement is economically motivated, such as the search for better jobs. Napoleon's march on Russia had another motive—to conquer the Russian Empire.

Geographic barriers, such as the Russian winter that stood in the way of Napoleon's plans, have prevented people from moving from one location to another. Mountains, rivers, and deserts are other physical factors that have hindered movement.

Today, technological advances in communication and transportation allow people to overcome many of these physical barriers. Yet other barriers exist. Repressive governments often deny their citizens the freedom to move to other countries. In addition, immigration laws and regulations keep people around the world from freely moving to other nations.

APPLYING GEOGRAPHY TO HISTORY

DIRECTIONS: Answer the questions below in the space provided.

1. What are different kinds of barriers to movement?

_____

2. How many troops did Napoleon lose between June and December 1812?

_____

3. How has the nature of barriers to movement changed?

_____

Critical Thinking

4. **Analyzing Information** How might geographical barriers to movement hinder a nation's development? How might they help it?

_____

Activity

5. Research the settlement of the area in which you live. What factors encouraged settlement? What factors prohibited settlement? What affects the movement of people in and out of your area today?

Mapping History Activity 18

CHAPTER 18

The French Revolution

Napoleon so dominated Europe that the years 1800 to 1815 are often called "the Napoleonic Era." At the height of his power, Napoleon controlled virtually the entire continent.

DIRECTIONS: The map below illustrates the remarkable extent of Napoleon's influence. Use the map to answer the questions and complete the activity that follow. Use a separate sheet of paper.

Europe at Height of Napoleon's Power, 1812

1. a. When was Napoleon's power at its height?

b. What nations did his empire comprise?

c. What nations did he make his allies?

2. Napoleon's major battles are listed in the chart at right.

a. Add a symbol for battle to the map key.

b. Using the symbol, mark on the map the location of each battle. Write the date of each battle next to its symbol.

Battle	Date	Approximate Location
Marengo	1800	300 miles northwest of Rome
Trafalgar	1805	off the coast of Cape Trafalgar
Austerlitz	1805	250 miles southwest of Warsaw
Auerstedt	1806	just southwest of Leipzig
Jena	1806	just southeast of Auerstedt
Friedland	1807	extreme northern Poland, about 100 miles from the Baltic Sea
Peninsular War	1808–1814	throughout Spain
Wagram	1809	just north of Vienna
Aspern	1809	just northeast of Vienna
Borodino	1812	about 100 miles west of Moscow
Lützen	1813	about 100 miles west of Leipzig
Leipzig	1813	at Leipzig
Ligny	1815	about 100 miles southeast of Waterloo
Waterloo	1815	at Waterloo

Historical Significance Activity 18

Three Ways Napoleon Changed the World

Napoleon was one of the most influential people in all of history. The passages below discuss three ways that Napoleon changed the world.

1. The Napoleonic Code

"One of Napoleon's reforms . . . was destined to have an impact far beyond the borders of France. That was the creation of the French civil code, the [Napoleonic Code]. In many ways the code embodied the ideals of the French Revolution. For example, under the code there were no privileges of birth, and all men were equal under the law. At the same time, the code was suffi-ciently close to the older French laws and customs to be acceptable to the French public and the legal profession. On the whole, the code was moderate, well organized, and written with com-mendable brevity and outstanding lucidity. As a result, the code has not only endured in France . . . but has been adopted, with local modifications, in many other countries."

2. The Invasion of Spain

"Napoleon also had a large, though indirect, effect on the history of Latin America. His invasion of Spain so weakened the Spanish government that for a period of several years it lost effective control of its colonies in Latin America. It was during this period of *de facto* autonomy that the Latin American independence movements commenced."

3. The Louisiana Purchase

"Of all Napoleon's actions . . . the one that has perhaps had the most enduring and significant consequences was one that was almost irrelevant to his main plans. In 1803 Napoleon sold a vast tract of land to the United States. He realized that the French possessions in North America might be difficult to protect from British conquest, and besides he was short of cash. The Louisiana Purchase, perhaps the largest peaceful transfer of land in all of history, trans-formed the United States into a nation of near-continental size. It is difficult to say what the United States would have been like without the Louisiana Purchase; cer-tainly it would have been a vastly differ-ent country than it is today. Indeed, it is doubtful whether the United States would have become a great power with-out the Louisiana Purchase.

"Napoleon, of course, was not solely responsible for the Louisiana Purchase. The American government clearly played a role as well. But the French offer was such a bargain that it seems likely that any American government would have accepted it, while the deci-sion of the French government to sell the Louisiana territory came about through the arbitrary judgment of a sin-gle individual, Napoleon Bonaparte."

—From *The 100: A Ranking of the Most Influential Persons in History* by Michael H. Hart

DIRECTIONS: Answer the following questions on a separate sheet of paper.

1. Which change has affected the most people? Explain your answer.

2. Which change was the most significant one for your ancestors? Explain your answer.

3. Which change has had the most significant effect on your life? Explain your answer.

4. Which change do you think is the most significant overall? Why?

★ Cooperative Learning Activity **18**★  ★

Stages of Change in France

BACKGROUND

The French Revolution did not simply replace one type of government with another, or replace a monarchy with a democracy. The remarkable events of the late eighteenth- and early nineteenth-centuries in France from the fall of the Bastille to the reign of Napoleon took place in stages. Through your research, you will learn about the unusual twists and turns that the transformation took as the people of France struggled to define French government.

GROUP DIRECTIONS

1. Your group will prepare a two-column chart to show the various stages of the French Revolution and the rise of Napoleon to become first consul. In the left-hand column, list the stages of the events that took place, and in the right-hand column, describe the stage, including a list of important associated leaders and documents.

2. Use Chapter 18 in your textbook and library or Internet resources to discover as much as possible about the stages of political changes.

3. Use what you learn to create a poster-sized two-column chart. You may include appropriate drawings or illustrations to add interest to the chart.

4. Think about the following events and any others you find in your research to include in your chart. Where would each fit in the stages of the revolution and its aftermath?

the three estates	Committee of Public Safety
National Assembly	Reign of Terror
Reign of Louis XVI	Republic of Virtue
Constitution of 1791	the Directory
National Convention	the Consulate

ORGANIZING THE GROUP

1. **Decision Making** Form a group with three other students. Review the information from your textbook and decide what the group thinks are the major stages. Consider the old regime and the meeting of the Estates-General as the first two stages. Assign research on each stage to individuals. Decide on and assign tasks that will be needed to complete the chart.

2. **Individual Work** Do research to find out as much as possible about your assigned stages and the related events and significant people. Make notes as you gather your information, including sources.

3. **Group Work** Share your information with the group. Give one another suggestions for improving descriptions, grammar, and spelling. Revise your information into final form. Make sure that the beginning and ending times or events of your stages are as clear as possible or determine where stages might overlap.

Cooperative Learning Activity 18 (continued)

4. **Additional Group Work** Together, organize your group's information into a chart as described previously.

5. **Group Sharing** Display your chart on the classroom wall. As a group, present your chart to the class. All group members should point to and describe the information they provided to their group's chart.

GROUP PROCESS QUESTIONS

- What is the most important thing you learned about the events of the French Revolution and its aftermath?
- What part of the project did you enjoy most?
- What problems did you have?
- How did you solve the problems?
- How was a two-column chart useful and appropriate for conveying your information?

1. Was the goal of the assignment clear at all times? If not, why?

_____

_____

_____

_____

2. Did you have problems working well together? If so, how did you solve them?

_____

_____

_____

_____

3. Were you satisfied with your work on this project? Why or why not?

_____

_____

_____

_____

Unrest in Blaat

This activity will help students understand how conflicts can lead to revolution or civil unrest.

Learning Objective To develop an understanding of conflicts within a society that can lead to revolution or civil war.

Activity In groups, students will assume the roles of people in the imaginary country of Blaat. The roles are the king, the head of the official state religion, a rival preacher, a member of Parliament, and two citizens.

Teacher Preparation Make six copies of the handout material on the next page.

Activity Guidelines

1. Introduce the activity by explaining its objective. Briefly review the concepts of conflict and revolution. Then give students the following background information:

   Blaat is a country of about 10 million people. Its major industry is growing and exporting blueberries. Most of its citizens depend on the blueberry industry. King Borax of Blaat, who inherited the throne from his father, is an absolute monarch who believes he was given his power by God. One of his chief allies is Archbishop Ladlepate, head of the church. Both the king and the archbishop believe that in order for a country to be unified, there should be only one official religion.

   The king is currently engaged in a very costly war with Bordovia and needs to raise money—an additional 100 million klaams. Although the king is an absolute monarch, there is a Parliament that meets at his request and authorizes new taxes and payments to the crown. Parliament often opposes the king's policies and, in the king's view, tries to interfere in government. Consequently, rather than call Parliament, King Borax instituted a tax on growers, pickers, and merchants of blueberries

   without the consent of Parliament. When citizens in the port city of Faavabin refused to pay the tax, King Borax closed the port and refused to allow any ships to come or go. Tons of blueberries lay rotting on the docks, and the people were outraged.

   When the opposition church leaders began preaching against these unfair measures and against the war, King Borax had them imprisoned. The archbishop's men searched every church in the land and expelled opposition church leaders.

   However, when the country of Frangland entered the war and invaded the northern border of Blaat, King Borax was forced to call a session of Parliament to ask for money.

2. Organize the class into six groups. Assign one of the roles listed on the handout to each group. Explain to the groups that their job is to prepare a position statement from the role they have been assigned addressing the king's need to raise money.

3. Allow groups 30 minutes to reach a conclusion. Have each group appoint one member to write the position statement based on the group's stance. Each group's position statement should both address the conviction of its assigned character as well as dismiss the concerns of the other citizens of Blaat.

4. Have a spokesperson from each group read the group's statement to the class.

5. Have students return to their groups to briefly consider and discuss the other groups' statements. Ask the groups to decide whether they should change their own stances based on the other groups' arguments and why.

CHAPTER 18

HISTORY SIMULATION ACTIVITY 18

HANDOUT MATERIAL

Unrest in Blaat—Roles

King Borax
You are God's lieutenant on Earth. Like your father before you, you have absolute power given to you by God to pass any law you wish, and the people owe you unquestioning allegiance.

Archbishop Ladlepate
You have been chosen by God to lead the one true church. As such, you are the second most powerful person in Blaat. You owe your allegiance to King Borax. If he falls, so will you.

Lady Bolingreen
Your family has owned the great Bolingreen blueberry plantation for generations, since the days of good Queen Gertrude. Your family has always been loyal to the monarch, as have most of the great lords, but this king offends your honor. However, he is your king, and perhaps he is no worse than those fanatic opposition preachers who might replace him.

Master Scarford
You are a blueberry merchant of means, respected by your fellows, and a member of Parliament. Your family has come a long way; just three generations ago, you were blueberry pickers on the Bolingreen plantation. But this king could drive you to bankruptcy with his taxes.

Preacher Baker
You are a preacher in the small opposition church in your county and deeply committed to your religion. The archbishop and his men have tried to silence your preaching, even imprisoning you once, but you are determined to purify the Church of Blaat and establish the kingdom of God on Earth.

Tamara Chattworth
You are a blueberry picker on the plantation of Lady Bolingreen, who is completely loyal to the king. You are a member of the opposition church. You have seven children to care for, and already the burden of taxes leaves you barely able to feed them.

Time Line Activity 18

The French Revolution and Napoleon

DIRECTIONS: In France, the years from 1789 to 1815 were turbulent. You can trace the changes that took place during this time in French history on a time line. Read the time line below. Then answer the questions that follow, adding information to the time line as directed.

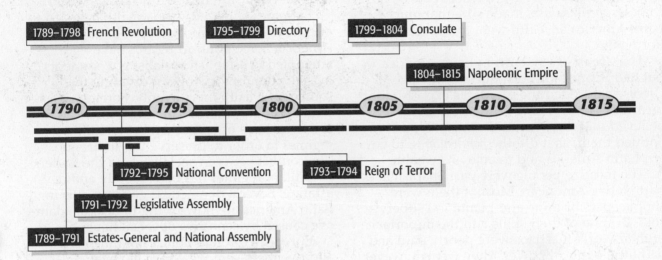

1. **A.** What event marked the beginning of the French Revolution? Add this point to the time line.

   _____

   B. How long did the French Revolution last? _____

2. **A.** What event marked the beginning of Napoleon's rule? Add this point to the time line.

   _____

   B. What event marked the end of Napoleon's rule? Add this point to the time line.

   _____

3. Napoleon ruled from 1799 to 1815. The Consulate accounts for the years 1799 to 1804. The remaining years are called the Napoleonic Empire. What 1804 event caused the change? Write your answer below. Then mark this point on your time line.

   _____

   _____

4. A French historian once said that the French Revolution "turned out badly." How does your time line illustrate this concept?

   _____

   _____

Legacy of Colonialism: Class and Tribal Conflict

THEN Like society in pre-Revolutionary France, Latin American society was rigidly stratified. Spanish and Portuguese colonists helped to set this class system in place.

In colonial times, *peninsulares*—people born on the Iberian Peninsula where Spain and Portugal are located—were at the top of the social hierarchy. As governors of the colonies, *peninsulares* made sure that much of Latin America's wealth went to Spain and Portugal.

The Creoles were born in Latin America but had Spanish or Portuguese parents. Creoles controlled the profitable export-import businesses and mining industries. They believed that their "pure European blood" entitled them, as it did the *peninsulares,* to govern Latin America and to enjoy its wealth.

The mestizo people were part Spanish and part Native American. Most of them were shopkeepers or mine and plantation supervisors. In spite of their skills and the importance of their work, mestizos were poorly paid and had little political power. They were, however, better off than the Native Americans and blacks. Many blacks were enslaved, while the Native Americans lived in abject poverty.

Latin Americans won their independence from Spain and Portugal when the focus of these countries shifted to thwarting Napoleon's attempt to conquer Europe. Independence somewhat improved social conditions. Most Latin American countries abolished slavery. Blacks and Native Americans who had fought in the revolution were often rewarded with land and political offices. Nonetheless, class structure remained a dominant characteristic of Latin American society.

NOW Tradition and neocolonialism have kept Latin America's divisive class structure alive. Neocolonialism developed when foreign corporations began to invest in Latin American plantations and mines. Like the countries of Europe that originally controlled the Latin American colonies, neocolonial investors have drained Latin America of much of its wealth.

Extremes of poverty and wealth have led to political instability and violence in Latin America. Some political figures have attempted to establish socialist governments in their countries in hope of dividing the sources of wealth more evenly. Foreign states with economic interests in Latin American countries have often backed brutal military regimes in order to preserve the status quo. The conflict between socialists and the leaders of military regimes has been bloody and devastating. Several democratic governments in Latin America are now trying to heal the damage caused by centuries of social injustice.

European colonial policies in nineteenth- and twentieth-century Africa have left a legacy of violence on that continent as well. Colonial administrators created countries by imposing artificial boundaries. The countries created by the administrators usually contained several tribal groups, often traditionally hostile to one another. Administrators ignored such realities as they drew the borders of new African nations.

Today, in the twenty-first century, warring tribes within one country often compete for political or military control or for resources such as diamond mines. Civil wars and conflicts within countries such as Nigeria, Rwanda, and Sudan have become commonplace, due in large part to the existence of old tribal conflicts.

CRITICAL THINKING

Directions: Answer the following questions on a separate sheet of paper.

1. **Drawing conclusions:** What was one reason that the *peninsulares* and the Creoles believed that they were entitled to rule and exploit Latin America?

2. **Making inferences:** How does neocolonialism contribute to the class hierarchy in Latin America?

3. **Synthesizing information:** How did race divide Latin American society? Do research in the library and on the Internet to learn about how Latin American racial attitudes originated in Spain with the Spanish Inquisition. Write a brief report of your findings.

People in World History Activity 18 — Profile 1

Marie Antoinette (1755–1793)

Courage! I have shown it for years; think you I shall lose it at the moment when my sufferings are to end?

Marie Antoinette on the way to the guillotine, 1793

From childhood, Marie had been told that she would someday be a queen. At the age of 15, she was married to the French *dauphin*, or crown prince. In only four years, he became King Louis XVI, and Marie Antoinette—at the age when people today graduate from high school—became the queen of France.

Like many royal marriages of the day, the one between Marie and Louis was based not on love, but on politics. The marriage was arranged to strengthen France's ties to Marie's native Austria. Unhappy in her marriage, Marie sought comfort in elaborate balls at Versailles, horse races, expensive parties, and lavish theater productions. In her extravagance, Marie became an important symbol of royal excess and indifference. As such, her influence on the French Revolution was incalculable.

Marie's reputation was under attack for much of her reign, although not always justifiably. The quotation most commonly associated with Marie is "Let them eat cake." This was supposedly her unthinking reply to a courtier's remark that the peasants were rioting outside her palace because they had no bread. She never said these words, but the fact that people were willing to believe otherwise says much about the way the public perceived her. Many French citizens viewed Marie as simply frivolous. Others thought she was dangerous, an untrustworthy foreigner who would plot against France. Indeed, Marie tried constantly to influence French foreign policy to benefit her native Austria. When France went to war with Austria in 1792, Marie, who hoped for the defeat of the French revolutionaries, passed information to the enemy. Her treason gave the Republicans their reason to try and convict the queen. She was guillotined on October 16, 1793.

The last years of Marie's life were full of heartache. She spent four years as a virtual prisoner of the revolutionaries. In her final months, her husband was executed and her surviving son was taken from her. Surprisingly, the superficial queen demonstrated remarkable character during these tragedies. Accounts of the time portray her as courageous, steadfast, and above all else, dignified as she approached the guillotine. Her noble death, in such contrast to her frivolous life, is one reason why Marie Antoinette has intrigued people for generations.

REVIEWING THE PROFILE

DIRECTIONS: Answer the following questions on a separate sheet of paper.

1. How did Marie Antoinette become queen of France?

2. Why was she so unpopular with the French people?

3. **CRITICAL THINKING** Drawing Conclusions. Does it surprise you that Marie Antoinette, famous for her frivolity, demonstrated such character toward the end of her life? Explain.

CHAPTER 18

People in World History Activity 18   Profile 2

Maximilien François Marie Isidore de Robespierre (1758–1794)

Any law which violates the inalienable rights of man is essentially unjust and tyrannical; it is not a law at all.

Maximilien Robespierre, (1793)

A bloody tyrant? An impractical dreamer? A valiant revolutionary? Even historians who do not admire Robespierre admit that he was the founder of French democracy and the French Revolution's greatest leader.

Maximilien Robespierre was born in Arras, France and raised by his maternal grandparents. When he was 11 years old, Robespierre won a scholarship to a university in Paris. He proved to be a brilliant student, especially in law and Greek and Roman literature. In 1781 Robespierre returned to Arras to set up a law office.

A talented lawyer, Robespierre was soon appointed a judge. The combined incomes from his two jobs allowed him to live comfortably in the house he had set up with his sister Charlotte. He was fast becoming well-known for representing poor people and helping those in need. He was most critical of royal absolutism and arbitrary justice.

In 1788 Robespierre wrote his first political paper, which voiced his opposition to the *ancien régime*, the royal rulers. Robespierre's political career began in 1789, when he was elected to represent Arras when the Estates-

General met at Versailles in May.

Robespierre made the most of his opportunity to help the common people. He spoke at debates and won a reputation as a strong supporter of democracy. In September 1792, he was elected to the National Convention and demanded that Louis XVI be executed as a traitor. The Convention agreed, and on January 21, 1793, the king was beheaded. By early June, Robespierre controlled the Convention.

For a year, Robespierre was one of the Jacobin leaders who halted inflation, instituted the Reign of Terror to eliminate the republic's enemies, and prepared for war. In June 1794, the Convention elected Robespierre their president.

After this quick rise to power, Robespierre's fall was even more sudden. His support began to crumble as people feared they would become the next victims of the Terror. On July 28, just a little over a month after being elected president of the Convention, Robespierre was arrested. He was guillotined the same day before a cheering mob.

REVIEWING THE PROFILE

DIRECTIONS: Answer the following questions on a separate sheet of paper.

1. When did Robespierre enter politics?

2. What did Robespierre do while he was a Jacobin leader?

3. CRITICAL THINKING Recognizing Ideologies. Why did Robespierre help lead the revolution against the king?

4. CRITICAL THINKING Drawing Conclusions. Why do you think Robespierre was able to rise so quickly in the rebel ranks?

PRIMARY SOURCE READING 18

Declaration of the Rights of Man and of the Citizen

Although the French Revolution later turned to violence and terror, the first bold public statement of the revolutionary National Assembly echoes the high ideals of John Locke, the Enlightenment, and the American Declaration of Independence. The Declaration of the Rights of Man and of the Citizen was issued in August 1789.

Guided Reading *In this selection, read to learn what problems and rights the Declaration addresses.*

The representatives of the French people, constituted in National Assembly, considering that ignorance, forgetfulness, or contempt of the rights of man are the sole causes of public misfortunes and the corruption of governments, have resolved to set forth in a solemn declaration the natural, inalienable, and sacred rights of man so that this declaration, being constantly before all members of the social body, may unceasingly recall to them their rights and their duties; so that the acts of the legislative power and those of the executive power may always be compared with the true aim of political organization and thus may be more respected; and so that the demands of the citizens, founded henceforth upon simple and incontestable principles, may always be aimed at maintaining the constitution and the happiness of all.

In consequence, the National Assembly recognizes and declares, in the presence and under the auspices of the Supreme Being, the following rights of man and citizen.

1. Men are born and remain free and equal in rights. Social distinctions can be based only upon the common good.

2. The aim of every political association is the preservation of the natural and imprescriptible rights of man. These rights are liberty, property, security, and resistance to oppression.

3. The source of all sovereignty is essentially in the nation [that is, the people]; no body, no individual can exercise authority that does not emanate from it expressly.

4. Liberty consists in the power to do anything that does not injure others; accordingly, the exercise of the natural rights of each man

has no limits except those that assure to the other members of society the enjoyment of these same rights. These limits can be determined only by law.

5. The law can forbid only such actions as are injurious to society. Nothing can be forbidden that is not forbidden by the law, and no one can be constrained to do that which it does not decree.

6. Law is the expression of the general will. All citizens have the right to take part personally, or by their representatives, in its enactment. It must be the same for all, whether it protects or punishes. All citizens being equal in its eyes, are equally eligible to all public dignities, places, and employments, according to their capacities, and without other distinction than that of their merits and their talents.

7. No man can be accused, arrested, or detained, except in the cases determined by the law and according to the forms which it has prescribed. Those who call for, expedite, execute, or cause to be executed arbitrary orders should be punished; but every citizen summoned or seized by virtue of the law ought to obey instantly; he makes himself culpable by resistance.

8. The law ought to establish only punishments that are strictly and obviously necessary, and no one should be punished except by virtue of a law established and promulgated prior to the offence and legally applied.

9. Every man being presumed innocent until he has been declared guilty, if it is judged indispensable to arrest him, all severity that

CHAPTER 18

may not be necessary to secure his person ought to be severely suppressed by law.

10. No one should be disturbed on account of his opinions, even religious, provided their manifestation does not trouble the public order as established by law.

11. The free communication of thoughts and opinions is one of the most precious of the rights of man; every citizen can then speak, write, and print freely, save for the responsibility for the abuse of this liberty in the cases determined by law.

12. The guarantee of the rights of man and citizen necessitates a public force [that is, law-enforcement officers]; this force is then instituted for the advantage of all and not for the particular use of those to whom it is entrusted.

13. For the maintenance of the public force and for the expenses of administration a general tax is indispensable; it should be equally apportioned among all the citizens according to their means.

14. All citizens have the right to ascertain, by themselves or through their representatives, the necessary amount of public taxation, to consent to it freely, to follow the use of it, and to determine the quota, the assessment, the collection, and the duration of it.

15. Society has the right to call for an account by every public agent of his administration.

16. Any society in which the guarantee of the rights is not assured, or the separation of powers not determined, has no constitution.

17. Property being a sacred and inviolable right, no one can be deprived of it, unless a legally established public necessity evidently requires it, under the condition of a just and prior indemnity.

INTERPRETING THE READING

Directions *Use information from the reading to answer the following questions. If necessary, use a separate sheet of paper.*

1. What does the Declaration blame for the social problems and government corruption in France?

2. According to the Declaration, what natural rights do people possess? How is this list different from that in the American Declaration of Independence?

3. If the Declaration had been put into effect, who would have been able to vote?

Critical Thinking

4. **Making Inferences** In what ways does the Declaration reflect France's specific problems and crises?

World Art and Music Activity 18

Jacques-Louis David

In the painting below, Jacques-Louis David [da • VEED] depicts one of the turning points in the history of Europe and of the world. Interestingly, the painting itself carries a historic importance all its own. Explore the painting's many details. Pay particular attention to its formal style and the faces of the individuals in the scene.

DIRECTIONS: Read the accompanying article about David. Then answer the questions in the space provided.

The Consecration of Emperor Napoleon I and the Coronation of the Empress Josephine (detail)

The painting you are looking at was one of Napoleon's favorites. When he first saw it, he exclaimed "How great! What relief! How true! This is not a painting; one can walk around in this picture; life is everywhere!"

It was not surprising that Napoleon, a ruler with a large ego, was thrilled by something that celebrated himself. Nevertheless, the painting *is* a remarkable piece. The actual canvas is huge—about 20 feet (6 meters) by 30 feet (9 meters). It was completed in 1807 after two years of painstaking work by the great French painter Jacques-Louis David.

Just as Napoleon dominated France politically and militarily, Jacques-Louis David dominated the country artistically. His influence was so great that he has been called "the virtual art dictator of France for a generation." Few other artists have ever had as much artistic influence during their own lifetimes.

Born in Paris in 1748, David demonstrated his talent at an early age. As a young man, he studied in

(continued)

World Art and Music Activity 18

Rome and became profoundly impressed with the art of that ancient civilization. David would soon become the leading proponent of neoclassicism in French art.

Neoclassicism was an artistic movement that celebrated the formal art of Greece and Rome. Neoclassical paintings are noted for their balance, detail, and realism. Sometimes they use subjects from ancient history in the context of modern events. David soon mastered and set the standard in neoclassical painting. His style and subjects became so well received by the French nobility that in 1785 he became the painter to the court of Louis XVI. Ironically, he would later vote for the king's death. David was an ardent republican and was elected to the Convention. He served as director of artistic affairs during the revolution and was associated with such revolutionary figures as Marat and Robespierre.

Even before the revolution, however, David met and was impressed by a young Napoleon Bonaparte. Napoleon epitomized many of the classical ideals that the painter so respected. "My friends," he said of Napoleon, "what a beautiful head he has! It is simple, great, beautiful, like a head from antiquity!" Upon becoming emperor, Napoleon made David "first painter." In that role, David painted pictures in a heroic, neoclassical style that celebrated Napoleon and his accomplishments.

The Consecration of Napoleon is one of these works. Many people are struck by the sheer number of individuals depicted. Each face is painted with an intensity and attention to detail that makes each one almost a portrait itself. Indeed, one art critic called this painting "the most extraordinary series of portraits painted in one picture." There are about 100 likenesses of actual people in the painting. Napoleon and Josephine, of course, take center stage. Pope Pius VII is seated to the right. The woman seated in the center left background is Napoleon's mother. In truth, not all of the people in the painting were actually at the event, and many who were, including David himself, are not pictured.

True to the neoclassical style, the painting is a formalized, heroic depiction. Its purpose is more to celebrate what happened than simply to record the event. The many individuals, although realistically pictured, are glorified. The painting is a fitting tribute to Napoleon, ruler of much of Europe, and to Jacques-Louis David, ruler of the art world.

Reviewing the Selection

1. Why was Jacques-Louis David called "the virtual art dictator of France for a generation"?

   _____

2. What are the characteristics of neoclassical painting?

   _____

   _____

Critical Thinking

3. **Analyzing Information** Reread the first paragraph of the article, which records Napoleon's reaction to the painting. On a separate sheet of paper, explain why you agree or disagree with Napoleon's appraisal of the work.

4. **Synthesizing Information** Jacques-Louis David created art that celebrated three very different governments: the monarchy, the republic, and the French Empire. Do you think David must have violated his principles in order to support all three regimes? Was he an opportunist, or was he following some higher artistic principle? On a separate sheet of paper, write a brief paragraph in which you justify or criticize David's support for these different regimes.

Reteaching Activity 18

The French Revolution and Napoleon

The increasingly bitter division of French society in the late 1700s was a fundamental cause of the French Revolution. Understanding these divisions, then, is essential to your understanding of this turning point in history.

DIRECTIONS: Answer the question below. Then complete the pyramid by placing the letter identifying each statement into the appropriate space below.

1. What were the estates? _____

_____

2. Description of estates:

A. comprised about .5 percent of the population	**G.** made up of peasants and the bourgeoisie
B. comprised about 1.5 percent of the population	**H.** most were very poor
C. comprised about 98 percent of the population	**I.** owned 10 percent of French land
D. held high posts in government and the military	**J.** owned 25 percent of French land
E. made up of higher and lower clergy	**K.** owned 65 percent of French land
F. made up of nobility	

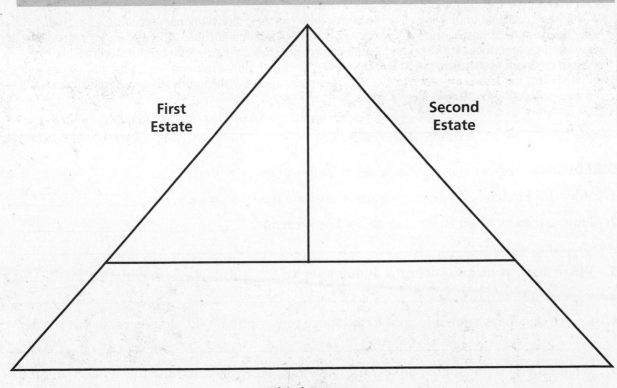

First Estate

Second Estate

Third Estate

★ Enrichment Activity 18 ★  ★

The *Levée en Masse*

CHAPTER 18

Four months after the French revolutionaries proclaimed the first day of the "Year 1 of Liberty," they faced fierce attacks from European monarchies that feared the spread of the revolution. Desperate, the leaders of the revolution made a decision that would change the face of warfare forever.

Almost all of the monarchies of Europe launched their armies against France to stamp out the sacrilegious revolutionaries, and when what was left of the old royal army, aided by volunteers, proved unable to stem the attacks, the National Convention decided on conscription: the *levée en masse*.

. . . the convention issued the call for a *levée en masse* in August [1793]. By New Year's Day, 1794, the French armies numbered about 777,000 men, and the wars of mass armies that ensued ravaged Europe for the next two decades.

Conscription was not an entirely new idea . . . but it had never really amounted to more than compulsory selection of an unfortunate minority, nor had it lasted long or been extended to an entire country. But the French Revolution, with its principles of liberty and equality, first stimulated and then exploited a fervent nationalism which made conscription acceptable. It also made French troops behave differently.

The "nation in arms" produced poorly trained soldiers . . . who had no time to master the intricate drill of close-order formations, but their enthusiasm and numbers made up for it: attacking in clouds of skirmishers and disorderly columns, they often simply overwhelmed their better-trained adversaries. . . . Battles rarely ended in draws any more—Carnot of the Committee of Public Safety instructed the French armies in 1794 "to act in mass formations and take the offensive. . . . Give battle on a large scale and pursue the enemy until he is utterly destroyed."

The basic principle underlying all this was that whereas the prerevolutionary regular soldiers had been scarce and expensive, the lives of conscripts were plentiful and cheap. The disdain for casualties grew even greater once Napoleon had seized control of France in 1799. "You cannot stop me," he boasted to Count Metternich, the Austrian diplomat. "I spend thirty thousand men a month." It was not an idle boast: the losses of France in 1793–1814 amounted to 1.7 million dead—almost all soldiers—out of a population of 29 million.

—From *War* by Gwynne Dyer, copyright © 1985 by Media Resources.

DIRECTIONS: Answer the questions below in the space provided.

1. Why did French revolutionary leaders institute the *levée en masse*? _____

2. How did the *levée en masse* change the French armies? _____
_____

3. What "basic principle" does the author refer to? _____
_____

4. France's enemies were reluctant to introduce conscription. Why do you think this was so?
_____

5. What do you think about Napoleon's statement? How do you think this reflects on him?
_____

GLENCOE
WORLD HISTORY

Chapter 18
Section Resources

GUIDED READING ACTIVITY 18-1   274

GUIDED READING ACTIVITY 18-2   275

GUIDED READING ACTIVITY 18-3   276

SECTIONS

Guided Reading Activity 18-1

The French Revolution Begins

DIRECTIONS: Answer the following questions as you read Section 1.

1. What two far-reaching international events took place in 1789?

   _____

   _____

2. How did the French Revolution compare to the American Revolution?

   _____

3. Describe the Three Estates of French society before the revolution.

   _____

   _____

4. Give a definition of the term *bourgeoisie*.

   _____

   _____

5. State the immediate cause of the French Revolution.

   _____

6. How did most members of the Third Estate want to fix France's financial problems?

   _____

   _____

7. What dramatic event took place on July 14, 1789, which saved the Third Estate from the King's forces?

   _____

   _____

8. What did the National Assembly do in response to peasant revolts and fear of foreign troops?

   _____

9. What name did the National Assembly give to its charter of basic liberties?

   _____

10. Why did Olympia de Gouges write a Declaration of the Rights of Woman and the Female Citizen?

    _____

11. The National Assembly took what action to control the Catholic Church?

    _____

Copyright © Glencoe/McGraw-Hill, a division of The McGraw-Hill Companies, Inc.

Guided Reading Activity 18-2

Radical Revolution and Reaction

DIRECTIONS: As you are reading the section, decide if a statement is true or false. Write **T** if the statement is true or **F** if the statement is false. For all false statements, write a corrected statement.

_____ **1.** The National Convention's first major step on September 21, 1792, was to reestablish the authority of King Louis XVI.

_____

_____

_____ **2.** The political faction known as the Mountain convinced the National Convention to pass a decree condemning Louis XVI to death.

_____

_____ **3.** During the Reign of Terror, revolutionary courts were established to settle property disputes between the church and state.

_____

_____

_____ **4.** In the new French Republic, the titles "citizen" and "citizeness" replaced "mister" and "madame."

_____

_____ **5.** In the dechristianization of France, the National Convention held a public ceremony dedicated to the worship of the monarchy.

_____

_____ **6.** Another change in French society was to no longer number years from the birth of Christ, but instead to number them from the birth of Muhammad.

_____

_____ **7.** After the death of Robespierre, revolutionary fervor began to cool.

_____

_____ **8.** In 1799 a coup d'etat led by Napoleon Bonaparte, toppled the Directory and Napoleon seized power.

_____

SECTION 18-2

Guided Reading Activity 18-3

The Age of Napoleon

DIRECTIONS: Fill in the blanks below as you read Section 3.

Napoleon Bonaparte dominated **(1)** _____ and
(2) _____ history from 1799 to 1815. He was born in 1769 on the
island of **(3)** _____ in the Mediterranean Sea. His education in French
military schools led to his commission in 1785 as a **(4)** _____ in the
French army. At the age of only 24, Napoleon was made a brigadier general by the
(5) _____. In 1796 he was made commander of the French armies in
(6) _____, where he won a series of victories.

Although theoretically the new government of 1799 was a republic, Napoleon
held **(7)** _____ power. In 1802 Napoleon was made
(8) _____ for life, and two years later he had himself crowned
(9) _____ Napoleon I.

Napoleon was a believer in reason who regarded religion to be at most a
(10) _____. Since most of the French were **(11)** _____,
Napoleon felt it was a good policy to mend relations with the
(12) _____. In an agreement made with the Pope,
(13) _____ was recognized as the religion of a majority of the French
people. Napoleon's most famous domestic achievement was to
(14) _____ the laws. The most important of the codes was the
(15) _____, or Napoleonic Code. This code preserved many of the
(16) _____ of the revolution. However, Napoleon also destroyed
some revolutionary ideals through **(17)** _____. He shut down 60 of 73
French **(18)** _____.

Two major reasons help to explain the rapid decline of Napoleon's Grand
Empire: the **(19)** _____ of Great Britain and the force of
(20) _____. The beginning of Napoleon's downfall came in 1812 with
his disastrous invasion of **(21)** _____.

Answer Key

CHARTING AND GRAPHING ACTIVITY 3

Conflict: The Spanish Armada—a fleet of warships—attacked the British fleet. **Resolution:** The larger, better-equipped British navy defeated the smaller Spanish ships.

Conflict: More than 100,000 people were accused of witchcraft. **Resolution:** By 1650 the hysteria over witchcraft began to fade. Governments grew tired of the disrupting effects of the witchcraft trials and began to discourage them.

Conflict: The Thirty Years' War began as a conflict between the Catholic forces led by the Hapsburg Holy Roman emperors and Protestants led by wealthy supporters of Calvin. The conflict developed into a political struggle and widened to include all major European powers except England. **Resolution:** The war ended with the signing of the Peace of Westphalia. This treaty also ended the Holy Roman Empire's political power.

ECONOMICS AND HISTORY ACTIVITY 3

1. Mercantilism is an economic theory that connects a country's wealth to its supply of gold and silver.

2. Raw materials are the different products that are used to make finished products. Finished products are ready for consumption by the public.

3. Adam Smith was an economist who wrote *The Wealth of Nations.* His book formed the basis of our capitalist economy.

4. Mercantilism is an economic system in which the government answers the three economic questions; capitalism is an economic system in which the consumer and business owners answer the three economic questions.

5. A positive trade balance would mean that a country was earning more than it was spending on products. This is a way of creating savings, or increasing the supply of gold and silver.

6. Answers may vary. Sample response: Labor may have value because it is willing to do a job few people want (such as a sanitation worker). Labor may have value because it requires special training (such as an electrician). It may have value because it provides something that society holds in high esteem (such as a movie star).

7. Answers may vary. Sample response: land—the property that my house is built on; labor—my teacher works in the school teaching students like me; capital—my mother uses her computer to do her job; entrepreneurial ability—the owner of the new electronics store on Main Street

WORLD LITERATURE READING 3

1. They predict that Macbeth will become Thane of Cawdor and king.

2. He is a brave and valiant warrior.

3. He names Macbeth Thane of Cawdor.

4. Banquo wonders if the witches aren't tempting them only to bring great misfortune. Macbeth is revealed as ambitious; Banquo, as cautious and thoughtful.

READING SKILLS ACTIVITY 12

Practicing the Skill
Answers will vary. Students should point out that the philosopher thinks that individuals have a free will and should be able to decide how to live their own lives apart from outside influences.

Applying the Skill
Answers will vary. Students should point out that de Pizan was standing up for women's intelligence and ability to be well educated.

HISTORICAL ANALYSIS SKILLS ACTIVITY 12

Practicing the Skill
The merchant has no respect or sympathy for the poorest citizens.

Answer Key

He could have been trying to convince people that charity given to the poor was wasted and that time spent trying to solve the problems of the poor was also wasted.

Applying the Skill
Answers will vary.

DIFFERENTIATED INSTRUCTION ACTIVITY 12

Answers will vary depending on the area students chose to focus on. Students' examples should reflect how the Renaissance affected the specific area.

ENGLISH LEARNER ACTIVITY 12

A.

1. Renaissance—revival of art and literature in the 14–16 centuries; reformation—a radical change for the better in religious, political, or social affairs. Answers will vary.

2. Characteristics of the Italian Renaissance: it was largely an urban society with city-states that became the centers of the Italian political, economic, and social life; it was an age of recovery from the many disasters of the 14th century; new view of human beings emerged as individual ability was emphasized.

B.

1. d
2. a
3. h
4. c
5. g
6. e
7. b
8. f

C.

1. b
2. a

3. a
4. c
5. b

D.

2. Each Anabaptist church chose its own minister, or spiritual leader.

3. Because all Christians were considered priests, any member was eligible to be a minister.

4. Anabaptists were regarded as dangerous radicals who threatened society.

CONTENT VOCABULARY ACTIVITY 12

1. dowry
2. secular
3. urban society
4. salvation
5. justification by faith
6. predestination
7. humanism
8. Reformation
9. mercenary
10. indulgences
11. fresco
12. Renaissance

ACADEMIC VOCABULARY ACTIVITY 12

A.

1. attempt
2. incline
3. studious
4. sound
5. damage
6. tool

Answer Key

7. incorrect

8. image

B.

1. e

2. a

3. g

4. d

5. c

6. h

7. f

8. b

C.

Answers will vary. Each sentence should include one of the vocabulary words listed and reflect information about The Renaissance period.

SKILLS REINFORCEMENT ACTIVITY 12

1. Answers will vary. In general, students should identify the meaning and duration of the Renaissance and the three most important characteristics of the Renaissance, including urban society and wealth; recovery from disasters and rebirth of ancient culture; and new view of value and potential of the individual.

2. Answers will vary. A possible summary follows:

The Renaissance, lasting from 1350 to 1550, was an age of rebirth. Renaissance Italy was characterized by (1) an urban society with increasing wealth, (2) a rebirth of ancient culture, and (3) an emphasis on the value and potential of the individual.

CRITICAL THINKING SKILLS ACTIVITY 12

1. Students should note that Franciscus Barbarus assumes that people think military leaders deserve more public recognition than do humanist scholars. They also think military feats are more permanent and important than scholarly accomplishments.

2. Niccolò Machiavelli believes morality is not necessarily needed to acquire and keep power, "that men shun danger and are greedy for profit." He assumes the prince need not be ethical, but only have an understanding of human nature. The two assumptions are similar in that both authors think men in power are justified to commit actions that lack morality.

HISTORY AND GEOGRAPHY ACTIVITY 12

1. As humans move themselves or goods from one place to another, they create paths or routes between those places. The places where goods are traded become market centers. Specialized commercial support activities also grow up in these market centers.

2. The Grand Canal provided a main thoroughfare for commercial traffic throughout Venice. Wider than any of the other canals in the city, the Grand Canal accommodated a large number of boats.

3. Venice was located midway between Asian markets and western European markets. Located on the Adriatic, Venice was slightly isolated from competitive Mediterranean cities. Thus, Venice could establish its own trading empire without interference from others.

4. Possible answers: war, famine, or other natural disasters; quest for political or religious freedom; desire to live in a different climate; opportunity to initiate trade in an area that had once been closed to trade.

5. Provide several classroom atlases. Encourage students to use current almanacs, nonfiction books, or geographic magazines to do their research on contemporary trade centers.

Answer Key

MAPPING HISTORY ACTIVITY 12

1. 75 percent Catholic; 25 percent Protestant

2. circled in blue: Wittenberg, Worms, Zürich, Geneva, Münster; circled in red: Rome, Trent

3. Answers will vary. Students may conclude that the Protestant Reformation was more successful in spreading Protestantism in urban areas, while the Catholic Reformation was more successful in rural areas. Remind students that geographical boundaries may have been at least partly responsible for either reformation's success.

HISTORICAL SIGNIFICANCE ACTIVITY 12

1. Students may answer that it is important to think of past ages as less advanced in some way than later ages because this comparison is the basis for our idea of progress. Others may argue that every age probably thinks of itself as best, but that is not really true. All ages, they may argue, are simply different from one another.

2. Students may argue that contemporary life is better than some things in the Renaissance but not better than others. They may admire the artistic achievements of that time but may criticize the religious intolerance. Or they may measure the technological advances of the Renaissance against modern times and argue that today far surpasses the Renaissance. Many will argue that no age is "half awake" or "childish."

3. Remind students to offer good evidence from all sectors of society—art, education, technology, government, commerce, and so on. Encourage them to think of the future in realistic terms by noting how many Renaissance developments continue today.

COOPERATIVE LEARNING ACTIVITY 12

Students should complete the activity and answer the Group Process and Quick Check questions. Have students share their responses with their groups or with the class as a whole.

HISTORY SIMULATION ACTIVITY 12

Students should work collaboratively in groups toward achieving the learning objective of the History Simulation Activity.

TIME LINE ACTIVITY 12

1. Gutenberg Bible is printed.

2. Desiderius Erasmus writes *The Praise of Folly*.

3. Martin Luther presents Ninety-five Theses.

4. Henry VIII annulled his marriage to his first wife.

5. the Jesuits, the Reform Commission, and the Council of Trent

6. *The Canterbury Tales*

7. John Calvin

LINKING PAST AND PRESENT ACTIVITY 12

1. They supported artists; therefore, they had the power to choose the subject matter of a painting or other work of art.

2. Congress has the option of reducing the budget of the NEA if it feels that money is being used to create works of art that the majority of the public does not like or support.

3. Some people claim that the lyrics of rap music encourage violence, defiance of authority, and contempt for women. Students who favor censorship of rap music should discuss how such things as music lyrics help to form young people's attitudes about violence, authority, and women. Students should also give examples, when possible, of specific events that may have been influenced by rap music.

Answer Key

Students who are against censorship of rap music should discuss the danger that censorship poses to freedom of expression and other rights guaranteed by the Constitution. Students against censorship should explain how and why they find the lyrics of rap music valuable.

PEOPLE IN WORLD HISTORY ACTIVITY 12, PROFILE 1

1. goldsmithing

2. Answers will vary, but may include that his use of tools and work with metals helped him in developing his printing equipment.

3. Paragraphs will vary, but should reflect an appreciation of the major effects of the spread of ideas through the printed word.

PEOPLE IN WORLD HISTORY ACTIVITY 12, PROFILE 2

1. Luther was a Roman Catholic priest.

2. Luther wrote the Ninety-five Theses, a German translation of the Bible, and many hymns.

3. Answers will vary, but may include a discussion of fairness and justice. Students might also suggest that his law studies may have influenced his style of argument.

PRIMARY SOURCE READING 12

1. jealous goldsmiths of the Guasconti family

2. Cellini was fined four measures of flour. Dissatisfied with this verdict, he attacked the Guasconti in their home. Although Cellini had a dagger, the Guasconti had various weapons. The fight was fierce, but no one was injured.

3. Answers will vary. Students are likely to question Cellini's reliability because he admits no fault whatever in himself or his views and because he depicts himself as an extraordinarily fearless hero, facing a dozen armed men by himself and armed only with a dagger.

4. Answers will vary. Students may suggest that he was brave, reckless, hot-tempered, egotistical, and a good storyteller.

WORLD ART AND MUSIC ACTIVITY 12

1. the *Pietà*, *David*, Sistine Chapel frescoes, the Laurentian Library, the Campidoglio, St. Peter's Basilica

2. His sculpture is perfectly proportioned, and the facial expressions are important. The same is true of his frescoes. His architecture was based on the best of what came before but also included new, innovative elements.

3. Answers will vary. Many students might say that seeing the size and detail of the sculpture in person would be a moving experience, and they empathize with the mother's sorrow at the loss of her son.

4. The main idea is that Michelangelo was an immensely talented artist. The examples of his sculptures, paintings, and architecture support this idea.

5. Answers will vary. We get pleasure from work we love. But most people also like praise and recognition.

RETEACHING ACTIVITY 12

A. 1. Using new techniques, artists made paintings more lifelike.
   2. Northern European painters developed the technique of painting in oils.

B. 1. Architects used columns and arches to create a human-centered environment.
   2. Reformers removed decorations from Protestant churches.

C. 1. Artists created lifelike, freestanding statues.

D. 1. Petrarch is called the father of Italian Renaissance humanism.

Answer Key

2. Humanists wrote in the vernacular.

3. With a new method of printing, books became more widely available.

E. 1. Protestantism was born as a result of Luther's conflicts with the Catholic Church.

2. The Catholic Reformation began in reaction to the spread of Protestantism.

ENRICHMENT ACTIVITY 12

1. The excerpts are describing different groups, but both writings are critical of the wealthy and privileged classes and sympathetic to the poor.

2. Students may conclude that the commonwealths of the Renaissance are very different from today's societies, stating that the rights of underclasses today are better protected. Or they may argue that the systems are, in reality, very similar, stating that the wealthy continue to wield greater power over other classes. Students should provide evidence from the passage and from society today to support their arguments.

3. Possible answers: The rich person might argue that his education, skills and abilities, or inheritance entitle him to the fruits of the commonwealth. A poor peasant might argue that his hard, productive work and his care for the land entitle him to the reasonable share of goods that he would receive in a utopia.

GUIDED READING ACTIVITY 12-1

1. People who lived in Italy believed they had witnessed a rebirth of the ancient Greek and Roman worlds.

2. an urban and wealthy society leading to a secular outlook on life; a rebirth of interest in ancient culture; a new view of human beings with regard for individual ability and worth

3. Milan, Venice, and Florence

4. Milan was located at the crossroads of the main trade routes from Italian coastal cities to the Alpine passes.

5. gambling, horseracing, swearing, painting, music, and books

6. France and Spain

7. The army had not been paid for months. The commander of the army allowed them to smash the gates and loot the city.

8. *The Prince* is one of the most influential works on political power in the western world.

9. Political activity should not be restricted by moral principles. For the sake of the state, he must let his conscience sleep.

10. A noble was born, not made. The perfect noble gained military skill and classical education. The noble was to follow a certain standard of conduct.

11. Their fathers went before a judge and formally freed them from his authority.

GUIDED READING ACTIVITY 12-2

1. False. A key movement was humanism.

2. True.

3. False. The *Divine Comedy* is the story of the soul's journey to salvation.

4. True.

5. False. Studies were considered "liberal" because by them, students could attain virtue and wisdom.

6. False. In the Renaissance view, human beings became the focus of attention.

7. False. They mastered the techniques for realistically portraying the world around them.

8. True.

9. True.

10. False. By 1500, artists from the north had begun to study in Italy.

Answer Key

GUIDED READING ACTIVITY 12-3

I. Catholic, Protestant
  A. humanists, reason
  B. Erasmus, reform
   1. politics, spiritual
   2. wealthy
II. certainty
  A. good works, salvation
  B. justification
   1. Ninety-five, indulgences
   2. reformed
   3. excommunicated
III. revolution
  A. state
  B. sided, peasant
  C. Holy Roman Empire
   1. organized
   2. Peace of Augsburg

GUIDED READING ACTIVITY 12-4

1. unity

2. Ulrich Zwingli; Martin Luther

3. Protestantism; France

4. all-powerful

5. Parliament

6. Edward VI

7. Anabaptists

8. equal; eligible

9. celibacy

10. husbands; children

11. the Jesuits, reform of the papacy, the Council of Trent

12. doctrine; leadership

READING SKILLS ACTIVITY 13

Practicing the Skill
In November, Eventually, began, In the fall of 1520, one year after, first, soon, about the time, Meanwhile, After four months, During the next 30 years

Applying the Skill
Answers will vary.

HISTORICAL ANALYSIS SKILLS ACTIVITY 13

Practicing the Skill

1. Mercantilism needed a favorable balance of trade. European countries were able to achieve this by using the resources of their many colonies. Trade and wealth increased for Europe. The costs were the time and effort and sometimes battles that were needed to govern colonies.

2. A subsidy is a payment that is invested in an industry to help it grow and succeed. Granting subsidies helped encourage exports and a favorable balance of trade.

Applying the Skill
Answers will vary, but should include the conflicts between England and the American colonies over trade and taxes that led to the American Revolution.

DIFFERENTIATED INSTRUCTION ACTIVITY 13

Answers will vary. Outlines should reflect the research students completed on the explorer. Presentations should include all required components.

ENGLISH LEARNER ACTIVITY 13

A.

1. God, glory, and gold. The Portuguese and Spanish had already explored the land and led the way to these journeys. Answers will vary.

2. Wealth, increased trade, new land to be claimed, recognition.

B.

1. exploration, explored

2. persuaded, persuasive

3. arrived, arrival

Answer Key

C.

1. B

2. C

3. A

4. D

D.

1. e

2. d

3. f

4. c

5. b

6. a

CONTENT VOCABULARY ACTIVITY 13

1. E

2. F

3. H

4. G

5. C

6. A

7. D

8. B

9. B

10. C

11. B

12. A

13. B

ACADEMIC VOCABULARY ACTIVITY 13

A.

1. overseas

2. percent

3. transportation

4. expansion

5. primary

6. labor

7. draft

B.

Answers will vary. Book titles should reflect the European exploration and expansion.

C.

1. transport

2. expansion

3. enable

4. discovery

5. explore

6. regulation

D.

1. S

2. A

3. S

4. S

5. A

6. A

SKILLS REINFORCEMENT ACTIVITY 13

1. Facts include what the English think of themselves, their way of thinking anyone "handsome" as being English, their questioning whether any "delicacies" exist in other countries.

2. He infers that the English are proud; suspicious of foreigners; and superficial, lacking personal friendships.

3. Students may question the author's conclusions, answering that the first evidence is more convincing because the author selects specific evidence directly related to the claim, whereas the second claim has evidence that is only tangentially related to it.

Answer Key

4. Find other primary and secondary sources on the subject to compare points of view.

CRITICAL THINKING SKILLS ACTIVITY 13

1. They are unhappy and want to be free.

2. They have halters around their necks and are whipped; they are separated from their families and sold in the same way as cattle; they are not given the benefit of modesty.

3. Prince says that the English "forget God and all feeling of shame" when they move to the West Indies. Students' explanations for this change will vary. Possible answers: Perhaps this is because they become obsessed with money, or perhaps they become accustomed to slavery.

4. Students will most likely argue that since Mary Prince is speaking from her own experience, she has credibility, and the reader tends to take her seriously and be sympathetic.

HISTORY AND GEOGRAPHY ACTIVITY 13

1. People's perceptions of regions are influenced by their experiences, by the knowledge they have about a land and its people, and by political motivations or restrictions.

2. Spanish: mineral wealth—gold and silver; French: furs; English: rich land for farming.

3. England's climate is wet and cool, not the best for growing a wide variety of crops. Discovering the mild climate and rich soil in Virginia, the English were eager to set up agricultural colonies that could supply the homeland with food.

4. When the pope divided the Atlantic Ocean between the Spanish and the Portuguese in 1493 by setting the line of demarcation (Treaty of Tordesillas), most of North and South America fell to Spain.

5. Supply students with resources such as almanacs, nonfiction books, and geographic magazines. Encourage them to share their perceptions of the same region with the rest of the class.

MAPPING HISTORY ACTIVITY 13

1. Students should select three distinct colors to represent Spanish, English, and French holdings and show these in a key.

2. Using colors that match their map key, students should indicate the following holdings:

Spain: northern South America, Central America, Mexico, and entire coast of Florida

England: most of New England and Long Island, except for its westernmost tip, and the eastern shore of Chesapeake Bay

France: St. Lawrence River, Nova Scotia, Prince Edward Island, eastern New Brunswick

3. Southwest, lower Eastern Woodlands

4. Eastern Woodlands

5. Subarctic, Eastern Woodlands

HISTORICAL SIGNIFICANCE ACTIVITY 13

Answers may vary. Possible answers:

1. If you own your own business, you stand to lose much more than an initial investment; all the responsibility falls on you (or your partners) to keep the company going.

2. Unlike owning your own business, the stockholders (while having some decision-making power) do not oversee the day-to-day business of the company; the stockholder's profit or loss is very much dependent on the larger operations of the company.

3. Students should be able to speculate that joint-stock companies no longer have the same kind of political authority. They are no longer like "mini countries"; all are highly regulated, and there are many more companies. Stocks are traded (in places such as the New York Stock Exchange) in huge volumes.

4. Students' letters should describe advantages and disadvantages of investing in a joint-stock company during the 1600s and today. Some students might relish the amount of power seventeenth-century companies had, while other students might criticize their oppression of others. Opportunities to make money exist in both time periods.

COOPERATIVE LEARNING ACTIVITY 13

Students should complete the activity and answer the Group Process and Quick Check questions. Have students share their responses with their groups or with the class as a whole.

HISTORY SIMULATION ACTIVITY 13

Students should work collaboratively in groups toward achieving the learning objective of the History Simulation Activity.

TIME LINE ACTIVITY 13

1. 3 years
2. 3 years
3. 148 years
4. 1534
5. the English; Jamestown

LINKING PAST AND PRESENT ACTIVITY 13

1. The Earth-centered model included the idea that planets were fixed inside concentric crystal spheres that could not be penetrated. The comet's path cut right through these supposed spheres.

2. It blocks and distorts light and other radiation that come from objects deep in outer space.

3. Some scientists believe that there is strong evidence of water on the surface of Mars, and water is necessary to support life. In their reports, students should mention that the purpose of the *Pathfinder* mission was to study Mars's terrain, its geology, and whether or not it contained water. They should also mention that the space vehicle *Pathfinder* carried a robot rover named *Sojourner*, which navigated the surface of Mars, photographed the terrain, and collected soil samples. Although *Sojourner* could not continue to function in Mars's extremely cold climate, it lasted two months longer than had been expected. Students should explain that the mission did not answer the question about the existence of life on Mars.

PEOPLE IN WORLD HISTORY ACTIVITY 13, PROFILE 1

1. Pizarro worked for Balboa as his chief lieutenant.

2. by playing one side in the Inca political turmoil against the other

3. Answers will vary. Possible answer: The Inca would have no reason to trust Pizarro since he executed their ruler Atahuallpa after they paid the ransom for his release.

PEOPLE IN WORLD HISTORY ACTIVITY 13, PROFILE 2

1. Cartier named a mountain at the foot of the St. Lawrence River Mont Réal, which became Montreal.

2. Answers will vary, but may include wanting to show the Native Americans to the French king.

PRIMARY SOURCE READING 13

1. lofty mountains; tall trees; a thousand kinds of birds; varieties of trees, fruits, and grasses; honey; mines of metals; the large population

Answer Key

2. in the Indies

3. gold, spices, cotton, mastic, slaves, rhubarb, cinnamon, and other valuable things

4. He omitted negative information such as the loss of the *Santa Maria*, the troubles with the commander of the *Pinta*, the mutinous mood of the crew, and courses taken or distance covered. He wanted to succeed in returning riches from the Indies.

5. Answers will vary. Some students may say that Columbus was so certain that he would reach Asia by sailing west that he was also certain he had reached his goal. Other students may say that Columbus should have been able to tell that the people and plants were not those of Asia, and that he did know he was not in Asia but would not admit this.

WORLD ART AND MUSIC ACTIVITY 13

1. rituals of myth, fertility rituals, initiations or rites of passage, and other related ceremonies

2. They were used in religious rituals, carvers and their tools were revered, masks were blessed after carving and before using, animal images held the spirit of the animal.

3. Answers will vary. Students should indicate that nationalist movements often seek to preserve African customs and society. The ritual use of masks might be one cultural tradition that Africans would want to retain.

RETEACHING ACTIVITY 13

Spain: Francisco Pizarro, Hernán Cortés, Ferdinand Magellan, Christopher Columbus

Portugal: Pedro Cabral, Vasco da Gama, Bartholomeu Dias

England: John Cabot

ENRICHMENT ACTIVITY 13

1. He states that many greater men have been wrong about the existence of the Americas, and he does not wish to commit a similar error.

2. The Europeans see the vastness of the newly discovered landmass and immediately wish to "consume" or control all it has to offer; unfortunately, this vast richness is too much for the Europeans to handle.

3. Contrary to what others have said or written, Montaigne does not see the inhabitants of the Americas as "savage" or "barbarous;" rather, Montaigne sees them as merely different from Europeans.

4. He thinks the Europeans are too narrow-minded: they assume that what they know is the best way of doing things and therefore do not attempt to learn from other people.

5. Students should give specific examples to back up their opinions.

GUIDED READING ACTIVITY 13-1

1. because of conquests by the Ottoman Turks

2. They were prompted by a desire for wealth, by religious zeal, and by a spirit of adventure.

3. Portugal

4. Da Gama sold his load of Indian spices in Portugal for a profit of several thousand percent.

5. The Spanish sought to reach it by sailing westward across the Atlantic Ocean.

6. He reached all the major islands of the Caribbean and Honduras in Central America.

7. This treaty gave Portugal control over its route around Africa, and it gave Spain rights to almost all of the Americas.

Answer Key

8. Within 30 years, the western part of Latin America had been brought under Spanish control.

9. there came a great sickness, a pestilence, the small pox

10. England, the Netherlands, and France

GUIDED READING ACTIVITY 13-2

1. False. Most slaves in Southwest Asia were used as domestic servants.

2. True.

3. False. The slaves were carried from Africa to the Americas.

4. True.

5. False. Local slave traders first obtained their supplies of slaves from nearby coastal regions. As demand increased, they moved farther inland.

6. False. King Afonso of Congo complained of his country being depopulated by the trade.

7. False. The traders always sought out the strongest and youngest people.

8. True.

9. True.

GUIDED READING ACTIVITY 13-3

I. South America
   A. peninsulares
   B. creoles
   C. mestizos, mulattoes
II. profit
   A. gold, silver
   B. Farming
   C. estates
   D. encomienda
      1. mita
      2. draft
III. Christianize
   A. Jesuits
   B. hospitals, orphanages, schools

READING SKILLS ACTIVITY 14

Practicing the Skill
Answers will vary. Students may answer that Louis XIV agreed with Jacques-Benigne Bossuet on how a king should rule a country, even though he didn't rule France in that way.

Applying the Skill
Answers will vary. Students may include that Peter wanted to synthesize European technology to make Russia's military stronger; and Western manners, dress, and ways of socializing.

HISTORICAL ANALYSIS SKILLS ACTIVITY 14

Practicing the Skill

1. If a person doesn't believe witches exist, he or she is a heretic. Witches are the most evil people that have ever lived.

2. Answers will vary. Students may answer that the arguments are not convincing because they are stated as "no exceptions" facts, but cannot be proven.

Applying the Skill
Answers will vary. Students' topics and conclusions should be well-documented.

DIFFERENTIATED INSTRUCTION ACTIVITY 14

Answers will vary. Charts should reflect the leadership of Louis XIV. Students' essays should clearly define their position and provide examples defending it.

ENGLISH LEARNER ACTIVITY 14

A.

1. Calvinism—theology of J. Calvin or his followers, in which predestination and justification by faith are important elements. Catholicism—faith, practice, or system of Catholic Christianity where believers' faith in Jesus and their good works will secure their eternal life in Heaven.

2. Answers will vary but may include Afghanistan, Uganda, Iraq, the Middle

Answer Key

East, and Northern Ireland. Civil war, death, persecution, and unrest may be cited.

B.

1. c
2. a
3. a
4. b

C.

1. T
2. F
3. T
4. T
5. F
6. T
7. F

D.
Definitions may vary.

1. influence based on recognized knowledge of expertise
2. refusal to comply
3. person or thing that succeeds another
4. factor or circumstance that induces a person to act a certain way
5. definite and unconditional

CONTENT VOCABULARY ACTIVITY 14

1. absolutism
2. armada
3. inflation
4. heretics
5. witchcraft
6. divine right
7. commonwealth
8. czar
9. boyars
10. Mannerism
11. baroque
12. natural rights

ACADEMIC VOCABULARY ACTIVITY 14

A.
Answers will vary. Each response sentence should use the underlined vocabulary word.

B.
Answers will vary. Students' sentences should include one of the words listed and be directly related to Louis XIV.

SKILLS REINFORCEMENT ACTIVITY 14

1. Elizabeth followed a moderate Protestantism, repealing laws that favored Catholics.

2. Student answers will vary. Students should address Elizabeth's references to Catholicism, including referring to Romish pastors as wolves, and references to inventions, heresies, and schisms in the Catholic Church. Elizabeth also argued that the Catholic faith was not the first in England.

3. Student answers will vary. In general, they should observe Elizabeth's rejection of Catholicism and support of Protestantism.

4. Student answers will vary. In general, they should indicate that the primary source document does support the generalizations in the text.

CRITICAL THINKING SKILLS ACTIVITY 14

1. Answers will vary. Possible answers: Sir Francis Drake was brave and a good leader, because he quashed a mutiny aboard the *Pelican* by beheading the ringleader, Thomas Doughty.

Answer Key

2. Sir Francis Drake most likely changed the name of the flagship from the *Pelican* to the *Golden Hind* to regain the favor of Sir Christopher Hatton.

3. The conclusion is supported by the fact that Sir Francis Drake remained in control when a mutiny occurred, and he beheaded the ringleader.

HISTORY AND GEOGRAPHY ACTIVITY 14

1. climate, soil conditions, energy and mineral resources, rivers, good natural harbors, access to distant markets or resources.

2. A location might be advantageous because of its nearness to someplace else. For instance, many suburban communities do not appear to gain any geographic advantages from locations, because they depend on their proximity to major urban areas, sometimes located more than 40 or 50 miles away, for jobs or markets.

3. Its harbor provided a launch point for troop ships. Caves could be carved from the rock, providing secrecy for Operation Torch. Gibraltar provided access from the Atlantic to the Mediterranean and to the African coast.

4. Answers will vary. Possible answers: Although English is the official language and the one used for business, Spanish is the language spoken at home.

5. You may want to suggest that students read the articles "Britain's Precarious Stronghold, Gibraltar" in *National Geographic*, vol. 190, no. 5, November 1996 and "Shadows on the Rock" in *The Smithsonian*, vol. 28, no. 6, September 1997. You may also want to have students research the political referendum held in Gibraltar in 2006. Encourage students to find examples in their research that link geographic location to commercial activity.

MAPPING HISTORY ACTIVITY 14

1. Answers will vary. Possible response: A central location such as the border of the Holy Roman Empire in France might have been better because it would have provided better access to all of the empire's holdings.

2. Possible response: France, because Philip II could have moved on three fronts: north from Spain, south from the Netherlands, and west from central Europe

3. Students should draw the borders of present-day France, Spain, Belgium, Germany, the Netherlands, the Czech Republic, Switzerland, etc., using the Reference Atlas. Students should realize that Spain, Portugal, and France are essentially the same configuration. The Netherlands are now smaller. Italy is larger. Belgium, the Czech Republic, Austria, Hungary, Slovenia, Croatia, Slovakia, and Germany have since been created.

HISTORICAL SIGNIFICANCE ACTIVITY 14

1. Mars was the Roman god of war. He bears comparing to Henry V because Henry won many victories over the French in the Hundred Years' War.

2. Henry V scored a decisive victory over the French at the Battle of Agincourt in 1415.

3. The Puritans believed that theatrical entertainments corrupted people, and the royalty, whom the Puritans opposed, supported the theatrical troupes.

4. Student answers will vary. This is a case were it looks like the end justifies the means, but that is not so. However bold the gesture and however good the outcome, dismantling the theater without the owner's permission was wrong because the lease had expired and the company's rights over the property no longer existed. In fact, their action appears to be theft.

Answer Key

COOPERATIVE LEARNING ACTIVITY 14

Students should complete the activity and answer the Group Process and Quick Check questions. Have students share their responses with their groups or with the class as a whole.

HISTORY SIMULATION ACTIVITY 14

Students should work collaboratively in groups toward achieving the learning objective of the History Simulation Activity.

TIME LINE ACTIVITY 14

1. her cousin, Mary Stuart

2. 1618

3. Possible responses: Protestant rebellion; religious freedom

4. Portugal

5. Possible response: Europe during this period was a place of great social and political upheaval and violence.

LINKING PAST AND PRESENT ACTIVITY 14

1. Both tried to eradicate the conquered peoples' cultures in order to secure a strong central government. The Hapsburgs changed their conquered subjects' governments and religions; the Soviets also changed their economies, family structures, art, and literature.

2. The leaders may feel that people who have the same values as their rulers may accept their laws more readily.

3. Students responses will vary. Their reports should mention Mahatma Gandhi's militant nonviolence against British rule in India and Martin Luther King, Jr.'s peaceful campaign against racism in the United States. They should describe Gandhi's tactics of boycotting British goods, refusing to pay taxes, and holding peaceful demonstrations, such as the March to the Sea. They should then discuss King's tactics—peaceful demon-strations, civil disobedience, sit-ins, and the bus boycott. Students should also discuss Gandhi's influence on Martin Luther King, Jr.

PEOPLE IN WORLD HISTORY ACTIVITY 14, PROFILE 1

1. Guy Fawkes tunneled into the cellar beneath the House of Lords, helped place the gunpowder, and was supposed to set it off.

2. The purpose was to spark a Catholic uprising, but it actually caused the perse-cution of Roman Catholics in England to become more vigorous and bitter.

3. November 5 was the day the Parliament would have been destroyed had the gun-powder not been discovered.

PEOPLE IN WORLD HISTORY ACTIVITY 14, PROFILE 2

1. The three areas of life that Pascal devoted himself to were mathematics, science, and religion.

2. Pascal's Wager argues that it is a good "bet" to believe in God. On the one hand, if one believes in God but God does not exist, one loses nothing. On the other hand, if one believes in God and God does exist, one gains eternal life. Therefore, believing in God is a good bet. You lose nothing and may gain every-thing. Pascal hoped to convert intellectu-ally those who did not care about religion in order to get them ready to experience the full conversion of the heart.

3. The basis of religious faith should be intu-ition and the heart's love of God.

4. Student answers may vary. Accept any an-swer that is relevant and thoughtful. The grave illness of a loved one might make one think of the meaning of human suffer-ing or of what happens to people after death, for example, both of which might make one consider religion seriously.

Answer Key

PRIMARY SOURCE READING 14

1. mainly the *valet de chambre*, the king's physician, surgeon, and nurse, the grand chamberlain, and privileged courtiers

2. The king met with his council about five mornings a week. He issued orders to officials and courtiers every morning; he held secret meetings with ambassadors. People could ask him for favors at certain other times of the day.

3. He had pet dogs. He regularly went hunting, shooting, or walking in his gardens. There were picnics and promenades.

4. The king said prayers regularly in the morning and at night, and he attended mass in the morning.

5. Answers will vary. Students who find it enjoyable may cite the luxury, the numerous servants to do his bidding, and the fact that he has few idle moments. Students who do not find it enjoyable may point to his lack of privacy and the huge number of courtiers all wanting his attention.

WORLD ART AND MUSIC ACTIVITY 14

1. The technique of using light and shadow is called chiaroscuro. Rembrandt had light shine on his subjects, but he also was able to make it look like light emanated from them.

2. He specialized in large paintings of biblical and historical themes as well as self-portraits. They are unique because he added compassion and humanity to whatever subject, including himself, that he painted.

3. Answers will vary. Some students may agree with the passage's assessment and point out realist elements of the painting to support their opinions. Others might argue that "scrupulous honesty" is difficult or impossible to represent in art and may emphasize elements of the portrait

they view as nonrealistic.

4. Answers will vary. Students should note that the demands of any patron, whether that patron is a church, a state, or an individual, will probably affect the choices an artist makes.

5. Answers will vary. The church or state probably would not have paid Rembrandt to paint self-portraits, so some of his greatest work would not exist.

RETEACHING ACTIVITY 14

Answers will vary. Possible responses are as follows:

Spain:
   K: Spanish history during this time reflected unrest. L: Philip's support of Catholicism led to conflict with Protestants; efforts to defeat Calvinism in the Netherlands led to rebellion; the reign of Philip II left Spain bankrupt with an out-of-date military and inefficient government.

England:
   K: Elizabeth I named supreme governor of both church and state. L: Elizabeth I maintained the balance of power; England defeated the Spanish Armada; brought stability and prosperity to England

France:
   K: Louis XIV was a powerful ruler known as the Sun King. W: What kind of monarchy developed in France under the Bourbon monarchs? L: The Bourbons developed an absolute monarchy, lavish and vigorous.

The German States:
   K: The Peace of Westphalia ended the Thirty Years' War. W: How was the Thirty Years' War different from prior European wars? L: The outcome of the war was the further weakening of Germany and the emergence of France as Europe's leading power; the war ended Hapsburg hopes of establishing an absolute monarchy over all of Germany.

Russia:
   K: Russian rulers included Ivan the Terrible, Michael Romanov, and Peter the Great. W: How did the power of the Russian czars differ

Answer Key

from that of other European monarchs? **L:** The Russian monarchy was all-powerful and easily crushed its opponents.

ENRICHMENT ACTIVITY 14

1. She is there to live or die with the troops.

2. Answers will vary. Possible answers: Elizabeth's presence at Tilbury reveals that she is extremely courageous.

3. Answers will vary. Possible answer: stirring, passionate, fiery, fervent, emotional

4. Answers will vary. Possible answers: It cheered them on, convinced them that their cause was just, and caused them to respect and revere their queen all the more.

5. Answers will vary. Possible answer: Philip's speech would be similar to Elizabeth's in tone but would likely be more fiery and urge the Spanish soldiers to show no mercy to the English, because the English are Protestants rather than Catholics.

GUIDED READING ACTIVITY 14-1

1. Calvinism and Catholicism were aggressive in trying to win converts and in eliminating each other's authority.

2. They were French Protestants influenced by John Calvin.

3. Towns and provinces were willing to assist nobles in weakening the monarchy, and most nobles were Huguenots.

4. In 1589 Henry of Navarre, the political leader of the Huguenots, succeeded to the throne of France and converted to Catholicism.

5. He insisted on strict conformity to Catholicism and strong monarchical authority.

6. Spain saw itself as a nation of people chosen by God to save Catholic Christianity from the Protestant heretics.

7. Violence erupted when Calvinists, especially nobles, began to destroy statues in Catholic churches.

8. The United Provinces of the Netherlands held center stage as one of Europe's great powers.

9. The small island kingdom became the leader of the Protestant nations of Europe and laid the foundations for a world empire.

10. The people of England would rise against their queen when the Spaniards arrived.

GUIDED READING ACTIVITY 14-2

1. silver
2. inflation
3. mines
4. pirate
5. artisans
6. merchants
7. witchcraft
8. confessed
9. unreasonable
10. Religion
11. political
12. territorial
13. Westphalia
14. Parliament
15. power
16. Oliver Cromwell
17. Orange
18. Mary
19. Glorious Revolution
20. Parliament's

Answer Key

GUIDED READING ACTIVITY 14-3

I. Absolutism; power
   A. right of kings
   B. Louis XIV
      1. monarchy
      2. Sun King
      3. foreign policy, church, taxes
II. Prussia, Austria
   A. frontiers
      1. army
      2. Frederick
   B. Hapsburgs
      1. German
      2. Hungary, Transylvania, Croatia, Slavonia
III. czar
   A. Romanov
   B. technology
   C. Sweden

GUIDED READING ACTIVITY 14-4

1. Mannerism; suffering; emotions, ecstasy

2. Reformation

3. baroque

4. Gian Lorenzo Bernini; Basilica

5. dramatists; William Shakespeare

6. lower classes

7. *Don Quixote*

8. Lope de Vega

9. Leviathan

10. natural; remove

11. constitutional

READING SKILLS ACTIVITY 15

Practicing the Skill
Class discussions will vary, but opinions should be critically formed and objective.

Applying the Skill
Opinions will vary, but should be well thought out and presented.

HISTORICAL ANALYSIS SKILLS ACTIVITY 15

Practicing the Skill

1. the mid- to late-sixteenth century; the domed mosques built by the Ottoman Turks

2. The mosques show that religion was very important to the Ottomans. Their magnificent architecture shows also shows that they were great artisans who appreciated beautiful things.

Applying the Skill
Answers will vary.

DIFFERENTIATED INSTRUCTION ACTIVITY 15

Diagrams should include the following: Ottoman Empire—could not be forced into marriage, permitted to seek divorce, served as senior officials (governors of provinces) in some instances; Mogul Empire—gave political advice, received salaries, practice of isolating women was common among upper-class Hindus, child marriage was common, custom of suttee continued; Both—were allowed to own and inherit property, could have political responsibilities

ENGLISH LEARNER ACTIVITY 15

A.

1. Answers will vary. Religious tolerance is allowing people to practice their own religion. A region that practices religious tolerance would be one filled with peace.

2. Answers will vary.

D.

1. occupation

2. pastoral

3. Peasants

4. guilds

5. Merchants

6. inherit

Answer Key

C.

1. however; to contrast
2. like; to show similarity
3. however; to contrast
4. in addition; to add information
5. for instance; to give examples

CONTENT VOCABULARY ACTIVITY 15

1. A
2. N
3. I
4. J
5. K
6. G
7. E
8. C
9. D
10. B
11. M
12. H
13. F
14. L

ACADEMIC VOCABULARY ACTIVITY 15

A.
Answers will vary, but should include the underlined vocabulary words.

B.

1. c
2. b
3. a
4. a
5. b
6. c
7. b

8. a

SKILLS REINFORCEMENT ACTIVITY 15

1. A
2. B
3. E
4. E *or* F
5. A *or* D
6. A *or* C
7. Answers will vary but should include at least three specific books or articles and at least two different types of research sources. Information sought in each book or article should be appropriate to the type of source.

CRITICAL THINKING SKILLS ACTIVITY 15

1. Adjectives used to describe India include *savage, fierce, barbarous,* and *teeming.* Adjectives describing Britain are *perfect, best,* and *mighty.*

2. The author believes that Indian civilization has little of value to offer the rest of the world. He feels that British civilization, on the other hand, has many rich traditions that have been of great benefit to India.

3. barbarous customs—Shah Jahan attempted to eliminate suttee, textiles highly valued in foreign trade.

   savage oppressions—Akbar's humane rule, reduced or suspended taxes when crops fail.

   endless wars of race and creed—policy of religious tolerance, both Muslims and Hindus in government.

HISTORY AND GEOGRAPHY ACTIVITY 15

1. Human characteristics of a place include cultural aspects such as language, religion, political systems, economic activities, and social structures.

Answer Key

2. Human characteristics of Constantinople include Greek language, descendants of various peoples, Christian beliefs, banking, trade, insurance, credit services, social and economic programs for the poor, and close ties between church and state.

3. Answers might include language(s) spoken, town or city government, religious organizations, social activities, types of industry, commerce

4. Differences among people can sometimes make it difficult to find common ground for understanding and cooperation. Willingness to learn from differences can enhance international relations.

5. Explain to students that newspapers present a perspective that might differ from other media. Ask them to keep this in mind when compiling their lists.

MAPPING HISTORY ACTIVITY 15

1. The battle at Chaldiran established a new border. Tabriz became a frontier city, uncomfortably close to the Ottoman enemy.

2. Uzbek

3. The Safavids were forced to defend two fronts at the same time.

HISTORICAL SIGNIFICANCE ACTIVITY 15

1. We are not sure why Mumtaz Mahal made her husband promise to remarry should she die before him, but the most likely reason is that she loved him so much she wanted to make sure he was happy after she died.

2. Student answers will vary. The description of the Taj Mahal as a "teardrop on the cheek of time" does capture beautifully the meaning of the Taj Mahal because the reference to the cheek evokes love, the reference to a tear evokes death, and the reference to time evokes Shah Jahan's desire to make his love eternal.

3. Student answers will vary. As a skyscraper, the Chrysler building symbolizes our conquest of nature and the power of human enterprise. Architectural details such as the hubcap motif towards the top of the building symbolize the automobile industry.

4. Shah Jahan spent the final eight years of his life under house arrest. Therefore, he could not visit the Taj Mahal in the sense of going into it. However, he could see the building from a window, so he could visit the Taj Mahal by looking at it.

COOPERATIVE LEARNING ACTIVITY 15

Students should complete the activity and answer the Group Process and Quick Check questions. Have students share their responses with their groups or with the class as a whole.

HISTORY SIMULATION ACTIVITY 15

Students should work collaboratively in groups toward achieving the learning objective of the History Simulation Activity.

TIME LINE ACTIVITY 15

1. 1123 years

2. 221 years

3. Safavid, Mogul, Ottoman

4. 1683

5. 1529 at Vienna and 1571 at Lepanto

6. Ismail in 1501

7. approximately 1517

8. Taj Mahal, c. 1632

LINKING PAST AND PRESENT ACTIVITY 15

1. The use of the mosque's courtyard as a political forum suggests that, originally, religious leaders also were political leaders.

2. It opens up space far above the crowded areas at ground level.

Answer Key

3. Answers will vary. The teacher might encourage students to choose a Renaissance artist for their report. They can then look for evidence in the paintings that the artist's culture valued classical Greek myths, individuality, the material world, and scientific aspects of painting such as the effect of light, perspective, and human anatomy.

PEOPLE IN WORLD HISTORY ACTIVITY 15, PROFILE 1

1. Selim killed all other possible heirs to the throne except Süleyman.

2. He invaded Egypt and annexed it into his empire.

3. He was known as the Grim for killing most of his family and his brutal treatment of his enemies.

4. Answers will vary, but may include a discussion of Selim's tactics of intimidation and fear.

5. Answers will vary. Possible answer: The sharif thought it was safer and smarter to acknowledge Selim's power.

PEOPLE IN WORLD HISTORY ACTIVITY 15, PROFILE 2

1. His country was being invaded by its two enemies, the Ottoman Turks and the Uzbeks.

2. Abbas created a standing army.

3. Abbas cared deeply that his subjects did well and did not suffer injustice.

4. The factors that led to Abbas's military victories were the training and arming of his soldiers, his strategies, and his use of artillery.

5. Abbas treated his own family badly because he developed an obsessive paranoia about assassination. This paranoia was caused by fear of being overthrown by his family.

PRIMARY SOURCE READING 15

1. It was considered legitimate to use force in support of trade.

2. Initially it was smaller, but later it rivaled the regular military in size.

3. Very little evidence is left. Even a small tavern called East India Arms was renamed.

4. a one-time colossus of trade

WORLD ART AND MUSIC ACTIVITY 15

1. Turkish village boys dueling using sung poetry; musical dramas staged by devout Iranian Muslims; singers in Egyptian coffee houses

2. Answers will vary depending upon which instrument is chosen. Oboes have changed very little; flutes have changed greatly.

3. Answers will vary. Students should include forces of cultural diffusion within Southwest Asia (for example, the unifying force of Islam and the unification brought about through large empires) as well as cultural contact with other regions (for example, Moorish control of Spain, international commerce, colonialism, and immigration).

RETEACHING ACTIVITY 15

Possible answers:

Ottoman Empire:
   Ulema: group administered the legal system and schools for educating Muslims

   Sultan: political and military supreme authority; hereditary; imperial rule; isolated

Safavid Empire:
   Shah Abbas: accomplishments in science, mathematics, and the arts

   Textiles: silk and carpet weaving

   Pyramid System: shah at top, bureaucracy and landed classes in the middle, the common people below

Answer Key

Shah Ismail: founder; called himself shah (king); used Shiite faith as a unifying force

Mogul Empire:

Architecture and Painting: Taj Mahal; blending of Persian and Indian cultures produced new styles

Akbar: religious tolerance; established state workshop for artists; foreign trade prospered

Babur: founder; advanced weapons, including artillery; established power in North India

Government Tolerance: upper ranks of government bureaucracy filled with non-native Muslims; many lower-ranking officials were Hindus; zamindars

ENRICHMENT ACTIVITY 15

1. via the Silk Road through Central Asia and through the coastal areas where ports were located; Muslim communities in China were located around the Silk Road in the northwest portion of the country and in port cities in southern China.

2. During the 1850s, the Qing dynasty was weakened by the Taiping Rebellion, leaving it decentralized and vulnerable to further unrest.

3. The Confucian civil service system, reinstituted by the Ming and Qing dynasties, emphasized loyalty first to the Chinese emperor. Muslims, believers in God, might be viewed as a threat because they chose to obey God's laws or those of a mullah before the laws of the Chinese emperor.

4. Chinese repression of minority religious groups differed markedly from Akbar's religious tolerance, which made life bearable for Hindus and other religious groups as long as they obeyed the Mogul emperor.

GUIDED READING ACTIVITY 15-1

1. The Osman Turks began to expand.

2. The janissaries were converted to Islam and trained as foot soldiers or administrators to serve the sultan.

3. "What a city we have given over to plunder and destruction."

4. The new caliph, defender of the faith and successor to Muhammad.

5. Collect taxes, maintain law and order, and be responsible to the sultan's court in Constantinople.

6. because its mastery of firearms helped it unify the regions that it conquered

7. both political and military

8. He would sit behind a screen and privately indicate his desires.

9. Istanbul

10. By far it was in architecture, especially the mosques of the last half of the sixteenth century.

11. Women were allowed to own and inherit property, could not be forced into marriage, and were permitted to seek divorce.

GUIDED READING ACTIVITY 15-2

1. Sunni
2. Shiites
3. Iran
4. Iraq
5. Abbas
6. Afghan
7. political
8. social
9. power
10. bureaucracy
11. merit
12. birth
13. government
14. trade

Answer Key

15. horse
16. camel
17. roads
18. Europeans
19. Ottomans
20. Europe
21. science
22. mathematics
23. flowering
24. Isfahan

GUIDED READING ACTIVITY 15-3

I. subcontinent
  A. Mogul
  B. Delhi
II. Akbar
  A. humane
    1. tolerance
    2. Hindu
  B. progress
III. domestic
  A. imprisoned
  B. Persians
IV. British
  A. French
  B. harass
V. Muslims, Hindus
  A. isolating
  B. wealthy
  C. Taj Mahal

READING SKILLS ACTIVITY 16

Practicing the Skill

1–3. Answers will vary.

Applying the Skill
Answers will vary.

HISTORICAL ANALYSIS SKILLS ACTIVITY 16

Practicing the Skill

1. F
2. C

3. H
4. D
5. A
6. B
7 G
8. E

Applying the Skill
Answers will vary.

DIFFERENTIATED INSTRUCTION ACTIVITY 16

Answers may vary slightly.

Warriors—Divided into shogun, daimyo, samurai, and ronin; Shogun was supreme ruler below the emperor and distributor of the national rice crop; Daimyo received land and rice from shogun in exchange for military service; Samurai received rice from the daimyo in exchange for their services as advisors, castle guards, and government officials; Ronin were warriors who had no masters and traveled the countryside seeking jobs; Role of Women—rights were restricted, males had authority over property, marriage, and divorce

Peasants—farmers who produced rice and held a privileged position in society; often poor; Role of Women—parents arranged marriages; wife had to move in with her husband's family; could be divorced if she did not meet family's expectations; women valued for their roles as childbearers and housemakers; worked in the fields

Artisans—included craftspeople such as swordmakers and carpenters; Role of Women—parents arranged marriages; wife had to move in with her husband's family; could be divorced if she did not meet family's expectations; women valued for their roles as childbearers and housemakers; worked in the fields

Merchants—distributed food and essential goods; profited from the labor of others; Role of Women—parents arranged marriages; wife had to move in with her husband's family; could be divorced if she did not meet family's

Answer Key

expectations; women valued for their roles as childbearers and housemakers; worked in the fields

ENGLISH LEARNER ACTIVITY 16

A.

1. Answers will vary.

2. A dynasty is a line of hereditary leaders. Answers will vary, but may include: trade commerce, aligning with other strong nations, socially, and politically.

B.

1. C
2. I
3. C

C.

1. c
2. a
3. b
4. a
5. c
6. b
7. b
8. a

CONTENT VOCABULARY ACTIVITY 16

1. daimyo
2. banners
3. commercial capitalism
4. porcelain
5. shoguns
6. clan
7. hans
8. samurai
9. hostage system

10. eta
11. queue
12. Ming
13. Qing
14. Imperial City

ACADEMIC VOCABULARY ACTIVITY 16

A.

1. T
2. F—The traditionalists were alarmed.
3. T
4. F—Women were subordinate to their husbands.
5. F—Banking flourished during the era.
6. T

B.

1. adjective
2. noun, verb
3. adjective
4. noun, verb
5. noun, adjective
6. adjective

C.

1. b
2. a
3. c
4. c
5. c
6. a

SKILLS REINFORCEMENT ACTIVITY 16

1. the e-mail name and address of the recipient; if the recipient is on the same network, the e-mail name is sufficient

Answer Key

2. either by pressing the [TAB] key on your keyboard or by using the mouse to point and click the cursor to the Subject text box

3. because the recipient will see the e-mail name of the sender before he or she opens the message

4. by clicking on the [SEND] button located on the toolbar

5. In many programs, the date, name, and address of sender are supplied automatically.

CRITICAL THINKING SKILLS ACTIVITY 16

1. Atsutane believes the Dutch are no better than dogs, and he pictures a Dutchman's life as short and animal-like.

2. Cultural superiority functions only if other nations or cultures are made to appear inferior and sub-human. Atsutane's portrayal of the Dutch helps him reinforce his own view of Japanese superiority.

3. *Barbarian* comes from the Greek *barbos*, which means "foreign, rude, ignorant." It may be related to the Sanskrit *barbara*, meaning "stammering." When two cultures meet for the first time, their language may seem strange to one another's ears. Therefore, *barbarian*, with its connotations of nonsense-sounding speech, might be an apt term to use.

4. Answers will vary. Most students will probably say no. Ways to minimize stereotyping include the following: learn foreign languages; study history; interact with people from other groups; travel to other countries. The more people learn about a foreign culture, the more familiar it will become to them, and the less tendency they will have to make oversimplifications about that culture.

HISTORY AND GEOGRAPHY ACTIVITY 16

1. Because any feature that is common throughout an area can define a region, regions can take almost any shape or size, depending on the common feature that defines them.

2. The main part of the shogun's region was located in the center of Japan and divided north from south. Other parts of the shogun's region were located throughout the country and thus served to separate daimyo domains from one another.

3. If the customs of a domain were secret, any outsider or fugitive criminal who came into the domain would quickly give himself away. He would then be caught and expelled, preventing him from establishing a conspiracy.

4. Examples include Romans versus barbarian regions, Muslim versus non-Muslim regions, and Protestant versus Catholic regions. Within American history, the Civil War is an example of a conflict between regions—North against South.

MAPPING HISTORY ACTIVITY 16

1. Tokugawa

2. Several military campaigns throughout Japan from 1582 to 1590.

3. They failed due to counterattacks by Ming and Korean forces.

4. The counterattack in the strait between Japan and Korea should be circled.

HISTORICAL SIGNIFICANCE ACTIVITY 16

Student answers will vary. Accept any answer that is thoughtful and relevant.

COOPERATIVE LEARNING ACTIVITY 16

Students should complete the activity and answer the Group Process and Quick Check questions. Have students share their responses with their groups or with the class as a whole.

Answer Key

HISTORY SIMULATION ACTIVITY 16

Students should work collaboratively in groups toward achieving the learning objective of the History Simulation Activity.

TIME LINE ACTIVITY 16

1. Zheng He's explorations
2. 270 years
3. 276 years
4. Qing
5. The Act of Seclusion

LINKING PAST AND PRESENT ACTIVITY 16

1. Both procedures are supposed to free blocked energy. Acupuncture is performed with needles. Acupressure is done by massage.

2. They might keep records over a long period of time of how people react to specific treatments. Then they could analyze the results of their findings to determine which treatments were effective the greatest number of times.

3. The branch of science is ecology. Student reports should explore how the health of an ecological system is affected if it gets too much or too little rain; if the population of one kind of plant or animal gets disproportionately large or small; if too many chemicals enter its water or oxygen supply; and if large amounts of harmful ultraviolet (UV) rays enter its atmosphere.

PEOPLE IN WORLD HISTORY ACTIVITY 16, PROFILE 1

1. floods, droughts, rebellions, and foreign invasion

2. Answers will vary. Possible answer: The Manchus might not have been able to take control of China, and the Ming dynasty might have continued.

PEOPLE IN WORLD HISTORY ACTIVITY 16, PROFILE 2

1. Hideyoshi completed the work of unifying Japan.

2. Student answers will vary. Accept answers that are relevant and thoughtful. Democratic reasons given against the policy probably will appeal to individual rights. Arguments in defense of Hideyoshi's policy probably will appeal to the need for order.

PRIMARY SOURCE READING 16

1. According to the law, drinking and gambling both lead to the destruction of a unified state.

2. Before a daimyo can build a castle or improve a castle, he must get approval from the proper authorities of the shogunate. This is necessary because the shogunate views big, fortified castles as dangers to the state.

3. People may not marry to form political alliances; all intended marriages must be approved by the shogun.

4. Samurai must not live ostentatiously because to do so makes the less fortunate people below them envious and willing to revolt.

5. The shogun and his officials benefit the most from the code of laws because it sets limits on the powers of the daimyo, who would otherwise be potential threats to the power of the shogun. The common people probably would benefit the least from these laws because they are barely mentioned at all. They would not be protected from brutality or other abuse by any of the laws stated above.

6. Students' answers may vary but should include some form of education that prepares people for roles in government and industry. Students may determine that a strong moral code is also necessary for

Answer Key

producing honest and efficient government officials.

WORLD ART AND MUSIC ACTIVITY 16

1. prepare the paper, select or make the proper pens and brushes, draw the lines in ink, add water to shade the gray areas

2. Japanese monks who were skilled in painting traveled to China and learned the technique from Chinese monks, then experimented with it when they returned to Japan.

3. Answers will vary. Possible answers: Zen Buddhism emphasizes peace and harmony with nature and its elevated significance in comparison to humans. This reverence is evident in the way this landscape was drawn. The wash drawing displays a landscape that is calm and peaceful. By showing all four seasons at once, the artist suggests the continuity and unity of nature.

4. Answers will vary depending on the second landscape students select.

RETEACHING ACTIVITY 16

1. Answers may include: protected values and institutions; limited exchange of ideas; limited foreign trade to firms licensed by the government; greater emphasis on agriculture; no development of commercial capitalism; heavy taxes on manufacturing, low taxes on farming

2. Answers may include: China extended its rule into Mongolia, central Asia, and Vietnam; effective government used a centralized bureaucracy; nationwide school system; manufactured goods produced in vastly higher numbers; new crops introduced; increased food production; completed the Grand Canal; weak rulers led to government corruption, high taxes, peasant unrest.

3. Answers may include: maintained the Ming political system; bannermen were the chief fighting force of the empire; important government positions shared equally by Chinese and Manchus; Kangxi's religious tolerance; Qianlong's rule leads to corruption, higher taxes, unrest, economic hardship for many peasants; White Lotus Rebellion; sold trade privileges to the Europeans

4. Answers may include: the shogunate controls daimyo by hostage system; long period of peace; trade and industry flourishes; banking flourishes; paper money becomes medium of exchange; intermarriage between social classes forbidden; role of women restricted; rise of popular literature written by and for townspeople

ENRICHMENT ACTIVITY 16

1. The Montagnards probably live in a rain forest environment inhabited by exotic animals, such as the toucan. In addition, rice is probably an important staple of their diet since it is represented in so many different patterns.

2. The patterns represent helicopters, guns, and men on horses. They probably represent the intrusion of the Vietnam War and modern technology into the lives of these relatively isolated agricultural people. The patterns also may help explain how widespread the effects of the war were on minority groups in Vietnam.

3. Student patterns should be clearly drawn and represent a familiar object. Students should make reference to the importance of preserving information about lifestyles and technology that may become obsolete in a hundred years.

GUIDED READING ACTIVITY 16-1

1. China extended its rule into Mongolia and central Asia and briefly reconquered Vietnam.

2. The canal made it possible to ship grain and other goods from southern to northern China.

3. the giraffes

4. It was the first direct contact between the Chinese Empire and Europe since the journeys of Marco Polo.

5. Chinese scholars marveled at European eyeglasses. Christian missionaries were impressed with teachings of Confucius and Chinese architecture.

6. He hanged himself from a tree in the palace gardens.

7. All Chinese males were to shave their foreheads and braid their hair into a pigtail.

8. The Qing tried to preserve their distinct identity, but also brought Chinese into the imperial administration.

9. Kangxi

10. corrupt officials and higher taxes

11. He wrote that China had no need of "your country's manufactures."

GUIDED READING ACTIVITY 16-2

1. agricultural

2. economy

3. population

4. capitalism

5. family

6. generations

7. clan

8. marriageable

9. novel

10. *Golden*

11. *The Dream of the Red Chamber*

12. Imperial City

13. imperial

14. porcelain

15. Europeans

GUIDED READING ACTIVITY 16-3

I. unification
  A. powerful
    1. Kyoto
    2. Osaka
    3. central
  B. Europeans
    1. Portuguese
    2. Francis Xavier

II. feudal
  A. "Great Peace"
  B. industry
  C. rural
  D. class
    1. warriors
    2. eta

III. cultural
  A. novel
  B. Kabuki
  C. Nobles

IV. Korea
  A. sixteenth
  B. foreign
  C. "Hermit Kingdom"

GUIDED READING ACTIVITY 16-4

1. stable

2. spice

3. Buddhist kings, Javanese kings, Islamic sultans

4. superior, universe

5. India

6. bureaucracy

7. Confucius

8. spices

9. conversion, trade

10. English, Dutch

READING SKILLS ACTIVITY 17

Practicing the Skill

Student answers will vary but they should draw on the chapter resources to explain that Enlightenment ideas about reason led

Answer Key

Wollstonecraft to use careful reasoning to argue against Rousseau's sexism rather than emotion.

Applying the Skill
Students should identify key parts of the Declaration and Bill of Rights that pertain to the ideas highlighted in the text. For example, students may underline the phrase *that they are endowed…with certain unalienable rights* and identify John Locke's theory of Natural rights as its basis.

HISTORICAL ANALYSIS SKILLS ACTIVITY 17

Practicing the Skill

1. Rousseau claims that a society that gives up its liberties to a king is allowing itself to be enslaved.

2. Rousseau claims that a society should be governed by the general will. A monarchy is therefore an evil institution, against the state of nature where men are born free.

3. This essay was published in France before the French Revolution deposed King Louis XVI. It would have been controversial because it was a challenge to the prevailing "absolutist" notion: that the king, not the people, was the highest power in France.

4. American politics was influenced by views such as Rousseau's in that the framers of the Constitution rejected the idea of having a monarchy. Instead of an executive branch of government headed by a king, born into office, they chose to have a President, elected by the people.

Applying the Skill
Answers will vary. Students outline the rights they feel they and their classmates should enjoy, with reference to specific documents and writings in their drafts. Responses should reflect that a school environment is not a perfect mirror of society, that they may not enjoy all of the same rights and privileges in school that they would be entitled to outside.

DIFFERENTIATED INSTRUCTION ACTIVITY 17
Answers will vary. Make sure students are using the correct type of reasoning in their examples.

ENGLISH LEARNER ACTIVITY 17

A.

1. Answers will vary but should reflect an understanding of the differences between a democracy and a monarchy.

2. A civil war is armed conflict between residents of the same country or nation. Student answers should demonstrate their knowledge of the U.S. or another country's civil war.

B.
After students review words, allow time for questions or quizzing with a fellow student.

C.

1. asserted

2. monarch

3. accountable

4. divine

5. eternal

6. solely

7. attributed

8. resolve

D.

Description of the Job	Job Title
1. a person who studies society by using reason	sociologist
2. a person who writes for a newspaper	journalist
3. a person who teaches college	professor
4. a person who works for social reform	reformist
5. a person who studies the economy	economist

Answer Key

CONTENT VOCABULARY ACTIVITY 17

1. I
2. H
3. E
4. J
5. G
6. N
7. L
8. B
9. D
10. K
11. M
12. C
13. A
14. F

ACADEMIC VOCABULARY ACTIVITY 17

A.

1. affect
2. conceptualize; conceptual
3. derivation; derivable
4. hypothesize; hypothesis

B.

1. a
2. b
3. e
4. c
5. d

C.

1. c
2. b
3. a

SKILLS REINFORCEMENT ACTIVITY 17

I. Colonial Unrest
   A. British impose Stamp Act to generate revenue needed after Seven Years' War, 1765
   B. Colonists protest
   C. Stamp Act is repealed in 1766

II. Fighting Begins
   A. First Continental Congress meets in Philadelphia, 1774
   B. Fighting begins at Lexington and Concord, 1775
   C. Second Continental Congress meets
      1. Forms Continental Army
      2. Appoints George Washington as commander in chief

III. The Declaration of Independence and War
   A. Approved by Second Continental Congress, 1776
   B. Written by Thomas Jefferson
   C. Declared colonies to be "free and independent states absolved from all allegiance to British Crown"

IV. Foreign Support
   A. French support
      1. Arms
      2. Money
      3. Soldiers
      4. Diplomatic recognition
   B. Spanish and Dutch Support

V. Surrender
   A. General Cornwallis surrenders at Yorktown, 1781
   B. British sign Treaty of Paris, 1783
      1. Recognized independence of colonies
      2. Granted control to colonies of territory from the Appalachians to the Mississippi River

CRITICAL THINKING SKILLS ACTIVITY 17

1. freedom
2. Answers will vary. Possible answer: Are there any means by which one person's power over another can be made answerable to the law?

Answer Key

3. As soon as you can resist this restraint, do so.

4. Answers will vary depending on the story that students select. You may wish to assign small groups of students to read the same article and work together to identify the central issues.

HISTORY AND GEOGRAPHY ACTIVITY 17

1. because they have different viewpoints and perceptions of an area

2. It was the "greatest" planet in the universe because it was where humans lived.

3. Answers will vary. Possible answer: Institutions can often shape the way people think about places in the world through the policies, teachings, or statements they present. For example, during war situations, governments often present the opposing government and country as being inherently evil.

4. Answers will vary. Possible answer: If the directions given are overly broad or vague, you can assume the direction-givers know little about world geography.

MAPPING HISTORY ACTIVITY 17

1. Answers may include Germany, Bosnia-Herzegovina, Albania, Slovenia, Italy, Czech Republic, Slovakia, Austria, Hungary, Croatia, Belgium, Luxembourg. Students may point out that the boundaries of many nations that existed in the Age of Enlightenment have changed.

2. Answers may include Paris, London, Rome, and Madrid.

3. Students should mark and label Kraków, Rome, London, and Paris.

HISTORICAL SIGNIFICANCE ACTIVITY 17

Students should list newspaper and TV stories that describe instances of people speaking out, exercising the right to assemble, freedom of religion, and freedom of the press. In their paragraphs, students should relate specific instances of how they have spoken out, assembled, worshiped, and/or enjoyed a free press in their own lives.

COOPERATIVE LEARNING ACTIVITY 17

Students should complete the activity and answer the Group Process and Quick Check questions. Have students share their responses with their groups or with the class as a whole.

HISTORY SIMULATION ACTIVITY 17

Students should work collaboratively in groups toward achieving the learning objective of the History Simulation Activity.

TIME LINE ACTIVITY 17

Science/Mathematics:
Event: Newton publishes his book *Principia*.
Significance: offered a new understanding of planetary motion, building on the work of Copernicus, Galileo, and Kepler; developed calculus

Government/Politics:
Event: Locke publishes his *Two Treatises of Government*; Maria Theresa rules Austria; Frederick II rules Prussia; the American Revolution begins. **Significance:** Locke introduced the idea that government was accountable to individuals; influenced American patriots. Maria Theresa was influenced by Enlightenment philosophy; introduced measures to free peasants, protect serfs, and provide public education. Frederick II tried to apply political ideals of the Enlightenment. The American Revolution used Enlightenment notions of individual rights as the basis for revolting against British rule.

Philosophy/Religion:
Event: The Enlightenment occurs; Diderot publishes the *Encyclopedia*; Rousseau's *Discourse on the Sciences and the Arts* seeks to balance emotion and reason. **Significance:** The Enlightenment spread the ideas of the Scientific Revolution and applied a scientific approach to areas previously defined by religion. The *Encyclopedia* criticized the Church

and government and spread ideas of religious tolerance throughout Europe. Rousseau's *Discourse* asserted the limitations of reason and the value of instinct and emotion in human life.

The Arts:
Event: Romantic movement occurs.
Significance: Artists broke with classicism to celebrate emotion and the individual.

LINKING PAST AND PRESENT ACTIVITY 17

1. He may have had a great curiosity in science, and he might have been suspicious of the scientific theories and ideas of the time.

2. Someone who knows he or she has such a gene might monitor his or her health more closely by following a healthy diet and exercise regimen to offset the likelihood of developing the disease.

3. When people learned that the microbes Leeuwenhoek saw under the microscope caused diseases, they discovered ways to destroy them. Student reports should mention Louis Pasteur, who discovered a vaccine preventing rabies; Joseph Lister, who discovered ways to prevent post-surgical infections; and Robert Koch, who studied the organisms that caused anthrax and tuberculosis. Students should understand that such discoveries could not have been made without a microscope.

PEOPLE IN WORLD HISTORY ACTIVITY 17, PROFILE 1

1. Copernicus understood that the Sun is stationary and located in the center of the universe. Further, he theorized that Earth was only one of the planets in the sky. As a result, it must move like the other planets.

2. Answers will vary. Possible answer: According to the Bible, Earth was a separate creation from the planets and stars. If Earth was no longer the center of the universe and was to be considered just another planet, this directly contradicted the Church's teachings about the universe and humankind's place in it.

3. Answers will vary. Possible answer: Copernicus's theory shook people's perceptions of the entire universe. If the basic structure of the universe could change, then it followed that nothing could be trusted.

PEOPLE IN WORLD HISTORY ACTIVITY 17, PROFILE 2

1. Smith addressed the question of how social order and human progress are possible in a society where people follow their own self-interests.

2. It is the policy that a government should impose the fewest possible restrictions on prices and trade.

3. Answers will vary. Possible answer: He assumed that people act out of self-interest—the consumer buys what he or she wants and the producer, in order to profit, will attend to the consumer's wants. In this manner, both consumers and producers are in harmony and so do not need rigid governmental controls on commerce.

4. Answers will vary. Possible answer: The government would regulate supply and demand to ensure fair commerce. A more controlling government would ensure that prices would not fluctuate.

PRIMARY SOURCE READING 17

1. He was warned that the *Encyclopedia* was dangerous to France.

2. They argued that people are afraid of new ideas they do not understand. The *Encyclopedia* shows how intelligent the French nation is compared to others. Even if, as the king has been told, some parts of the book are faulty, the entire work should not be banned.

Answer Key

3. Those who distrusted or feared the *Encyclopedia* continued to attack it.

4. Almost anyone would be able to afford a small, inexpensive book. Whatever information the *Encyclopedia* contained that might cause the masses to revolt would probably be read only by the wealthy, whose support for the king was unlikely to change.

WORLD ART AND MUSIC ACTIVITY 17

1. portraits of individuals

2. In England he learned to paint large groups of people and historical scenes.

3. Answers will vary. Possible answer: He was supported by the wealthy people who commissioned portraits. Since nothing in the passage indicates that Copley was poor, there must have been many wealthy art lovers in Boston. Students might also conclude that Bostonians valued art.

4. Answers will vary. Possible answer: He was trying to rectify the superficiality of earlier portraits. Students might conclude that Copley thought society was superficial and wanted people to look more deeply into themselves and others.

RETEACHING ACTIVITY 17

I. A. stated that the earth was round and rotated on its axis as it revolved around the sun, the center of the universe
    B. proved that the planets move in elliptical orbits with the Sun toward the end of the ellipse
    C. used the telescope to observe moons circling Jupiter; heavenly bodies are composed of material substance
    D. proposed theory of universal gravitation to explain motion of planets

II. A. made discoveries in anatomy by dissecting human bodies
    B. showed that blood makes a complete circuit as it passes through the body

III. A. conducted controlled experiments; Boyle's Law: the volume of a gas varies with the pressure exerted on it
     B. invented system of naming the chemical elements

IV. A. people had adopted laws and government in order to preserve their private property; liberty is achieved by being forced to follow what is best for "the general will," because the general will represents what is best for the entire community
    B. promoted the idea of separating governmental powers among branches

V. A. penned *Treatise on Toleration*, reminded governments that "all men are brothers under God"
    B. edited a 28-volume collection of knowledge: the *Encyclopedia;* attacked religious superstition and supported religious toleration

ENRICHMENT ACTIVITY 17

1. Answers will vary. Possible answer: Religious dogma keeps us obedient and prevents us from being truly free; Galileo is a heretic and should be condemned.

2. Ballads, poems, and plays will vary but should reflect that, because their work was controversial in the Church's view, Copernicus worked in secret without publishing and Diderot went to prison.

GUIDED READING ACTIVITY 17-1

1. These writings made it obvious that some ancient thinkers had disagreed with Aristotle and other accepted authorities of the Middle Ages.

2. the printing press

3. Earth is placed at the center of the universe.

4. He argued that the Sun, not Earth, was at the center of the universe.

5. mountains on the Moon, four moons revolving around Jupiter, and sunspots

Answer Key

6. The Copernican system threatened the Church's entire conception of the universe and seemed to contradict the Bible.

7. He defined the three laws of motion that govern the planetary bodies, as well as objects on Earth.

8. Harvey showed that the heart—not the liver—was the beginning point for the circulation of blood in the body.

9. astronomy

10. He emphasized the importance of his own mind and asserted that he would accept only those things that his reason said were true.

11. Francis Bacon, an English philosopher

GUIDED READING ACTIVITY 17-2

1. Enlightenment
2. Scientific
3. Reason
4. progress
5. balances
6. Christianity
7. *Encyclopedia*
8. Physiocrats
9. regulations
10. laissez-faire
11. contract
12. governed
13. Wollstonecraft
14. attacked
15. devotion
16. Methodism

GUIDED READING ACTIVITY 17-3

I. politics
  A. Prussia
  B. lawmaker
  C. impractical
II. condemned
  A. Austrian
  B. Seven
  C. Great War for Empire
III. music
  A. rococo
  B. music
    1. Bach
    2. Mozart
  C. novelists

GUIDED READING ACTIVITY 17-4

1. Great Britain
2. thirteen
3. revenues
4. Stamp Act, Britain
5. Lexington, Concord
6. Declaration of Independence
7. Yorktown
8. Treaty of Paris, independence, Mississippi
9. federal
10. Bill of Rights

READING SKILLS ACTIVITY 18

Practicing the Skill

Student answers may vary, but the lead lines on the graphic organizer could include the following:

represented the king's absolute power
symbol of government's harsh policies
members of the French Guard joined the people
represented imprisonment for political reasons
the people won out over the troops
people died fighting the government
symbol of the power of the wealthy over
the rules of law

Applying the Skill

Student answers should identify Napoleon's personal victories, such as the Italian Campaign, as well as conditions in France at the time,

Answer Key

such as the corruption of the Directory's members.

HISTORICAL ANALYSIS SKILLS ACTIVITY 18

Practicing the Skill

1. Answers will vary. Students should describe the scene depicted: Napoleon in uniform, wrapped in a cloak, with his right arm outstretched, riding a white horse with his soldiers in the background. Other possible observations may include the name Bonaparte inscribed in stone above that of Hannibal and Napoleon personally leading his troops into battle.

2. Answers will vary. Students should conclude that the artist was attempting to portray Napoleon as a heroic figure based on the scene depicted in the painting as well as the look of confidence evident on the face of the painting's subject. Observant students may recognize the symbolism of the white horse as a signal that David wished to depict Napoleon as heroic.

3. Answers will vary. Students should conclude that the artist was biased in favor of Napoleon based on the heroic depiction of the subject.

Applying the Skill

Answers will vary. Students should present summaries of their articles along with an explanation of whether or not they found evidence of bias in the first-hand accounts. They should present the words and phrases that signal the bias, if any, they found in the articles they chose.

DIFFERENTIATED INSTRUCTION ACTIVITY 18

Answers will vary. Example: Only the desire of the public should drive the government. The reason the government is powerful is because the power of the people is invested in it. Once the government begins to act without the general will of the people behind it, it stops acting on behalf of the people. If the government's will becomes the strongest and it uses the people's power to accomplish its own goals—when the government misuses its power—then the public's trust in the government fades, and the state will break up.

ENGLISH LEARNER ACTIVITY 18

A.

1. Answers will vary but should mention leadership qualities.

2. Answers will vary but should include major changes.

B.

After students review words, allow time for questions or quizzing with a fellow student.

C.

1. b
2. d
3. a
4. b
5. d

D.

1. S
2. S
3. A
4. A
5. A

CONTENT VOCABULARY ACTIVITY 18

1. estates
2. *taille*
3. duties
4. bourgeoisie
5. Tennis Court Oath
6. monarchy
7. *sans-culottes*
8. radicalism

Answer Key

9. Committee of Public Safety

10. coup d'état

11. consulate

12. nationalism

ACADEMIC VOCABULARY ACTIVITY 18

A.

administration; administer

benefit; beneficial

demonstration; demonstrate

exclusion; exclude

expansion; expand

B.

1. c

2. a

3. a

4. b

5. c

6. a

7. a

8. c

9. a

SKILLS REINFORCEMENT ACTIVITY 18

1. percentage of population and percentage of land ownership

2. **a.** approximately .5 percent
   b. approximately 10 percent

3. **a.** approximately 1.5 percent
   b. approximately 25 percent

4. **a.** approximately 98 percent
   b. approximately 65 percent

5. Answers may vary but should refer to the fundamental importance of agriculture.

6. the Second Estate

7. **a.** It was the only estate whose percentage of population exceeded its percentage of land ownership.
   b. Answers will vary but should refer to the fundamental inequality of this situation and to the resentment it bred.

CRITICAL THINKING SKILLS ACTIVITY 18

1. Answers will vary but may include: inspiring—the storming of the Bastille; unacceptable—the Reign of Terror; hope—the formation of the National Assembly; fear—the Great Fear; violence—the wars; fraternity—the spirit of the *sans-culottes*.

2. Answers will vary. Perhaps he spoke about both its positive and negative aspects because he felt it was important for the French people to remember them equally.

3. Answers will vary but may allude to such things as the Declaration of Rights and noble goals of the Revolution.

4. Answers may vary but should refer to the loss of the republic and the dictatorship of Napoleon.

5. that one of his ancestors stormed the Bastille

6. Answers will vary. Perhaps he would disagree, since he takes so much pride in his ancestor's actions.

7. Answers will vary but should be supported with explanations. Delmas's is probably the most positive; Furet's is probably the most negative.

8. Answers will vary, but students should support their opinions with explanations.

HISTORY AND GEOGRAPHY ACTIVITY 18

1. mountains, deserts, climate, laws

2. more than 500,000 troops

Answer Key

3. Modern barriers are more likely to be repressive governments and immigration laws than geographical features.

4. Possible answers: Hinder: prohibits flow of people and ideas that could help to improve the nation. Help: prohibits warfare with other countries that could damage the nation

5. Answers should reflect an understanding of the geographic theme of the movement.

MAPPING HISTORY ACTIVITY 18

1.
   a. 1812
   b. France, the Netherlands, the Italian states, Poland
   c. Spain, Norway, Denmark, the Austrian Empire

2.
   a. Map symbols should be appropriate, placed in the map key, and labeled.
   b. Students should mark battles (with dates, according to the chart) at the following points on the map: Marengo—approx. 1/2 inch NW of Rome; Trafalgar—just off Cape Trafalgar; Austerlitz—approx. 7/16 inch SW of Warsaw; Auerstedt—just SW of Leipzig; Jena—just SE of Auerstedt; Friedland—extreme northern Poland, approx. 3/16 inch from Baltic Sea; Peninsular War—Spain; Wagram—just N of Vienna; Aspern—just NE of Vienna; Borodino—about 3/16 inch W of Moscow; Lützen—about 3/16 inch W of Leipzig; Leipzig—at Leipzig; Ligny—about 3/16 inch SE of Waterloo; Waterloo—at Waterloo

HISTORICAL SIGNIFICANCE ACTIVITY 18

1. Answers will vary. Possible answers: The Napoleonic Code has affected all of the people of France since its creation and has served as a model for other countries. The independence of Latin America has had a fundamental impact on all of the peoples of that region and on the nations that had colonized them. The Louisiana Purchase has affected the people of the United States and, by enabling the United States to become a great power, it has affected people around the world.

2.–3. Answers will vary but should be supported with explanations.

4. Answers will vary. Possible answers: The Napoleonic Code revolutionized law. The independence of Latin America changed the history of that region and of the European colonial powers. The Louisiana Purchase was instrumental in making the United States a major global power.

COOPERATIVE LEARNING ACTIVITY 18

Students should complete the activity and answer the Group Process and Quick Check questions. Have students share their responses with their groups or with the class as a whole.

HISTORY SIMULATION ACTIVITY 18

Students should work collaboratively in groups toward achieving the learning objective of the History Simulation Activity.

TIME LINE ACTIVITY 18

1. **A.** the fall of the Bastille in 1789
   B. 9 years

2. **A.** Napoleon's coup d'état in 1799
   B. the Battle of Waterloo in 1815

3. He named himself Emperor of France in 1804.

4. Answers will vary, but should be supported with explanations. The original noble goals of the National Assembly deteriorate into the Reign of Terror within two years; less than a decade later, France is ruled by a dictator.

Students should mark the fall of the Bastille in 1789, Napoleon's coup d'état in 1799, the Battle of Waterloo in 1815, and Napoleon's naming of himself as emperor of France in 1804 on their time lines.

Answer Key

LINKING PAST AND PRESENT ACTIVITY 18

1. They believed that their "pure European blood" made them superior to Latin Americans of mixed ancestry and that this gave them special privileges.

2. By investing in plantations and mines, neocolonialism keeps the upper-class landowners wealthy and powerful.

3. In their reports, students should discuss how, during the Middle Ages, northern Spanish rulers tried to unify a country that was divided into separate kingdoms and inhabited by diverse ethnic groups. Because the rulers felt that making Christianity the state religion would accomplish this, they decided to convert all Spanish Jews and Muslims to Christianity. During the reign of King Ferdinand and Queen Isabella, Spaniards began to suspect that the converted Jews were secretly practicing Judaism. Often using torture, the leaders of the Spanish Inquisition interrogated the suspected Jews about their religious practices. In 1492 Ferdinand and Isabella expelled all unconverted Jews from Spain. As the Spanish lost tolerance for different races and cultures, they began to feel the well-being of their country depended on everyone being Christian and having "pure Spanish blood." The Spaniards that colonized Latin America brought this attitude with them.

PEOPLE IN WORLD HISTORY ACTIVITY 18, PROFILE 1

1. She married the crown prince.

2. Answers will vary, but should refer to the fact that she was not of French birth, that she was extravagant and aloof, and that her bad reputation was exacerbated by false rumors.

3. Answers will vary but should be supported. Students might point out that the two characteristics are not mutually exclusive.

PEOPLE IN WORLD HISTORY ACTIVITY 18, PROFILE 2

1. Robespierre's political career began in 1789, when the residents of Arras chose him to represent them.

2. He halted inflation, instituted the Reign of Terror to eliminate the republic's enemies, and prepared for war.

3. Robespierre felt the monarchy was an unjust system of government. He wanted to reduce extreme inequalities of wealth, ensure work and education for all, and give everyone a voice in government.

4. Answers will vary. Possible answers: He was a natural leader; he was brave and decisive; he had an unshakable sense of duty and sacrifice.

PRIMARY SOURCE READING 18

1. "ignorance, forgetfulness, or contempt" for people's natural rights

2. liberty, property, security, and resistance to oppression (freedom); the American Declaration lists "Life, liberty, and the pursuit of happiness"

3. "all citizens or their representatives"; probably only men

4. Students should note special mention of religious freedom, censorship, fair apportionment of taxation, ex post facto laws, illegal arrests, and rights of accused persons, which reflected problems of the time.

WORLD ART AND MUSIC ACTIVITY 18

1. David was enormously influential in his roles as court painter to Louis XVI, director of artistic affairs for the republic, and first painter to Napoleon.

2. a celebration of the formal art of ancient Greece and Rome; balance; realistic detail; use of subjects from ancient history

Answer Key

3. Answers will vary, but should address each of Napoleon's specific comments.

4. Paragraphs will vary, but should be supported with explanations. Some students will argue that by supporting three regimes, each with its own ideology, David showed himself to be an opportunist. Others will say that as an artist, he may have felt drawn to the personalities and dynamics of each regime and ignored their individual politics.

RETEACHING ACTIVITY 18

1. In France, the estates were orders of society that determined a person's legal rights and status.

2. First Estate: A, E, I; Second Estate: B, D, F, J; Third Estate: C, G, H, K

ENRICHMENT ACTIVITY 18

1. The French army was unable to stem the attacks of the armies of the European monarchies with what was left of the old royal army.

2. Answers may include that they fought in a less orderly fashion and that they fought for complete victory.

3. "whereas the prerevolutionary soldiers had been scarce and expensive, the lives of conscripts were plentiful and cheap"

4. Answers will vary. France's enemies were monarchies, and they feared the potential threat to their own authority of an armed populace.

5. Answers will vary, but should be supported with explanations.

GUIDED READING ACTIVITY 18-1

1. The beginning of a new United States of America and the beginning of the French Revolution.

2. The French Revolution was more complex, more violent, and far more radical.

3. The First Estate consisted of the clergy. The nobility made up the Second Estate. The Third Estate were the commoners.

4. This was the middle class of the Third Estate—merchants, bankers, industrialists, as well as professional people.

5. the near collapse of government finances

6. They wanted to set up a constitutional government that would abolish the tax exemptions of the clergy and nobility.

7. A mob of Parisians stormed the Bastille, an armory and prison in Paris, and dismantled it brick by brick.

8. On August 4, 1789, they voted to abolish all legal privileges of nobles and clergy.

9. the Declaration of the Rights of Man and the Citizen

10. She refused to accept an exclusion of women from political rights in France.

11. They determined that bishops and priests would be elected by the people and paid by the state.

GUIDED READING ACTIVITY 18-2

1. False. Their first major step was to abolish the monarchy and establish a republic, the French Republic.

2. True.

3. False. The courts were established to prosecute internal enemies of the revolutionary republic.

4. True.

5. False. The ceremony was dedicated to the worship of reason.

6. False. Years were numbered from September 22, 1792—the first day of the French Republic.

7. True.

8. True.

Answer Key

GUIDED READING ACTIVITY 18-3

1. French
2. European
3. Corsica
4. lieutenant
5. Committee of Public Safety
6. Italy
7. absolute
8. consul
9. Emperor
10. social convenience
11. Catholic
12. Church
13. Catholicism
14. codify
15. Civil Code
16. principles
17. despotism
18. newspapers
19. resistance
20. nationalism
21. Russia

ACKNOWLEDGMENTS

TEXT

9   From *The Tragedy of Macbeth* by William Shakespeare.

30   From *Two Renaissance Book Hunters: The Letters of Poggius Bracciolini to Nicolaus de Niccolis* translated by Phyllis Walter Goodhart Gordon, copyright © 1974, 1991 by Columbia University Press.

34   From *The Common Reader* by Virginia Woolf, quoted in the *Beacon Book of Quotations by Women* compiled by Rosalie Maggio, copyright © 1992 by Rosalie Maggio.

From *The Civilization of the Renaissance in Italy* by Jacob Burckhardt, translated by S.G.C. Middlemore, published 1990 by Penguin Books.

43   From *The Autobiography of Benvenuto Cellini*, translated by John Addington Symonds, published 1948 by Doubleday & Company, Inc.

45   From "Michelangelo" from *The Thames and Hudson Dictionary of Art and Artists* edited by Herbert Read, copyright © 1994 by Thames and Hudson Ltd.

67   From *A Relation . . . of the Island of England . . . c. 1500* translated by C. A. Sneyd from *The Portable Renaissance Reader* edited by James Bruce Ross and Mary Martin McLaughlin, copyright © 1953 by the Viking Press.

68   From *The History of Mary Prince, A West Indian Slave, Related by Herself* edited by Moira Ferguson, published 1993 by the University of Michigan Press.

81   From *The Discoverers* by Daniel J. Boorstin. Copyright © 1983 by Daniel J. Boorstin. Reprinted by permission of Random House, Inc.

117   From *Memoirs of the Duke of Saint Simon on the Reign of Louis XIV and the Regency*, Vol. III, translated by Bayle St. John. London: Bickers & Son, 1880, pp. 21–27.

155   "400 Years of the East India Company" by Huw V. Bowen, July 2000 *History Today*. Copyright © EBSCO Publishing. Reprinted by permission.

178   From Donald Keene, "Hirata Atsutane and Western Learning," *T'oung Pao*, 42:5 (1954), 374–76.

191   From *Sources of Japanese Tradition* by Ryusaku Tsunoda, Wm. Theodore de Bary and Donald Keene. Copyright © 1958 by Columbia University Press. Reprinted with permission of the publisher.

216   From *Treatise on the Social Compact* by Jean-Jacques Rousseau from *The Enlightenment* edited by Frank E. Manuel, copyright © 1965 by Prentice-Hall Inc.

229   From *Candide and Other Writings by Voltaire*, edited with introduction by Haskell M. Block. Copyright © 1956 and renewed 1984 by Random House, Inc. Reprinted by permission of Random House, Inc.

258   From *The 100: A Ranking of the Most Influential Persons in History* by Michael H. Hart, copyright © 1978 by Hart Publishing Company, Inc.

266   Translated by H.H. Hill from *Europe in Review: Readings and Sources Since 1500*, edited by G.L. Mosse, R.E. Cameron, H.B. Hill, and M.B. Petrovich (University of Wisconsin). Chicago: Rand McNally, 1957, 1964, pp. 162–164.

PHOTOGRAPHS

31   Art Archive/Museo Correr, Venice/Dagli Orti

41   CORBIS

42   SuperStock

45   Scala/Art Resource, NY

79   Mary Evans Picture Library

ACKNOWLEDGMENTS

80 British Library, London © British Library Board. All Rights Reserved/Bridgeman Art Library

83 Christie's Images/CORBIS

115 Hulton Archive/Getty Images

116 Time & Life Pictures/Getty Images

119 Scala/Art Resource, NY

143 Vanni/Art Resource, NY

153 Mary Evans Picture Library

154 Art Archive/Palace of Chihil Soutoun, Isfahan/Dagli Orti

157 Private Collection/Bridgeman Art Library

189 National Palace Museum, Taipei

190 Bettmann/CORBIS

193 The Metropolitan Museum of Art, Gift of John D. Rockefeller, 1941. 41.59.1

217 Time & Life Pictures/Getty Images

227 Bettmann/CORBIS

228 Michael Nicholson/CORBIS

231 Andrew W. Mellon Fund, Image © Board of Trustees, National Gallery of Art, Washington

244 SuperStock

265 SuperStock

266 Erich Lessing/Art Resource, NY

269 Erich Lessing/Art Resource, NY

Teacher Notes

Teacher Notes